D1555027

SEMICONDUCTOR STATISTICS

SEMICONDUCTOR STATISTICS

J. S. BLAKEMORE

Oregon Graduate Center

Beaverton, Oregon

DOVER PUBLICATIONS, INC.

NEW YORK

Copyright © 1962, 1987 by J. S. Blakemore.
All rights reserved under Pan American and International Copyright Conventions.

Published in Canada by General Publishing Company, Ltd., 30 Lesmill Road, Don Mills, Toronto, Ontario.
Published in the United Kingdom by Constable and Company, Ltd.

This Dover edition, first published in 1987, is an unabridged, corrected and slightly enlarged republication of the work first published by Pergamon Press, New York, 1962, as Volume 3 in the International Series of Monographs on Semiconductors, edited by Heinz K. Henisch. A new Preface updating the original text has been written specially for the Dover edition by the author, and replaces the original Preface.

Manufactured in the United States of America
Dover Publications, Inc., 31 East 2nd Street, Mineola, N.Y. 11501

Library of Congress Cataloging-in-Publication Data

Blakemore, J. S. (John Sydney), 1927–
Semiconductor statistics.

Bibliography: p.
Includes index.
1. Semiconductors—Statistical methods. 2. Excess carriers (Solid state physics)—Statistical methods. 3. Energy-band theory of solids—Statistical methods. 4. Fermi surfaces—Statistical methods. I. Title.
QC611.B52 1987 537.6′22 87-585
ISBN 0-486-65362-5 (pbk.)

CONTENTS

PREFACE TO THE DOVER EDITION

In their haste to get to the "meat" of a scientific book, readers often pass the preface by. I hope that will not happen this time, for this preface, prepared for this Dover reprint edition, is designed specifically to alert the reader to topics for which the treatment in this book, which was written in the 1960 era, can usefully be supplemented by a consultation of more recent published accounts.

It has interested me to confirm that many topics treated in *Semiconductor Statistics* remain valid as written, despite the large amount of semiconductor research during the intervening years. Descriptions of some other topics have inevitably become dated. The decision reached by Dover in discussions with me was that a verbatim reprint would be most useful if preceded—in this preface—by some author's comments, including citation of some of the key relevant papers of the last twenty-five years. (Note: throughout the text, the symbol (§) will serve to direct the reader to the Preface for updated information and citations of post-1960 literature.)

I should emphasize, as in the first preface, that this is a book written by one experimentalist to help other experimentalists understand the implications of carrier populations and Fermi energies. These quantities are of course not measured directly but are inferred from experimental observations of conductivities, etc. A semiconductor at or near thermodynamic equilibrium is considered in Part I, comprising Chapters 1 through 3. The additional complexities of an overtly non-equilibrium condition appear in Chapters 4 through 10 of Part II.

I have also been interested and pleased to observe that many of the literature citations for *Semiconductor Statistics* over the years have been for the material in Sections 3.2 and 3.3, dealing with the extrinsic carrier density consistent—at thermal equilibrium—with one or more species of impurity level. Less explicable has been the relative paucity of citations for some topics in Part II, such as the extensive treatment of carrier trapping in Sections 8.2, 8.4 and 8.5, especially since some of the material appears in print nowhere else! Nevertheless, it is up to the reader to find needed topics, while ignoring material irrelevant to his or her needs—at least for the present.

In noting a few post-1960 publications and commenting on which parts of this book have or have not weathered the last twenty-five years in good order, it will be simplest for the reader if my comments here are made on a chapter-by-chapter basis:

CHAPTER 1 was written to introduce the band model of semiconductor physics, at a time when relatively few textbooks on the subject existed. The exposition in Sections 1.1 through 1.4 is now less important, in view of the many solid-state textbooks now available. With some relief, I can note that nothing written in Section 1.5 about band-shape complications for Si, Ge and InSb has been proved *wrong*, though improved numbers are now available for effective masses, nonparabolicity factors and the like. The valence and conduction band systems for these three semiconductors, and for seven other zincblende lattice III–V and II–VI solids, were reviewed in the nonlocal pseudopotential band calculation exposition by Chelikowsky and Cohen [*Phys. Rev.* B **14**, 556 (1976)]. Silicon and germanium were also among the semiconductors considered by Wang and Klein [*Phys. Rev.* B **24**, 3393 (1981)] in calculations using a linear combination of Gaussian orbitals. That study emphasized both critical energy separations and effective mass parameters.

With regard to silicon (the topic of Section 1.5.1), cyclotron resonance measurements of conduction electrons [Ousset et al., *J. Phys.* C **9**, 2803 (1976)] have provided more precise effective mass parameters, pleasantly close to those quoted on p. 58. The classic optical measurements of Si intrinsic gap by MacFarlane et al. (1958:**3**) were considered, along with newer measurements by Bludau et al. [*J. Appl. Phys.* **45**, 1846 (1974)] when Thurmond [*J. Electrochem. Soc.* **122**, 1133 (1975)] recommended a three-parameter equation for the variation of gap width with temperature. As for the silicon valence bands, appreciable modifications of the A, B and C parameters from the values of Eq. (151.3) were dictated by the cyclotron resonance work of Hensel and Feher [*Phys. Rev.* **129**, 1041 (1963)]. However, all of this has left the density-of-states masses as expressed on p. 63 virtually unchanged!

For germanium effective mass parameters (as discussed in Section 1.5.2), post-1960 studies have also provided improved numerical accuracy without invalidating the concepts and numbers of the original text. Several cyclotron resonance studies of Ge conduction electrons at low temperatures (including the paper by Ousset et al. noted above) have been supplemented by magnetophonon resonance measurements [Harper et al., *Repts. Prog. Phys.* **36**, 1 (1973)] extending to higher temperatures; and these imply that the density-of-states m_c does not have a major temperature dependence. The valence band parameters A, B and C, as determined in the cyclotron resonance studies of Hensel and Suzuki [*Phys. Rev.* B **9**, 4219 (1974)] and of Skolnick et al. [*J. Phys.* C **9**, 2809 (1976)], become shifted slightly from the numbers of Eq. (152.2), but with no substantial effect on the density-of-states effective masses.

Indium antimonide was selected to have its band parameters discussed in Section 1.5.3 as an example of a zincblende-structured compound with a direct gap and hence a nonparabolic conduction band of small initial m_c, heavy-hole maxima slightly displaced from the zone center, etc. The $\mathbf{k}.\mathbf{p}$ model of Kane (1957:**5**) has certainly proved of great value in interpreting the mutual influences of the various band extrema for InSb itself and for other direct-gap III–V semiconductors, including GaAs [Blakemore, *J. Appl. Phys.* **53**, R123 (1982)]. Thus, for both InSb and GaAs, the **k . p** model is able to account for the increase of m_c with energy and the decrease of the band-edge curvature mass m_{co} with rising temperature (due to the attendant reduction of gap width). Stradling and Wood [*J. Phys.* C **3**, L94 (1970)] tracked the decline of m_{co} for InSb over the 40–300 K range.

The InSb valence bands are less mysterious now than in 1960, though some uncertainties remain. Cyclotron resonance was used by Pidgeon and Brown [*Phys. Rev.* **146**, 575 (1966)] to show that light holes have a mass $m_1 \simeq 0.016\ m_o$ not much larger than m_{co}, but the heavy-hole band is a different matter. Eaves et al. [*J. Phys.* C **10**, 2831 (1977)] found considerable anisotropy for heavy holes—with a density-of-states equivalent near $0.4m_o$—and the enlargement of m_2 along [111] directions fits the picture that this heavy-hole band has multiple extrema very slightly higher in energy than that for the zone center. A number of post-1960 experimental investigations have sought information about that small energy elevation, as summarized in a report by Bol'shakov et al. [*Sov. Phys. Semicond.* **14**, 1018 (1980)].

The final part of Chapter 1, Section 1.6, contains very brief comments on the nature of "flaw" (impurity or defect) localized states, and this subject has generated a vast experimental and theoretical literature in the past twenty-five years. Pantelides [*Rev. Mod. Phys.* **50**, 797 (1978)] has reviewed in detail the effective mass theoretical approach to relatively shallow impurities, while the present author has attempted elsewhere [Blakemore and Rahimi, *Semiconductors and Semimetals* **20**, 233 (Academic Press, 1984)] to survey the numerous ways that a midgap flaw can appropriately be modeled. (That survey is also relevant to the subject matter of Chapter 7, in dealing with mechanisms for capture of a free carrier by a localized center.) The final paragraphs of Chapter 1 comment on the defect chemistry of a compound semiconductor with a volatile major constituent, and it may be of interest to some readers that the eventual outcome of the article cited by Kröger and Vink (1956:**27**) has been a multivolume monograph by Kröger [*Chemistry of Imperfect Solids* (North-Holland, 1974)].

CHAPTER 2 deals with the mutual relationships of temperature, Fermi energy and free carrier densities, including the intrinsic condition. The first part of the chapter concerns identification of $\mathcal{F}_{1/2}(\eta) = (n_o/N_c) \equiv u$ as the $j = ½$ member of the $\mathcal{F}_j(\eta)$ family of Fermi–Dirac integrals, the family member necessary for relating Fermi energy and temperature with carrier density in a parabolic band. Members of that family, in addition to the $j = ½$ member, are required in describing n_o versus reduced Fermi energy η for a non-parabolic band and in describing various electronic transport properties. For that reason, tables of $\mathcal{F}_j(\eta)$ appear in Appendix B for various integer and half-integer values of j, while some asymptotic approximation for $\mathcal{F}_{1/2}(\eta)$ and other $\mathcal{F}_j(\eta)$ are discussed in Appendix C. As some readers will know, there has been considerable published activity in the past two decades on the analytic modeling of Fermi–Dirac integrals, from two points of view: as in Appendix C and Chapter 2, approximations that yield $u \equiv (n_o/N_c)$ from a knowledge of the Fermi energy and the temperature; and those that yield the reduced Fermi energy $\eta = [(\phi - E_c)/kT]$ from a knowledge of how large n_o is compared with the effective density of band states, N_c. Useful approximations for that second direction of attack were described by Nilsson [*Phys. Stat. Sol.* (a) **19**, K75 (1973)], and by Joyce and Dixon [*Appl. Phys. Lett.* **31**, 354 (1977)]. The present writer has reviewed elsewhere [Blakemore, *Solid St. Electron.* **25**, 1067 (1982)] the variously published proposals for modeling both $\eta(u)$ and $u(\eta)$, and it must be observed that further ingenious analytic approximate forms continue to be offered in print. It is now possible, with reasonable accuracy, to use one analytic approximate form all the way from non-degeneracy to complete degeneracy.

Following the discussion in Section 2.2 (still quite pertinent) of how a magnetic field affects the states of a band and their occupancy, Section 2.3 describes the intrinsic carrier populations of a semiconductor. The theory that the gap E_i varies linearly with temperature has by now been discredited, with the three-parameter form $E_i = [A - BT^2/(T + C)]$ proposed by Varshni [*Physica* **34**, 149 (1967)] representing a considerable improvement. In connection specifically with GaAs, the present writer has elsewhere [*J. Appl. Phys.* **53**, R123 (1982)] discussed the thermodynamic consequences of a nonlinear $E_i(T)$ for the enthalpy and entropy of transition as well as for the free energy itself.

The final section of Chapter 2 concerns spatial fluctuations of carrier density (caused by variations of E_i and/or doping) and was of course written many years before the great interest in ternary and quaternary III–V and II–VI materials, superlattices, quantum wells, etc. that developed in the mid-1980s. In writing the first paragraph of Section 2.5.1, my presumption that such alloys would have random allocation of atomic species on a given kind of lattice site mirrored the expectations of that day—and of the next quarter-century. Not until 1985 was it discovered, with considerable surprise [Kuan et al., *Phys. Rev. Lett.* **54**, 201 (1985)], that $Al_xGa_{1-x}As$ alloys grown epitaxially on GaAs show a preference for an ordering of Al and Ga on the Group-III sublattice. Some possible wider implications of this remain to be explored.

CHAPTER 3 concerns extrinsic semiconductors in thermal equilibrium: the distribution of available carriers between one band and one or more sets of impurity levels. One of the more important parts of this chapter is Section 3.2.2, which discusses an extrinsic material dominated by one set of impurities but affected also by some compensating levels, as evidenced by the "mass action" equation, Eq. (322.13), for a non-degenerate situation. Further implications of this method of analysis, and a more incisive computer-based analytic approach, were discussed elsewhere by the present writer [Blakemore, *J. Appl. Phys.* **51**, 1054 (1980)] more recently. In this regard, see also Hoffman [*Appl. Phys.* **19**, 307 (1979)] and Partain et al. [*Phys. Rev.* B **21**, 2432 (1980)] for further ways to analyze an extrinsic situation.

The final section of Chapter 3 concerns interactions among impurity states and the formation of impurity bands, a subject that has amassed a large literature since 1960. When the total impurity density is small, the relatively improbable transitions from one impurity site to another can occur only from an occupied site to an empty one (requiring finite compensation), as discussed by Miller and Abrahams (1960:**23**) and demonstrated by some of this author's earlier data (1959:**6**). More comprehensive data have since been published [Davis and Compton, *Phys. Rev.* **140**, A2183 (1965)] on these compensation-dependent phenomena.

Other principles come into play, however, when the doping in a semiconductor becomes stronger, including band tailing [Halperin and Lax, *Phys. Rev.* **148**, 722 (1966)], which can lead to appreciable gap narrowing and the development of an impurity band. The latter is discussed in the text in connection with Fig. 35.4 and was extensively studied by Hubbard [*Proc. Roy. Soc.* **A.277**, 237, 281 and 401 (1964)]. The roles of the "lower and upper Hubbard bands" and their merger when the impurity concentration is large enough are discussed in Chapter 6 of Mott's *Metal-Insulator Transitions* (Taylor & Francis, 1974). The entire subject of communication among states that are partially localized is of great interest also in connection with amorphous semiconductors, as reviewed by Mott and Davis [*Electronic Processes in Non-Crystalline Solids* (2nd Ed., Oxford, 1979)].

Part II of this book (Chapters 4 through 10) discusses problems that concern a semiconductor disturbed from thermal equilibrium. Appearing shortly before the original edition of *Semiconductor Statistics* was the valuable book by Bube (1960:**10**) on photoconductivity of solids. Within the next few years came the disarmingly slim (but subtle) book *Concepts in Photoconductivity* by Rose (Interscience, 1963) and the English translation of Ryvkin's book *Photoelectric Effects in Solids* (Consultants Bureau, 1964). Further refinements of these subjects have been published in forms briefer than full-scale monographs, though there have of course been many books on semiconductor devices that depend in varying degrees on non-equilibrium phenomena.

CHAPTER 4 sets the scene for all of this by commenting on detailed balance, as a preliminary, among other things, for discussing upwards and downwards radiative transitions in subsequent chapters, in defining quasi-Fermi levels and carrier lifetimes and in commenting on the relative probability of various electronic transition phenomena. It is ironic that Ge and Si, elemental solids for which purification has been highly successful, still have flaw-dominant recombination because their band structures do not facilitate the simplest band-to-band transition processes. The more favorable direct band structure has allowed band-to-band recombination to dominate in the $Hg_{1-x}Cd_xTe$ and $Pb_{1-x}Sn_xTe$ alloy systems [Gerhardts et al., *Solid St. Electron.* **21**, 1467 (1978), for example], in tellurium, as noted in the text (1960:**11**), and even in a semiconductor with a gap as wide as GaAs [Casey and Stern, *J. Appl. Phys.* **47**, 631 (1976)] under optimized conditions.

CHAPTER 5 was written to describe band-to-band radiative and radiationless (multiphonon, but not flaw-assisted) types of transition, of which the latter (as noted on page 203) is considered to be—at best—highly unlikely. Thus, the important processes for Chapter 5 are the spontaneous and stimulated radiative ones. As far as the spontaneous recombination regime is concerned, what I wrote then is still useful, as is the van Roosbroeck and Shockley (1954:**15**) analysis of how recombination probability can be assessed from the strength of optical absorption, controlled by the matrix element for upwards stimulated radiative transitions.

A dated aspect to part of Chapter 5 is evident on pages 201–202, a source of frustration to me at the time of writing (1960) since I knew that stimulated recombination must have further consequences but did not have time to investigate the matter further! Bernard and Duraffourg showed the following year [*Phys. Stat. Sol.* **1**, 699 (1961)] that the intrinsic absorption coefficient becomes negative if the difference of quasi-Fermi levels exceeds the gap width. That is not a sufficient, but is certainly a necessary, condition for lasing—which can happen with appropriate geometry. Injection-pumped GaAs soon showed laser action in the work of Hall et al. [*Phys. Rev. Lett.* **9**, 366 (1962)] and other groups. The Bernard-Duraffourg condition is, of course, embodied in subsequent treatments of combined stimulated/spontaneous recombination, such as Lasher and Stern [*Phys. Rev.* **133**, A553 (1964)] and Casey and Panish [*Heterostructure Lasers* (Academic Press, 1978)].

CHAPTER 6 concerns band-to-band Auger recombination, the fundamentals of which were enunciated by Landsberg and Beattie (1959: **15**, **16**). Landsberg has continued to be interested in this topic, pointing out [*Solid St. Electron.* **21**, 1289 (1978)] the many processes of this genre. Even for a direct gap semiconductor, band-shape complexities can enhance the Auger transition probability [Benz and Conradt, *Phys. Rev.* B **16**, 843 (1977); Haug et al., *Phys. Stat. Sol.* (b) **89**, 357 (1978)]. It has also become recognized since the mid-1970s that phonon-assisted transitions can become a significant contributor in an indirect gap semiconductor—such as Ge or Si—under conditions of heavy doping and/or strong excitation [Dziewior and Schmid, *Appl. Phys. Lett.* **31**, 346 (1977); Haug, *J. Lumin.* **20**, 173 (1979)].

CHAPTER 7 devotes most of its space to discussing solutions of the continuity equation for steady state and transient situations involving generation-recombination between one set of flaw states and one band. That subject was discussed in even more detail in the book by Ryvkin (1964). The material in Chapter 7 should be useful in interpreting information about capture and emission rates for deep-level flaws, a subject of intense continuing interest. The emphasis in multiphonon-aided capture has now, of course, shifted from the phonon cascade of Lax (1960:**15**) to multiphonon relaxation [Kovarskii, *Sov. Phys. Sol. St.* **4**, 1200 (1962); Henry and Lang, *Phys. Rev.* B **15**, 989 (1977)] based on configurational coordinate lattice relaxation models. Further models for flaw-related Auger capture at a localized trap have also been proposed over the years. The various carrier capture processes (embedded via detailed balance into any consideration of emission coefficients) were discussed in chapters of two mid-1980s volumes in the Academic Press *Semiconductors and Semimetals* series [Neumark and Kosai, **19**, 1 (1983); and Blakemore and Rahimi, **20**, 233 (1984)].

That subject, a comparison of relative probabilities for processes of energy transformation in transferring an electron between a trap and a band state, is, of course, fully relevant for any semiconductor in which band-to-band recombination traffic ocurs predominantly via midgap flaw states. Such flaw-mediated generation-recombination traffic via one dominant set of midgap flaws is the preoccupation of Chapter 8, including the lifetime model of Hall (1952:**8**) and Shockley and Read (1952:**7**), when these centers are few enough in numbers to make recombination more important than trapping. However, Chapter 8 does discuss the tricky conditions occurring when traps are numerous, perhaps in more detail than the average reader can use! There is no post-1960 literature that renders the exposition in that chapter obsolete.

CHAPTER 9 deals rather briefly with some additional aspects of a flaw-controlled generation-recombination environment. The first of these (Section 9.1) is one affected by the presence of multivalent flaws, and experimental work over the years has made us increasingly aware of amphoteric and/or multivalent behavior both by foreign impurities and by various kinds of native defect [Baraff and Schlüter, *Phys. Rev. Lett.* **55**, 1327 (1985); Bourgoin and Lannoo, *Point Defects in Semiconductors* (Springer, 1983)].

The next section of Chapter 9 makes no more than a token allusion to the fact that more than one type of flaw is almost invariably present in a semiconductor, even though one species *may* dominate recombination over a substantial range of temperature and/or excess carrier density. What can happen when states are broadly dispersed through the intrinsic gap was considered in the 1963 book by Rose, and again by Simmons and Taylor [*Phys. Rev.* B **4**, 502 (1971); B **15**, 964 (1975)]. Those models, appropriate for a compound with many kinds of native defect, are applicable to the non-linear and quenching phenomena found in insulating photoconductors. In contrast, the Haynes–Hornbeck model discussed in Section 9.3 requires only two distinct species of flaw; one is able to mediate electron-hole recombination, while the other is so asymmetric in its capture cross-sections as to serve just as a trap site. I find it interesting that Hornbeck and Haynes (1955:**36**) devised their model to describe properties of the (rather dirty) silicon of that time. Silicon now can exist in a highly "clean" form, but the trapping complications of Hornbeck and Haynes still hold sway in numerous "dirty" samples of various semiconducting compounds.

The final section of Chapter 9 mentions trapping and recombination at dislocations, a subject that (despite its apparent importance for technology) has attracted a meager literature. Does the dangling bond sequence along a dislocation provide a half-filled 1-D band, as proposed by Schröter and Labusch [*Phys. Stat. Sol.* **36**, 539 (1969)]? Or, as suggested by Figielski [*Solid St. Electron.* **21**, 1403 (1978)], is localization of these enough to form narrow upper and lower Hubbard bands? The latter would endow dislocations with interestingly non-linear recombination properties. Unfortunately, no resolution of these matters can be reported as this Dover edition goes to press.

CHAPTER 10 does not make a serious attempt to cover the full range of problems associated with excess carriers distributed non-uniformly in space. That is one of the imperatives for a book on solid-state electronics, such as that by Sze [*Physics of Semiconductor Devices* (2nd Ed., Wiley, 1981)], for which the two pages of Section 10.2 were never intended to provide competition. The rest of Chapter 10 concerns the distribution of excess carriers—in space and time—for a piece of semiconductor that may be homogeneous in its bulk properties but that can have excess carriers distributed (as a consequence of the way they appeared or arrived) non-uniformly, and that are also susceptible to surface recombination [Many et al., *Semiconductor Surfaces* (Interscience, 1965); Morrison, *The Chemical Physics of Surfaces* (Plenum, 1977)]. This subject matter has proved to be of limited reader interest, even though its principles were embodied in the prescribed procedures for lifetime measurement by the photoconductive decay method (ASTM Standard F28-75). The writer hopes that this Dover edition occasionally passes before the eyes of someone who does need the material in Section 10.3.

The ten chapters of the main text are followed by three appendixes. The Fermi–Dirac distribution law of Appendix A is hopefully familiar to most readers; the tables of Fermi–Dirac integrals in Appendix B are believed to be numerically reliable. As commented earlier in this Preface, Appendix C describes a subject on which there has been a considerable recent literature, which I have attempted to review [*Solid St. Electron.* **25**, 1067 (1982)], though various people have continued to attack the subject and appear inclined to continue to do so.

The original Pergamon Press 1962 edition of *Semiconductor Statistics* owed much to the support of Heinz Henisch as editor of a Pergamon monograph series, and it is a pleasure to acknowledge this again. Nick Holonyak encouraged Dover Publications to consider reprinting this book, and I am glad to recognize the value of his endorsement.

JOHN S. BLAKEMORE

Beaverton, Oregon
1986

SEMICONDUCTOR STATISTICS

PART I.

SEMICONDUCTORS IN THERMAL EQUILIBRIUM

Chapter 1

BASIC CONCEPTS IN THE ELECTRON THEORY OF SOLIDS

1.1 CLASSICAL THEORIES OF METALLIC CONDUCTION

CONSIDERABLE insight into the nature and behavior of semiconductors (and metals) comes from an examination of the band theory of solids. This theory can be regarded as arising naturally from the broadening of the discrete quantized energy levels of an isolated atom, but it is also useful to observe the development of band theory from the so-called collective electron point of view. We accordingly start with a review of the classical and quantized free electron models of metallic conduction. This discussion serves to introduce in historical sequence the important ideas which led to the band model and to an explanation of the distinction between metals, semiconductors and insulators.

1.1.1 DRUDE'S MODEL

Not long after the discovery of the electron, the suggestion was first made that the outer electrons of each atom in a metal might not be tightly bound to their individual atomic cores, but might rather form a free electron gas, collectively owned by the entire set of atoms which make up a crystal. That electrons should be free to move anywhere in a crystal seems reasonable in view of the validity of Ohm's law; and that their density might be comparable with that of atoms is indicated by the very large electrical and thermal conductivities of metals. Drude (1904:**1**) investigated the consequences of a simple model in which all the free electrons moved with a classical momentum $\bar{p} = (3m_0kT)^{1/2}$ and were presumed to be scattered in random directions by the positive ion cores. The model did not have any features from which the absolute strength of this scattering could be determined, thus conductivities could be quoted only in relative terms. Drude's model did, however, give a result for the ratio of thermal to electrical conductivities:

$$\frac{\kappa}{\sigma} = 3\left(\frac{k}{e}\right)^2 T \tag{111.1}$$

which was in surprisingly good agreement with the experimental law of Wiedemann and Franz (1853:**1**).

1.1.2 Lorentz's Model

Attempts were made by Lorentz (summarized in 1909:**1**) to improve upon Drude's model, particularly in recognizing that not all free electrons will move with the same speed and momentum. Of course, from general thermodynamic principles it is evident that if a system contains a large number of particles (such as electrons), then the particles will normally tend to find positions of lowest energy. At the same time, for any temperature other than absolute zero, particles are continually receiving and emitting energy in a way which tends to oppose the process of settling towards minimum energy.

Lorentz assumed that electron velocities and momenta varied in accordance with the classical Maxwell–Boltzmann distribution law. For a classical population of $\mathcal{N}$ free electrons in thermal equilibrium, the number with momenta in an infinitesimal range $\mathrm{d}p$ is

$$\mathrm{d}\mathcal{N} = \frac{4\pi \mathcal{N} p^2}{(2\pi m_0 kT)^{3/2}} \,.\, \exp\left[\frac{-p^2}{2m_0 kT}\right] \,.\, \mathrm{d}p \tag{112.1}$$

The Lorentz theory considered the deformation of this distribution in applied fields, and the manner in which a perturbed distribution tends to return to normal. By an ironic chance, these sophisticated calculations yielded apparently less satisfactory results than Drude's crude model in several respects:

(a) Drude had obtained a ratio of thermal to electrical conductivity of $3(k/e)^2T$, in good agreement with the experimental law of Wiedemann and Franz. Lorentz's result was one-third smaller.

(b) The more elaborate theory made it impossible to explain the actual temperature dependence of conductivities in ordinary metals if scattering was based on any central law of force, elastic or inelastic!

(c) Lorentz was able to predict values for other metallic properties such as thermoelectric, magnetoresistive and Hall coefficients. The Hall effect expression

$$R = -3\pi/8ne \qquad (112.2)$$

confirmed that free electrons are as numerous in metals as atoms—yet this served only to deepen the mystery that the free electron gas does not give metals a large additional specific heat.

From the foregoing, it will be seen that classical theory could do little to account for electronic behavior in metals—let alone semiconductors, whose existence was barely noted at the beginning of this century. It was not until the 1920's that any significant advances were made by the application of quantum ideas to the problem.

1.2 QUANTUM STATISTICS AND THE FREE ELECTRON THEORY

Arnold Sommerfeld (1928:**1**) retained a number of the important features in Drude's and Lorentz's earlier theories. Thus, like them, he assumed that free electrons enjoy a constant potential energy $-W$ inside a metal. (Whereas the potential experienced by an electron must actually depend on its relationship to other free electrons and to the periodic array of positively ionized atomic cores.) Also he was forced to accept that some form of scattering takes place to set the absolute value of the resistivity, yet he could not cite the specific cause of this scattering. Even so, a number of mysteries on the classical theories were easily explained by Sommerfeld's model, based on quantum statistics.

1.2.1 **p**-Space and **k**-Space. The Density of States

Consider a space for which the co-ordinates are the x, y and z components of electron momentum (Fig. 12.1). An electron of any momentum $\mathbf{p}$ can be represented by the vector from 0 to some point in $\mathbf{p}$-space. This electron has kinetic energy $E = p^2/2m_0$, and it is evident that a sphere centered on the origin of $\mathbf{p}$-space will be a constant energy surface.† Applying the concept of **p**-space to the classical distribution (112:1), it can be seen that the density of electrons in **p**-space for a given energy is

$$\frac{d\mathcal{N}}{4\pi p^2 \,.\, dp} = \frac{\mathcal{N}}{(2\pi m_0 kT)^{3/2}} \exp\left[\frac{-p^2}{2m_0 kT}\right]$$

$$= \frac{\mathcal{N}}{(2\pi m_0 kT)^{3/2}} \exp\left[\frac{-E}{kT}\right] \qquad (121.1)$$

when classical conditions hold.

In expressing the result (121:1), it is assumed that an electron may have any momentum and energy. This does not hold true when the

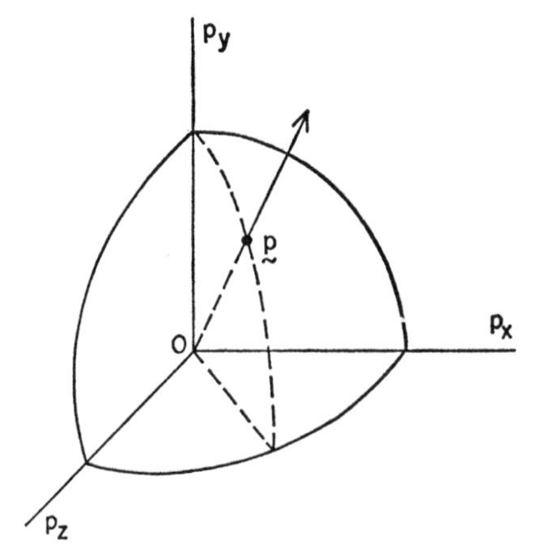

FIG. 12.1. Momentum space. The vector **p** represents the momentum of a particle, $p = \sqrt{(p_x^2+p_y^2+p_z^2)}$. Thus any sphere centered on the origin of momentum space is a surface of constant kinetic energy.

additional postulates of quantum theory are taken into account. According to quantum theory, when the motion of an electron is restricted by boundary conditions (as it is for an electron moving within

† In discussing the free electron model, the origin of energy is arbitrarily set as that of zero electronic kinetic energy. This is convenient for our present purposes since we are concerned only with differences of kinetic energies, and do not discuss problems of thermionic emission, contact potential, etc. (for which the height W of the surface potential barrier would be important). In discussions of the more complicated band models later in the book, different criteria of the most convenient origin for energy are encountered, and adopted where appropriate.

a crystal of finite size), there is a finite number of possible electron states (distinguishable patterns of electron behavior) within any specified range of energy and momentum.

In order to determine how many separate quantum states there are within a range of momentum, it is convenient to recall that—in quantum-mechanical terms—a free electron of momentum **p** can be represented by a wave of wavelength $\lambda = h/p$, or wave-vector $\mathbf{k} = \mathbf{p}/\hbar$. Thus as a companion to **p**-space, we can construct the corresponding **k**-space (Fig. 12.2), in which a vector **k** shows the direction and periodicity of the wave representing an electron of component momenta

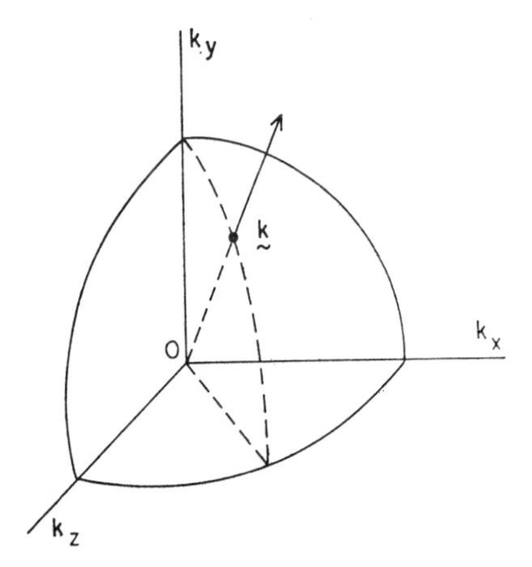

FIG. 12.2. **k**-space. The vector **k** represents the periodicity and direction of the wave representing an electron for which $k_x = (p_x/\hbar)$, $k_y = (p_y/\hbar)$, $k_z = (p_z/\hbar)$. For free electrons a sphere of radius k, centered on the origin, is a surface of constant energy.

$p_x = \hbar k_x$, $p_y = \hbar k_y$, and $p_z = \hbar k_z$. The kinetic energy of such an electron can be written

$$E = \frac{\hbar^2}{2m_0}(k_x{}^2 + k_y{}^2 + k_z{}^2) = \frac{\hbar^2 k^2}{2m_0} \qquad (121.2)$$

It is necessary to be temporarily concerned not only with the energies but also with the wave-functions ψ of electrons. According to wave-mechanical principles [for a very readable account see (1957:**1**)], ψ is to be interpreted as a probability function such that $|\psi|^2\,\mathrm{d}\tau$ is the probability of finding an electron in the volume element $\mathrm{d}\tau$. The permissible functions must satisfy Schrödinger's equation

$$-\frac{\hbar^2}{2m_0}\nabla^2\psi = E\psi \qquad (121.3)$$

subjcct to appropriatc boundary conditions. Now any real crystal is very large compared with atomic dimensions, and the properties of electrons in the bulk are imperceptibly affected by the true nature of the surface. Thus all boundary conditions will give the same result for the density of states, and one might as well be chosen which gives the wave functions a convenient analytical form (1942:**1**). Let ψ be periodic with period L along each Cartesian axis. Then solutions of (121.3) having the form of plane waves

$$\psi = C\exp(i\mathbf{k}\,.\,\mathbf{r}) \qquad (121.4)$$

are acceptable provided that

$$k_x = (2\pi n_x/L), \qquad k_y = (2\pi n_y/L), \qquad k_z = (2\pi n_z/L) \quad (121.5)$$

when n_x, n_y and n_z are any integers, 0, ± 1, ± 2, ± 3, ... This is all consistent with Heisenberg's uncertainty principle (on which the Schrödinger equation is based) that when an electron is restricted to having co-ordinates determinate to distance L, momentum is indeterminate over a range $\Delta p = h/L$ for each co-ordinate, or an indeterminacy in wave-vector of $\Delta k = (2\pi/L)$.

Thus now only certain positions in **k**-space correspond to acceptable wave-functions, such that **k**-space would be filled if each of these positions were to be surrounded with a cubic cell of volume $(2\pi/L)^3$ (Fig. 12.3). For a real metal of macroscopic dimensions, these cells are exceedingly small, and calculus procedures can be adopted to write the number of cells lying between spheres of radii k and $(k+\mathrm{d}k)$ as $(k^2L^3/2\pi^2)\mathrm{d}k$. Per unit volume of material, then, there are $(k^2/2\pi^2)\mathrm{d}k$ cells available within a range $\mathrm{d}k$ of wave-vector.

The density of available *electron states* is actually twice as large as the cell density, since wave-functions with spin $s = \pm\frac{1}{2}$ are separate permitted states for any permitted wave-vector and energy. Thus the number of *states* per unit volume within an infinitesimal range of energy or wave-vector is

$$g(E)\,.\,\mathrm{d}E = g(k)\,.\,\mathrm{d}k = (k/\pi)^2\,\mathrm{d}k \qquad (121.6)$$

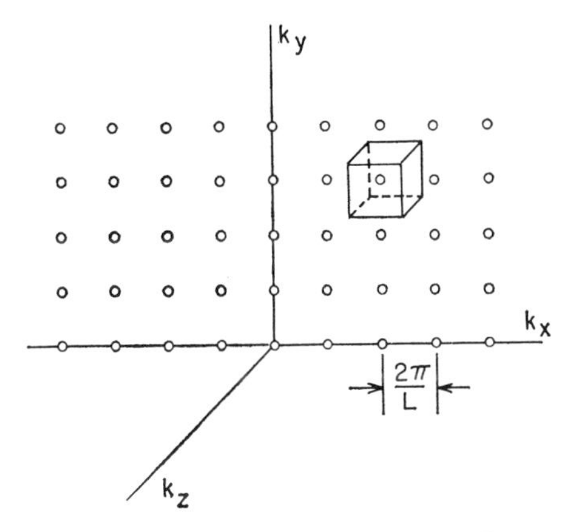

FIG. 12.3. Permitted states in **k**-space for cyclical boundary conditions, indicated by the points in the plane for $n_z = 0$. All of **k**-space would be filled if each allowed point were surrounded by a cubical cell of side $(2\pi/L)$, as exemplified by the cell for $n_x = +2$, $n_y = +3$, $n_z = 0$.

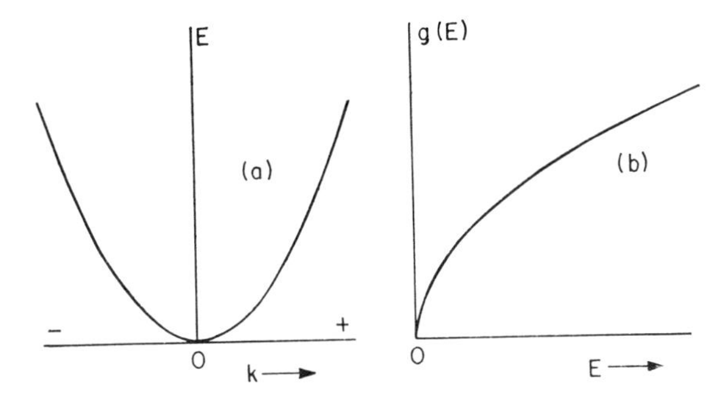

FIG. 12.4. (a) The parabolic relationship $(E) = (\hbar^2 k^2/2m_0)$ between wave-vector (in one dimension) and kinetic energy; and (b) the density of states as a function of kinetic energy for free electrons in a metal.

Now the energy and wave-vector of an electron state are connected by Eq. (121.2). Differentiating this and eliminating k in the combination with Eq. (121.6), the density of electron states at energy E is

$$g(E) = 4\pi(2m_0/h^2)^{3/2}E^{1/2} \tag{121.7}$$

Having considered the *electronic states* permitted by quantum theory, we must now turn to considerations of how *electrons* are distributed over the various states.

1.2.2 Pauli's Exclusion Principle and Fermi–Dirac Statistics

Consider a number of particles whose individual wave-functions (including spin) are $\psi_a^{(1)}$ for the first, $\psi_b^{(2)}$ for the second, $\psi_c^{(3)}$ for the third, and so on. The wave-function Ψ for the system as a whole is determined by these one-particle functions. Now if the particles are indistinguishable one from another, the function Ψ must be constructed in such a way that $|\Psi|^2$ is not affected by the interchange of a pair of particles. There are two possibilities for this:

(a) The symmetrical combination

$$\Psi_s = \sum_P \psi_a^{(1)}\psi_b^{(2)}\psi_c^{(3)}\ldots \tag{122.1}$$

with the sum taken over all permutations P of the arguments. For this method of combination, Ψ itself is not affected by any interchanges.

(b) The antisymmetrical combination

$$\Psi_a = \sum_P (-1)^r \psi_a^{(1)}\psi_b^{(2)}\psi_c^{(3)}\ldots \tag{122.2}$$

where r is the number of interchanges which must be made to obtain a permutation from the standard form. In determinantal form,

$$\Psi_a = \begin{vmatrix} \psi_a^{(1)} & \psi_a^{(2)} & \psi_a^{(3)} & \ldots \\ \psi_b^{(1)} & \psi_b^{(2)} & \psi_b^{(3)} & \ldots \\ \psi_c^{(1)} & \psi_c^{(2)} & \psi_c^{(3)} & \ldots \\ \cdot & \cdot & \cdot & \ldots \\ \cdot & \cdot & \cdot & \ldots \end{vmatrix} \tag{122.3}$$

Ψ_a changes sign when permutations are made, but $|\Psi|_a^2$ remains the same.

Note an interesting feature of the antisymmetrical arrangement, that Ψ_a vanishes whenever two particle functions are the same (since two rows of the determinant are then identical). In view of the Pauli principle that no two electrons in an atom can be in the same quantum state, this suggests that *electron* wave-functions combine in antisymmetrical ways.

Pauli's principle is a postulate introduced to explain certain experimental facts (notably the absence of a ground state in orthohelium). It acquires additional strength as a postulate when further results follow, such as the shell structure of the periodic system, and the success of Fermi–Dirac statistics in accounting for the behavior of large systems of electrons. For while Pauli applied his principle to electrons in an atom, Fermi and Dirac applied the same idea to any assemblage of electrons, that no two could have the same set of quantum numbers.

The relevance of this to the discussion in the previous sub-section of electronic states is that not more than one electron can be in any given state. Recalling the distribution of states in k-space for free electrons (Fig. 12.3) it can readily be seen that when electrons are placed in a system, as many as possible will execute motions characteristic of states with small $\mathbf{k}$ (and low energy), but it will still be obligatory for many electrons to occupy states of high energy—no matter how low the temperature. This is very different from the classical notion that all electrons would come to rest at the absolute zero of temperature.

The reasoning which leads to the distribution function of Fermi–Dirac statistics is rather detailed; this has been placed in an appendix in order to avoid going through all the arguments at this point. The final and important result is that for a system of indistinguishable particles which occupy quantum states in accordance with the Pauli principle, the thermal equilibrium probability of occupancy for a state of energy E is

$$f(E) = \frac{1}{1+\exp\left(\dfrac{E-\phi}{kT}\right)} \tag{122.4}$$

This is consistent with the classical distribution of (112.1) and (121.1) as a limiting case for energies considerably higher than ϕ, but for energies comparable with or lower than ϕ, Eq. (122.4) represents a far from classical situation. The form of the probability of occupancy function $f(E)$ as a function of energy is shown in Fig. 12.5 for the absolute zero of temperature and for a finite temperature T. For an energy equal to $\phi, f(E) = 0{\cdot}5$; while for energies higher or lower by an interval kT, $f(E) = (1+e)^{-1} = 0{\cdot}27$ or $f(E) = (1+1/e)^{-1} = 0{\cdot}73$, respectively. Only for energies within a few kT of ϕ is the probability of occupancy appreciably different from zero or unity.

The quantity ϕ is variously known as the Fermi level, Fermi surface, and electrochemical potential. The Fermi level behaves as a normalizing parameter, characterized by the number of electrons per unit volume, n_0, and by the density of states function. For ϕ is determined by the condition that the number of occupied states at all energies must be equal to the total number of electrons present:

$$n_0 = \int_{-\infty}^{\infty} n(E) \, . \, \mathrm{d}E = \int_{-\infty}^{\infty} f(E) \, . \, g(E) \, . \, \mathrm{d}E \qquad (122.5)$$

This is quite generally true, for the density of states function (121.7) characteristic of free electrons in a simple metal, or for the more complicated $g(E)$ required with semiconductors and multivalent metals.

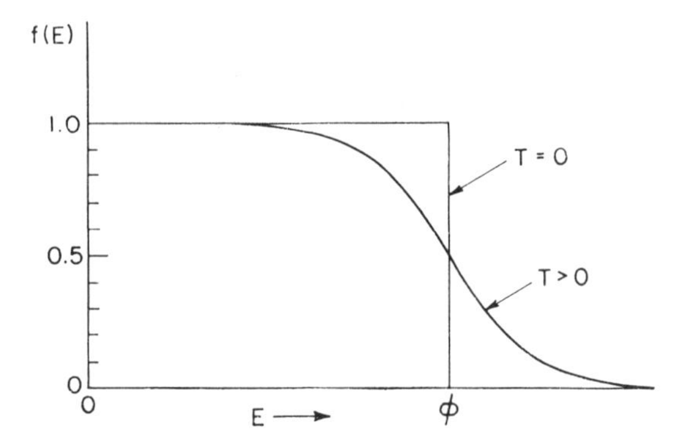

FIG. 12.5. The Fermi–Dirac probability function $f(E)$ as a function of energy for a finite temperature and for absolute zero temperature.

Continuing the historical approach it will be noted first how Sommerfeld fused Eqs. (121.7) and (122.4) to explain several characteristics of monovalent metals. In subsequent chapters it will frequently be necessary to reckon with Eq. (122.5) when $g(E)$ takes complex forms.

1.2.3 Degeneracy of an Electron Distribution. Sommerfeld's Model

Classical theories predict that each free electron should have a specific heat of $3k/2$. Then a metal with one free electron per atom should have a specific heat of 9 cal/mole, compared with 6 cal/mole for a non-metal above the Debye temperature. But the additional specific heat of the electron gas in a metal is experimentally very small and proportional to the absolute temperature. This is explained by Sommerfeld's quantized model, which is based on the following argument.

The density of permitted states is given by (121.7) when there is no variation of potential energy within a metal. In conformity with Eq. (122.5), the Fermi level must have an energy such that

$$n_0 = \int_{-\infty}^{\infty} f(E)g(E)\,.\,\mathrm{d}E = \int_{-\infty}^{\infty} \frac{4\pi(2m_0/h^2)^{3/2}E^{1/2}\,.\,\mathrm{d}E}{1+\exp\left[\dfrac{E-\phi}{kT}\right]} \qquad (123.1)$$

Fig. 12.6 illustrates how $n(E)$ will vary with energy above the supposed origin of zero kinetic energy, at 0°K and at a finite temperature.

The integration of Eq. (123.1) is very simple at $T = 0$°K, when *all* states are occupied up to the Fermi energy ϕ_0, and *all* those of higher energy empty:

$$n_0 = \int_0^{\phi_0} 4\pi\left[\frac{2m_0}{h^2}\right]^{3/2} E^{1/2}\,.\,\mathrm{d}E = \frac{8\pi}{3}\left[\frac{2m_0\phi_0}{h^2}\right]^{3/2} \qquad (123.2)$$

This statement can equally well be inverted, to note that corresponding with an electronic volume density n_0, the Fermi level at low temperatures must be

$$\phi_0 = \frac{h^2}{2m}\left[\frac{3n_0}{8\pi}\right]^{2/3} \qquad (123.3)$$

For a monovalent metal with a typical interatomic spacing of about 3Å, this Fermi energy comes to the surprisingly large value of $\phi_0 \sim 5$ eV, or 200 times larger than kT for room temperature!

Thus the curve drawn for $T > 0$ in Fig. 12.6 would actually require a temperature of several thousand degrees. At normal temperatures the levels are completely occupied *almost up to* the Fermi level, and *very few* electrons are to be found in states above the Fermi energy. ϕ does decrease on heating, as shown in the figure; but the change,

$$\phi_T - \phi_0 = -\frac{\pi^2 k^2 T^2}{12\phi_0}, \qquad kT \ll \phi_0 \qquad (123.4)$$

is very small at attainable temperatures.

The term *degenerate* is applied to an electron distribution for which the energy range of completely occupied levels is large compared with the width $\sim 2kT$ of the transition range. In a degenerate system, only a small fraction $\sim (kT/\phi_0)$ of electrons are capable of changing their energies in infinitesimal amounts.† This fraction alone is effective in determining those properties of a material which depend on electrons making a graduated response to a stimulus. As an example, we should expect the specific heat of an electron gas to be *degenerated* to a small

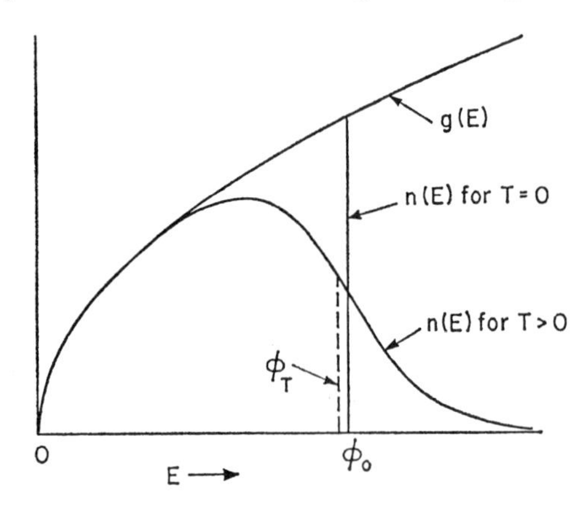

FIG. 12.6. Distribution of electron states $g(E)$ and of electrons in these states for the Sommerfeld free electron model, when the population in the metal is degenerate.

fraction (kT/ϕ_0) of its classical value—which is just the observed behavior in a metal at normal temperatures. The paramagnetic susceptibility of the electron gas is similarly degenerated (1927:**1**).

Sommerfeld noted that when the simple quantum conditions are applied, only electrons in states near the Fermi level contribute significantly to conductivities and galvanomagnetic coefficients. His expressions were calculated from the Boltzmann transport equation,

† Two electrons occupying low lying states may interchange, but since electrons are indistinguishable there is no observable result of such an exchange. An electron in a low energy state can only change significantly by being raised to an empty state near the Fermi level. In view of indistinguishability, this is equivalent to requiring all intermediate electrons to move up one step—a process of very low statistical weight.

solved on the assumption of isotropic elastic scattering. The flow of electrons in response to an external stimulus—electrical, magnetic or thermal—was always proportional to a member of the set of integrals

$$I_m = -\int_0^\infty E^m \lambda \frac{\partial f(E)}{\partial E} \,.\, \mathrm{d}E \tag{123.5}$$

where m is an integer and λ is the electron mean free path between scattering collisions. Now $\partial f/\partial E$ is finite only for the energy range immediately around the Fermi level (Fig. 12.7); then if λ is any reason-

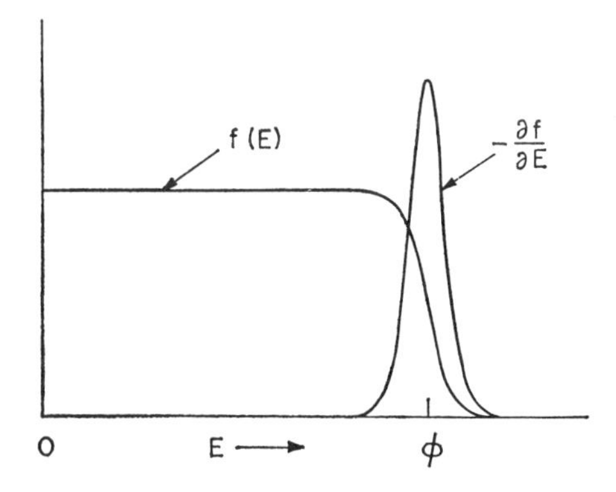

FIG. 12.7. The functions $f(E)$ and $-\partial f/\partial E$ for a degenerate electron distribution.

able function of energy, an integral of the form (123:5) receives appreciable contributions only from this small energy range. Sommerfeld showed, for example, that the electrical conductivity of a degenerate electron gas is given by

$$\sigma = \frac{n_0 e^2 \lambda(\phi)}{(2m_0\phi)^{1/2}} \tag{123.6}$$

where $\lambda(\phi)$ denotes the mean free path for an electron with the Fermi energy.

The only term in this expression which can be temperature-dependent is the mean free path. This is a little awkward, for the conductivity of simple metals is proportional to $1/T$, yet such a dependence of mean free path is not compatible with elastic scattering. Thus a correct theory of metallic behavior cannot be based on the approximations used so far. Nevertheless, the Sommerfeld theory is a considerable improvement over classical approaches, explaining specific heat degeneration, providing an improved value for the Wiedemann–Franz ratio, and giving results for Thomson, Seebeck, magnetoresistance and Hall coefficients which describe fairly well the behavior of the simplest monovalent metals.

A. H. Wilson (1953:**4**) has remarked that the most important feature of Sommerfeld's model is separation of the concepts of free electron and conduction electron. Only electrons in the energy range for which $(\partial f/\partial E)$ is finite can be regarded as conduction electrons.

The Sommerfeld approach to scattering is, however, unsatisfactory. For this model, as for the classical models, the theory gives no clue as to the proper numerical magnitude for the mean free path λ. Comparison with experimental conductivities suggests that $\lambda \sim 400$ Å at room temperature and may be as much as a factor of 10^4 larger at low temperatures.

If elastic scattering is rejected as being incompatible with the observed temperature dependence, then two sources of inelastic scattering present themselves. One source is that of point imperfections (impurity atoms, lattice vacancies, etc.)—this scattering is temperature-independent and gives a low-temperature residual resistance. A second inelastic scattering mechanism is provided by phonons (thermal lattice vibrations). Phonons could make the mean free path proportional to T^{-1} since λ is of the same order of magnitude as the wavelength of average acoustic phonons.

Before investigating this attractive possibility, it is necessary to explain how the electronic mean free path can be very large in perfectly periodic crystal lattices. An answer to this problem is given by the band theory of solids.

1.3 THE BAND THEORY OF SOLIDS

The free electron theory of the previous section introduced the important concepts of quantized distribution in an electron population. This theory foundered on the insertion of the concept that electrons are elastically scattered by nuclei, which could not be reconciled with the temperature dependence of conductivities in metals. Now inelastic scattering could be imposed on Sommerfeld's model—for example, interaction with phonons—but this is hardly a wise procedure when it is not obvious why *elastic* scattering does *not* occur in a perfect crystal. Moreover, the free electron model cannot cope with complicated multi-valent metals and does not explain why some materials are metals and others are semiconductors or insulators.

A good reason for these deficiencies is that the free electron theory ignores the potential fields in a solid. We shall now explore the theory resulting from one method of taking the crystalline potential into account, supposing a perfect lattice in order to calculate the distribution of electrons in energy.†

1.3.1 Schrödinger's Equation—One-electron Functions

The band theory of solids is based on a single electron approximation, whereby the permissible properties of one electron are calculated from an equation allowing for the effect of everything else in the crystal. The use of one-electron wave-functions permits the use of Fermi–Dirac statistics. The advantages and limitations of the band model as compared with other possible schemes for representing outer shell electrons in a solid are discussed in Sub-section 1.3.5.

The adoption of single electron wave-functions involves the important assumption that an *effective field* can be introduced into the wave-equation to replace that due to all other electrons present. This is a *self-consistent field*, as used by Hartree (1928:**2**), Fock (1930:**1**) and others in extensive attempts to solve the multi-electron problems of atoms and molecules. In his approach to electrons in solids, Bloch (1928:**3**) assumed that one-electron wave-functions could be constructed which would satisfy Schrödinger's equation with an appropriate expression for this crystal field. The potential experienced by an electron depends on:

(1) The periodic array of atomic cores in the crystal. The term "core" includes the nucleus and all inner electronic shells which are not appreciably affected by the proximity of other atoms.

† The concept of a finite mean free path resulting from some scattering mechanism is necessary for an evaluation of transport phenomena. But this idea can be inserted *after* the model of a perfectly periodic crystal lattice has been set up.

(2) All other outer shell electrons from every atom in the crystal.

If the atoms remain rigidly fixed in position, the contribution of the cores to the potential will vary spatially with the periodicity of the lattice. It seemed reasonable to Bloch that the time-averaged effect of all the outer shell electrons should *also* be the same in each unit cell of the crystal—this satisfies requirements for electrical neutrality and crudely takes account of electron–electron repulsion.

On this basis, then, the *total* crystal potential $V(\mathbf{r})$ will have the threefold periodicity of the lattice. Bloch showed that the solutions of the Schrödinger equation

$$\frac{\hbar^2}{2m_0}\nabla^2\psi+[E-V(\mathbf{r})]\psi = 0 \tag{131.1}$$

are then of the form

$$\psi = U_k(\mathbf{r}) \,.\, \exp(i\mathbf{k}\,.\,\mathbf{r}) \tag{131.2}$$

where U is a function (depending in general on the wave-vector $\mathbf{k}$) which also has the periodicity of the lattice.† When $\mathbf{k}$ is real, the solutions are running plane waves modulated with the periodicity of the lattice; these solutions are well behaved and acceptable. But solutions corresponding with an imaginary $\mathbf{k}$ must be discarded, since the wave-function (131.2) is not then well behaved.

This has interesting consequences. For whatever the concrete form of the potential $V(r)$, there must be some ranges of the eigen-energy E which correspond with real values of $\mathbf{k}$ and other ranges for which $\mathbf{k}$ can only be imaginary. For the ranges of E where $\mathbf{k}$ is real, electron functions exist. For the energy ranges where $\mathbf{k}$ is imaginary, no electron can exist in a perfectly periodic lattice.

The energy ranges for which stable solutions exist are known as the *permitted electron bands* of the solid. We are very interested in finding out the positions (on an energy scale) of these bands and of the *forbidden energy gaps* between the bands, and also to know the distribution of permitted electron levels within the bands. All of this depends on the symmetry of the crystal structure, the interatomic spacing and on the types of atom setting up the crystal field.

† This result was previously known in pure mathematics as Floquet's theorem (1927:**2**).

As an indication of the complexity in a real three-dimensional solid, it should be noted that constant energy surfaces in **k**-space will not normally be spherical. This marks a difference from the free electron model, where energy was expressible as $(\hbar^2 k^2/2m_0)$ and a sphere centered on the origin of **k**-space was always a constant energy surface. Referring to Fig. 13.1, for the free electron model OA was the direction of the waves associated with the state A and was also the direction of motion of an electron—considered as a packet of waves around the

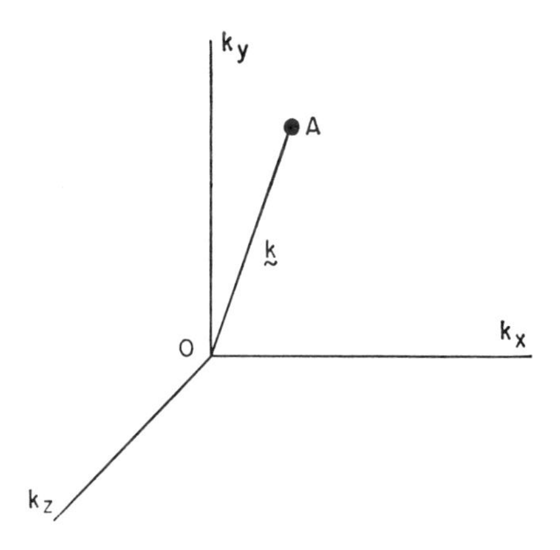

FIG. 13.1. **k**-space.

point A. The electron moved (in real space) along the direction normal to the energy contour (in **k**-space) and this was just the direction OA.

For band theory, taking into account the periodic crystal field, individual waves around A have a phase velocity in the direction OA, but the group velocity of the wave-packet (which describes the direction of motion of the electron) must be normal to the energy contour in **k**-space, and this may have a direction quite different from OA.

At the risk of repetitiousness, it is again remarked that permitted wave-functions (131.2) are the same in every unit cell of a periodic lattice. Thus the packet of waves describing an electron in an allowed state is not attenuated as the electron moves through the crystal. This is relevant to the earlier discussion of free electron theory, which was unable to explain why electronic mean free paths should be so large, particularly at low temperatures. It now emerges in an entirely natural way that an electron moving under the influence of a perfectly periodic potential undergoes no scattering—the mean free path is infinite. Scattering can only occur to yield a finite mean free path if the periodicity of the potential is broken; this occurs at grain boundaries, under the influence of localized imperfections such as foreign atoms or lattice vacancies, and through the modulation of interatomic spacings by thermal vibrations.

That an electron wave should be transmitted without attenuation by a periodic lattice is a result which has many analogies in physics. Brillouin (1946:**1**) has discussed this topic at length, illustrating the same mathematical methods in connection with acoustical and electrical circuit problems as well as band theory. Shockley (1950:**1**) uses the multi-section electrical transmission network as a foil with which to demonstrate many features of band theory. For instance, he remarks on the formal similarity between the problem of attenuation in a non-uniform transmission line and that of electron scattering by thermal vibrations in semiconductors.†

Localized imperfections are a source not only of scattering but also of localized energy states. Whereas the only states in an infinitely large perfectly periodic crystal are those described by Bloch waves and forming the "permitted bands", the states introduced by impurities may have energies within the forbidden gaps. In many cases the impurity states are not truly new, but are descended from states which have been split off from the bands by the powerful potential of the imperfection.

There is an important difference between a band state and an impurity state. For the former is non-localized, representing a charge density spread uniformly throughout the crystal; yet the wave-function of the latter is localized in the vicinity of the impurity. An electron occupying an impurity state is said to be *bound* to the impurity, for such an electron is not free—as the band electrons are free—to move anywhere in the crystal. Many properties of semiconductors are controlled by the extent to which electrons can be released from these bound impurity states.

† In the deformation potential approach of Shockley and Bardeen (1949:**1**) to this type of scattering, it is assumed that the modulation of interatomic spacing involved in the thermal vibration perturbs the edges of the energy bands. This has consequences analogous to those of mismatch in a transmission line.

1.3.2 The Energy–Wave-Vector Relationship. Brillouin Zones

A number of attempts have been made in recent years to calculate the band structures of real solids. As an example, one may note the work of Herman (1954:**1**, 1955:**7**) on germanium and silicon. Complicated iterative techniques must be used, effective wave-functions being synthesized from series of terms with appropriate atomic configurations. For the results to have much rapport with reality, the amount of work required is enormous. Even so, the results of Kronig and Penney's simple calculations (1930:**2**) give some insight into the relationship of energy E and wave-vector $\mathbf{k}$ when there is a periodic crystal potential. Kronig and Penney supposed a monatomic one-dimensional crystal of lattice spacing a in the x-direction, and represented the potential by a rectangular pulse at each lattice site. They then proceeded to the limiting case of a potential pulse with given area as this became infinitely high and infinitesimally wide (a delta function potential). Fig. 13.2 shows the type of result they obtained for the dependence of E on k_x. The forbidden ranges of energy will be noted. As the amplitude of the delta function potential is reduced to zero, the forbidden gaps disappear and the curve merges with the dashed parabola.

$$E = (\hbar^2 k_x^2/2m_0) \tag{132.1}$$

of the Sommerfeld model. On the other hand, when the potential becomes infinitely strong, only the discrete set of energies

$$E_n = (n^2 h^2/8m_0 a^2) \tag{132.2}$$

are allowed. (These are just the eigenvalues of an electron in an enclosure of length a.) In all cases, the wave-function is of the form

$$\psi = U_k(x)\,.\,\exp(ik_x x) \tag{132.3}$$

It is evident in Fig. 13.2 that the energy discontinuities occur for $k_x = (n\pi/a)$ where n is any (positive or negative) integer. These are the values of k_x which give ψ itself the perfect periodicity of Kronig's and Penney's one-dimensional lattice, and form an essential feature of solutions in terms of Bloch waves, which is preserved in the description of real three-dimensional structures.

Brillouin (1946:**1**) and Seitz (1940:**1**) have discussed in detail the permissible wave-functions for lattices in more than one dimension, and the values of $\mathbf{k}$ which correspond with an energy discontinuity. The positions in $\mathbf{k}$-space for which discontinuities occur depend on the

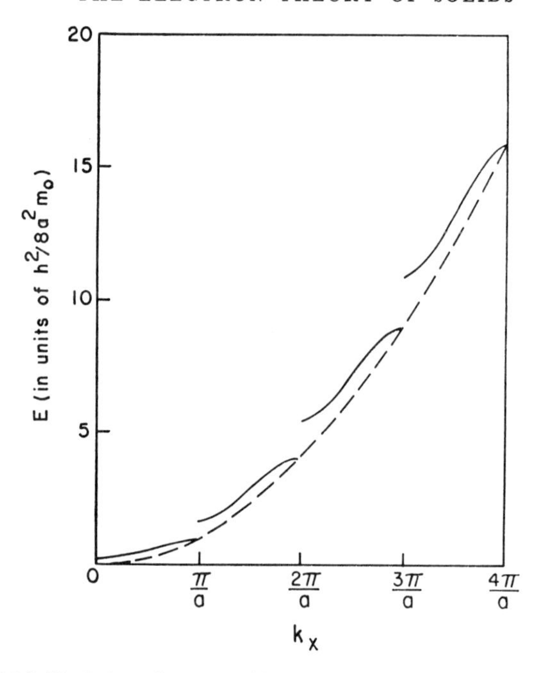

FIG. 13.2. Variation of energy with wave-vector (one-dimensional) for the Kronig–Penney model with a finite delta function crystal potential.

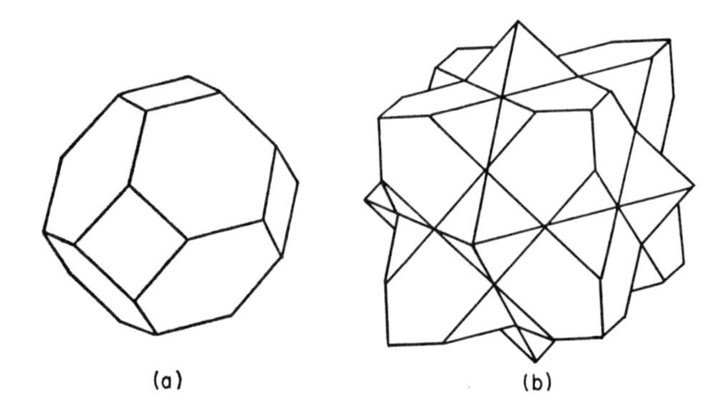

FIG. 13.3. The first two Brillouin zone boundaries for a face-centered cubic lattice. Zones of the same shape are found for lattices derived from F.C.C., such as the zincblende and diamond structures. After Seitz (1940:**1**).

symmetry of the crystal structure and on the interatomic spacings; they form a series of surfaces centered on the origin of **k**-space. These surfaces are polyhedral, with faces corresponding to crystallographic directions. Fig. 13.3 shows the first two members of the series of surfaces when the crystal structure is face-centered cubic, and Fig. 13.4 similarly

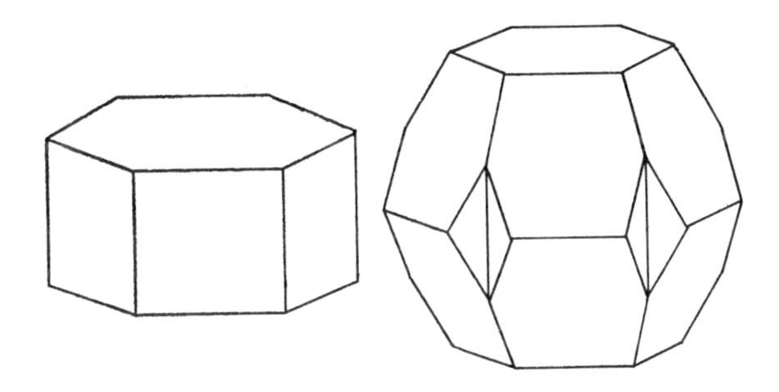

Fig. 13.4. The first two Brillouin zones for a close-packed hexagonal lattice. After Seitz (1940:**1**).

illustrates the first two surfaces in **k**-space when the atoms are in a close-packed hexagonal array.

The region lying *between* two successive polyhedra in **k**-space is known as a *Brillouin zone*. The relationships of the polyhedra are such that each Brillouin zone occupies the same volume of **k**-space. This volume is sufficient to accommodate $2N$ electron states, where N is the total number of atoms in the crystal.†

That each Brillouin zone should contain two states (one of each spin choice) for every atom is entirely to be expected, since the band system of a solid arises naturally from the discrete energy levels of an isolated atom. Each level becomes broadened through interaction between the closely spaced atoms of a solid in such a way that the energy range of a band is independent of the number of atoms in the crystal but depends upon their interatomic spacing and on the energy level from which the band arose. Fig. 13.5 illustrates this schematically for two successive quantum states when a small number of atoms are brought together.

† This follows from the volume of **k**-space encompassed by a Brillouin zone and from the density of electron states in **k**-space (Sub-section 1.2.1).

When the number of atoms in the crystal is very large (as is the case for any real crystal), the $2N$ states in each band are exceedingly closely spaced in energy, but the *distribution* of states in energy is still the same.

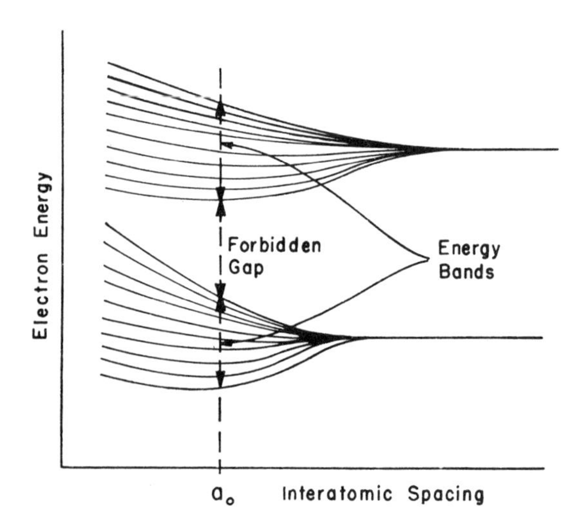

FIG. 13.5. Qualitative picture of the manner in which permitted energy bands and forbidden gaps arise from discrete atomic energy levels, broadened by interatomic coupling.

We shall expect to see:

one zone arising from atomic $1s$ states	K shell
one zone arising from atomic $2s$ states three zones arising from atomic $2p$ states	L shell
one zone arising from atomic $3s$ states three zones arising from atomic $3p$ states five zones arising from atomic $3d$ states	M shell

and so on. Electrons which occupied inner shell states in an isolated atom are not much affected by the proximity of other atoms—these electrons are still very closely associated with a single nucleus. Accordingly, the first few Brillouin zones describe states with very limited ranges of energy. But the zones corresponding with the outermost electrons may cover a broad range of energy; electrons in such states belong to the crystal as a whole rather than being identifiable with any one atom.

After the first few zones of tightly bound electrons are over, it is frequently found that subsequent zones overlap in energy. Now for a given direction in **k**-space there is an increase in energy on passing a zone boundary, but it often happens that the highest energy attainable

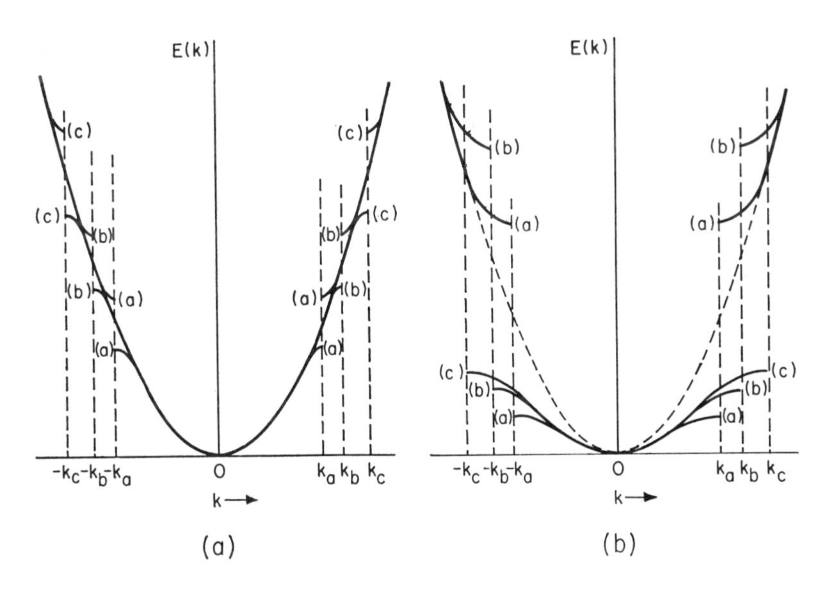

FIG. 13.6. Dependence of energy on wave-vector (a) for a case where overlap occurs between two Brillouin zones (the second zone starts in some directions with energy lower than the highest energies attainable for other directions in the first zone) and (b) for a situation with no overlap. After Seitz (1940:**1**)

in one zone is larger than the lowest energy for a *different* direction in the next zone. There is then no forbidden energy gap between the pair of zones, and they are said to *overlap*, forming a band of $4N$ states. Part (a) of Fig. 13.6 shows a situation of overlapping zones, while there is evidently no possibility of overlap for the case of part (b).

The actual resultant bands of a crystal may have $2N$, $4N$, $6N$, etc., states, and perhaps show little superficial resemblance to the original atomic levels. When a band does show characteristic features of atomic states, it is often referred to by the atomic designation.†

1.3.3 Filling of Energy Bands—Metals and Insulators

Band theory offers a highly satisfactory reason for the distinction between metals and non-metals. This may be appreciated by visualizing a solid from which all the outer electrons of each atom have been removed, leaving just the periodic array of atomic cores (nucleus plus tightly bound closed shells). If the electrons are now restored to the solid, one by one, the first ones added will assume the lowest states in the lowest empty band. As more electrons are added, this band fills up until every state in it is occupied. Further electrons must enter the lowest state in the next band, and so on until the full complement is present and the solid is electrically neutral.

In each completely full band, electrons do not enjoy freedom of response to an externally applied field—they cannot take part in conduction. This follows from the arguments used in Sub-section 1.2.3, that electrons can only *interchange* states, with no observable result.

Whether a solid is a metal or insulator now depends on the occupancy of the highest band containing any electrons. If this band is only partly full, the Fermi level is part way up the band. Electrons near the Fermi energy can take part in conduction, etc. But if the highest occupied band is *completely full*, then no electrons are available for conduction in *any* band and the material is an insulator. The condition depends on the number of electrons per atom since each band has $2N$ states or a multiple of this.

As an example, sodium has eleven electrons. Of these, two occupy states in the $1s$ band (K shell), eight occupy states in $2s$ and $2p$ bands (L shell), one is available for the lowest band in the M shell. Then if the $3s$ band in sodium is a simple zone, this band is half full. If there is any overlap between $3s$ and $3p$ zones, the resultant band is less than half full. In either case, sodium would be expected to behave as a metallic conductor.

The next element, magnesium, has twelve electrons, two of which are available for the M shell bands. This element would be insulating if the

† Thus for example in discussing the properties of the iron group of transition elements, reference is often made to the $4s$ band (of $2N$ states) and to the $3d$ band (of $10N$ states, formed by overlap of the five $3d$ Brillouin zones).

$3s$ band were completely lower in energy than any states of $3p$ bands. The interatomic potential in Mg actually takes a form which produces a small overlap of the $3s$ and $3p$ bands, and so metallic behavior is made possible.

Silicon has fourteen electrons per atom, of which four must go into $3s$ and $3p$ states. The periodic potential in this material is such that, for the interatomic spacing of solid silicon, the eight states divide into a band of $4N$ states, then a gap, then an upper band with the remaining $4N$ states. The electron supply is just sufficient to fill the lower band and leave the upper band completely empty. We expect then to find that silicon is an insulator, and indeed the electrical conductivity of pure silicon is extremely small at low temperatures.

1.3.4 Thermal Excitation in Semiconductors

On warming any insulator, a conductivity is found which increases with temperature. It was pointed out by Wilson (1931:**1**) that this can result from thermal excitation of electrons from the highest occupied band (known as the valence band) to the lowest empty band (the conduction band). The term *intrinsic semiconductor* is used to denote a material which derives its conduction from this mechanism, and the energy difference by which an electron must be elevated is known as the intrinsic gap (Fig. 13.7). Thermal vibrations co-operate to raise electrons into the conduction band, and while there they are capable of taking part in conduction. The density of electrons in the conduction band for thermal equilibrium is determined by a dynamic balance of thermal excitation and subsequent de-excitation. This depends principally on the intrinsic gap width and the temperature, in the form

$$n_i \propto \exp(-E_i/2kT) \qquad (134.1)$$

All of this will be discussed in much more detail in Sub-section 2.3.

When an electron has been raised to the conduction band, a vacant state exists in the valence band. This provides some slight freedom for other electrons in that band to change their energies in response to a field. The overall effect is that of a particle with positive mass and charge; this particle is called a positive "hole". The wave-function for a full band with one electron missing shows properties formally equivalent to the situation of one positive charge in an otherwise empty "hole" band (1931:**4**). Shockley (1950:**1**) has shown this in

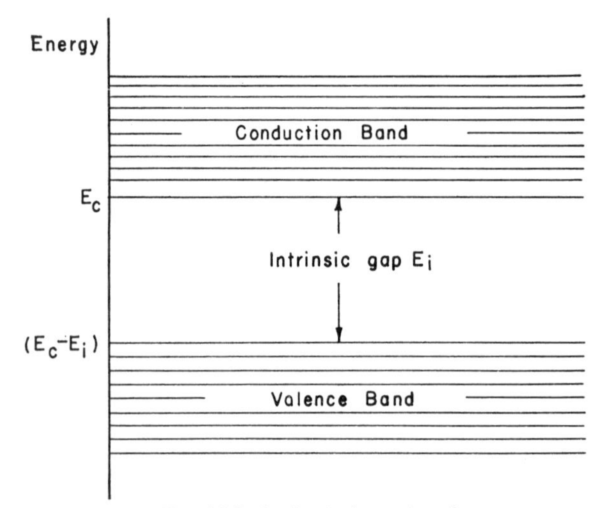

FIG. 13.7. An intrinsic semiconductor.

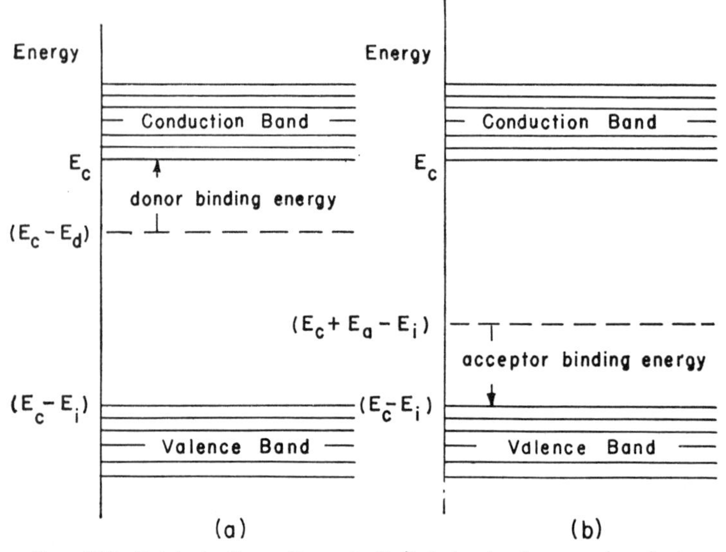

FIG. 13.8. Extrinsic (impurity-controlled) behavior in a semiconductor, showing the action of (a) donor impurities to provide possible free electrons (*n*-type semiconductor), and (b) acceptor impurities to make hole conduction possible (*p*-type semiconductor).

considerable detail, and such arguments give one confidence in dealing with holes as "real" particles. Electrical conductivity and other associated properties reflect the response both of free electrons *and* free holes to an applied stimulus.

Shortly after his first paper on intrinsic excitation in semiconductors, Wilson (1931:**2**) discussed the influence of impurity states.† He noted that since localized levels may correspond with energies within the intrinsic gap, either free electrons *or* free holes may be thermally excited at temperatures too low for appreciable intrinsic excitation. When the free carriers produced are predominantly electrons, the semiconductor is said to be extrinsic *n*-type. Conditions are said to be extrinsic *p*-type for a semiconductor containing predominantly free holes. The two kinds of situations can arise in the manner shown in Fig. 13.8.

An impurity or flaw which—when electrically neutral—has an electron fairly weakly bound to it is called a *donor center*. The weakly bound electron can be described in terms of a level at energy E_d below the bottom of the conduction band, and the opportunities for exciting this electron thermally to the free states are proportional to

$$\exp(-E_d/kT)$$

The number of free electrons for thermal equilibrium at any temperature depends on a dynamic balance of excitation *from* donors and recapture *by* these impurities.

Another class of impurity is the *acceptor center*, which in electrical neutrality offers a level with an electron vacancy at an energy E_a above the valence band. A valence band electron has a probability proportional to $\exp(-E_a/kT)$ of being excited into the acceptor state, leaving a free hole behind in the valence band. The acceptor can be considered as having a "bound hole" in its neutral condition, which is capable of being thermally excited *down* to the valence band.

Some kinds of flaw provide more than one donor or acceptor level, and can indeed take on the attributes of donor *and* acceptor in different states of ionization. This complicates the picture but does not obscure the general classification of excitation modes. More will be said about localized levels in Section 1.6.

† Impurity states are discussed in more detail in Section 1.6. For the present we may note that any disturbance of the periodicity of the crystal lattice may give rise to localized "impurity" or "flaw" states.

1.3.5 Validity of the Band Model

The movement of electrons in crystals is governed by more complex laws than the movement of a smaller number of electrons in an atom or a molecule. This is due, in the first place, to the larger number of electrons and nuclei in a macroscopic body. The problems of electron motion in solids require the use of special approximate methods. Since it is often difficult to determine the limits of applicability for these approximations, doubts can arise as to the extent to which theoretical results correspond with reality.

In the previous pages we have introduced the basic concepts of band theory, based on a one-electron approximation for motion in a solid; the problem of the interaction of electrons is in this theory reduced to a single-electron problem by the device of the self-consistent field. Before using the band concept freely (as we shall for the remainder of this book), it is useful to review the validity of this model. To what extent then is the band theory legitimate for describing solids? Slater (1959:**1**) suggests that this question may be asked in two ways. Firstly, how well do the *consequences* of band theory agree with experiment? And secondly, how well does the band picture agree with the more elaborate theory which we should find by rigorously applying wave-mechanical principles to the problem of a solid?

Only positive answers to the latter question can be reassuring to a theoretician; for apparent agreement of theory and experiment carries no guarantee that the theory is the correct one. Even so, the ever-broadening areas of agreement which have developed since the early 1950's between energy band calculations and more detailed experimental observations [compare for instance (1958:**1**) and (1958:**2**)] both for semiconductors and metals provide considerable encouragement for the theory. While metals are probably less understood in detail than certain semiconductors at the present time, it is interesting to note that band theory has traditionally and successfully been used for a description of the metallic state (1952:**1**). This despite the objections of some Russian writers (e.g. 1951:**1**, 1951:**2**) who evidently feel that agreement between band theory and the behavior of degenerate semiconductors or metals occurs in spite of the theory rather than because of it! Falicov and Heine (1961:**4**) comment on a wide range of experimental results which point to the existence of a "sharp" Fermi surface in metals. This, of course, is the expectation of the one-electron model.

Before turning to theoretical, rather than experimental, justifications of the band model, it should be remarked that a one-electron theory is not to be abandoned lightly. For only within the framework of a one-electron theory is it possible to use the Fermi–Dirac distribution function for a statistical description of the total electron population, and to use the Boltzmann kinetic equation for the distribution function in applied electric and magnetic fields. Multi-electron theories of electron transport are possible (1959:**2**) but far from simple.

Having said this, let us consider some respects in which the simple theory has been held to be possibly inadequate. By band theory we mean that electron wave-functions are solutions of Eq. (131.1) and that the interaction of an electron with the diffused charge of all other electrons in the system may be represented by a suitable potential. Electrons in different states do not necessarily see the same potential. Now the Hartree–Fock self-consistent field approach is known to be highly successful for multi-electron atoms, but as applied to a crystal it takes but poor account of correlations in electron motion. This means that, even with the most diligent search for the best effective potential, a set of energy bands calculated for a crystal is not likely to correspond too closely with the actual electronic configuration of the crystal. It does *not* mean that the concept of electrons distributed in a set of energy bands is false.

A variety of multi-electron methods have been developed to describe the correlation between electrons more completely. In the plasma oscillation method of Bohm and Pines (1953:**1**, 1955:**1**), a screened Coulomb interaction is used between electron pairs. Hubbard (1955:**2**) has explored some variations of the plasmon approach. Methods based on use of the density matrix have been used by several authors (e.g. 1955:**3**, 1948:**1**), A very interesting approach is that of "elementary excitations" (1959:**3**, 1957:**2**, 1949:**2**); the energy of a system of interacting electrons is represented as the sum of the energies of separate non-interacting "quasi-particles", governed by some statistical law.†

The impressive conclusion of all these—and other—multi-electron theories is that they validate all the qualitative features of the simple band theory. Alternation of permitted and forbidden ranges of energy, the concepts of reduced wave-vector and effective mass (see Section 1.4) all are preserved in the more exotic theories. Herman (1958:**1**) remarks "there is good reason to believe that the success of the energy band

† The treatment of quasi-particles has much in common with the methods of quantum electrodynamics (field theory). The unity of the several branches of physics involving many-particle interactions is well brought out by ter Haar (1958:**7**).

theory in accounting for a wide variety of experimental observations is far from accidental. The essential features of the energy band theory will probably persist in future, more sophisticated, theories". He notes that the multi-electron methods provide a great deal of physical insight into the reasons why the one-electron methods are actually as successful as they are.

Aside from the question of the self-consistent field, a prominent feature of band theory is that the nuclei are supposed to form a perfectly periodic array. At any temperature other than absolute zero, thermal lattice vibrations will ensure that this is not the case; it is conventionally supposed that the modification of internuclear distances by these vibrations can be allowed for by perturbation methods *after* the band scheme of the unperturbed array has been set up. A possibly more potent threat to the ideas of electron bands lies in the question: how much does an electron deform the lattice in its vicinity? This is the question of the distinction between a free electron and a polaron.

If atoms near to an electron in an ionic crystal are polarized and displaced through Coulomb interaction with the electron, the term polaron is given to the complex of electron plus accompanying polarization. Landau (1933:**1**) noted that the energy of the system is lowered as a result of this polarization and suggested that the electron might be "trapped" by its own field.† Early calculations by Pekar (1946:**2**) led to a result that an electron *could* be self-localized in an ionic crystal, but subsequent work of the same author (1949:**3**, 1953:**9**) revealed that this was not the case. Pekar still found that a polaron should be much less mobile than a "free electron", with a different temperature dependence of mobility. (Polaron states do form a set of bands which are filled in accordance with Fermi statistics, but the "inertia polarization" modifies the dependence of energy on wave propagation vector in a way which tends to give the polaron a very large effective mass.) Gubanov *et al.* (1960:**8**) have reported an experimental polaron mass in Cu_2O which agrees well with Pekar's theory.

While Pekar and some other Russian writers evidently feel that polaron states must be used for semiconductors with ionic lattices, another school of thought (e.g. 1950:**2**, 1956:**1**) feels that the distinction between an electron and a polaron is not a very strong one. This school recognizes that some inertia polarization does occur in an ionic crystal,

† It was at one time thought (1936:**2**, 1937:**3**) that self-trapped electrons might be responsible for the well-known color centers in alkali halide crystals, but it is now known that color centers arise from electron trapping at vacant lattice sites.

but concludes that this produces only a minor shift of the energies corresponding with band edges.

Band theory in its basic form fails in another respect to give full expression to the behavior of the electron system in a solid—it ignores multiplet structure. In metals with partially filled *d* and *f* shells the opportunities for complicated multiplet structure are overwhelming, and even in the highly simplified case of a semiconductor the structure known as an exciton can persist for a finite time. Frenkel (1931:**3**) described an exciton as an electron and a hole situated at the same lattice cell, which jump simultaneously from cell to cell. It was soon appreciated (1937:**1**, 1938:**1**) that in an exciton the electron and hole may be many lattice spacings apart; they form a rotating pair with a coulombic attraction modified by the crystal. The system has a ground state and a series of excited states,† terminating with the liberation of hole and electron.

It is interesting that, while excitons do not form an integral result of a one-electron theory, they can be described very well once the properties of the valence and conduction bands are known (1956:**9**).

We have been attempting in the face of some objections to justify the use of the Bloch collective electron model which generates the band theory. It should now be noted that there are some materials whose behavior is at variance with the normal provisions of band theory. Oxide semiconductors such as αFe_2O_3, CoO and NiO provide excellent examples of this apparently paradoxical situation.

It has been known for a long time that these materials have the properties normally associated with semiconductors. In the pure state they have an extremely low electrical conductivity, and a many-fold increase can be provoked by departures from lattice perfection. Thus extrinsic conduction in NiO can be encouraged by departures from stoichiometric proportions (1949:**7**, 1951:**12**), which is easily accomplished by controlling the oxygen vapor pressure at high temperatures (1934:**1**). Vacant anion sites then behave as acceptors. An acceptor can also be produced by a "controlled valency" procedure (1948:**3**, 1950:**6**) such as the replacement of a nickel atom in the NiO lattice with a lithium one.

Now the nickel ion in NiO is in the $(3d)^8$ configuration; thus whether the 3*d* band of 10 states per atom is split by the cubic crystal field into sub-bands of 4 + 6 states or not, nickel oxide should—according to the

† When the electron–hole spacing is large, the energy levels may be hydrogenic, renormalized by the dielectric constant.

Bloch model—have a partially filled band. In accordance with Wilson's classification,this compound (and the others like it) should be metallic, yet it is not. The paradox was first discussed by de Boer and Verwey (1937:**2**), who suggested that metallic conduction is inhibited by a very large interatomic potential barrier. This means in essence that the Bloch picture is not applicable to materials such as NiO; perhaps, then, the Heitler–London (1927:**3**) procedure should be used, in which electrons are associated with individual atoms.

The inapplicability of the Bloch approach for materials of large interatomic spacing has been argued very persuasively by Mott (1949:**6**, 1956:**3**), who points out that the Heitler–London and Bloch models are *not* different approximations to the same exact wave-function. Mott shows that when a material of large interatomic spacing such as NiO is treated from the Heitler–London viewpoint, energy is required to create the polar states (such as some Ni^{+} and Ni^{3+} in NiO rather than all Ni^{2+} ions) which are necessary for conduction. According to this picture, if the lattice constant were progressively decreased, a point would be abruptly reached where a lower energy could be obtained with many electrons available for conduction. From this critical lattice constant downwards, the Bloch picture would be appropriate.

In another approach to these compounds, Yamashita and Kurosawa (1958:**19**) start essentially from the Heitler–London viewpoint, but treat the electron–phonon interaction in zero order to argue that electrons should be self-trapped. The periodic potential is then used as a perturbation to show that the self-trapped configuration can migrate through the crystal. This is a concept similar to those applied (e.g. 1959:**12**) in the theory of impurity conduction via weakly interacting impurities.

Slater (1951:**11**) and Heikes (1955:**24**) think it significant that the anomalous compounds of the NiO type are antiferromagnetic. They suggest that a system of energy bands would be modified by the additional field of the magnetic superlattice, superimposed on the normal crystal potential, and that for an antiferromagnetic material this could split the bands in a manner which would make the highest occupied one completely full. This approach sounds attractive, but it does not explain why these compounds do not become metallic in nature above the Néel temperature. Moreover, Katz (1952:**10**) points out that the conditions necessary for band splitting will rarely be achieved.

It is not really surprising that some groups of materials elude the ordinary classifications. It is more a matter for surprise that *so many* materials can be classified from a rather small number of general principles.

The transport properties of electrons in the bands of a semiconductor or metal are conventionally developed from a kinetic approach (see 1953:**4** and 1960:**19**) based on the Boltzmann equation. As Joffé (1960:**22**) emphasizes, this is improper for low mobility semiconductors. When $\mu \lesssim 5$ cm^2/volt sec [as is the case for elemental semiconductors such as boron (1957:**38**) and selenium (1951:**19**), for many inorganic compounds, and for almost all organic semiconductors], the mean free path deduced from a kinetic approach turns out to be smaller than interatomic distances. For such materials the "mean free path" concept loses its meaning, and "mobility" has a changed significance. Of course, this affects only the way electrons must be regarded as undergoing scattering from one state to another in a band. The existence of energy bands in these solids is not directly in question.

As a final reflection on the reality of energy bands for electrons in many solids, we may take note of the fact that the conductivities and other electrical properties of some metals and semiconductors are virtually unchanged in melting, suggesting that a band structure is preserved even though there is no longer any long-range order.† This is not really surprising if we recall that in band theory the influence of everything beyond one or two atomic spacings is lumped into a self-consistent field. The division of permitted electron states into groups or bands is dictated by the nature of the short-range order, and this can be the same in a highly ordered crystalline lattice, in an amorphous phase of the same solid (1960:**22**) or in the liquid phase.

1.4 THE EFFECTIVE MASS OF CHARGE CARRIERS

It is now necessary to consider in more detail the mathematical formulation of the band model. This leads to a description of the E–$\mathbf{k}$ relationship and the distribution of states in energy in terms of an "effective mass" tensor.

† Some other semiconductors become metallic on melting. This is true for instance of germanium, in which a change of co-ordination number (from 4 to 6) occurs at the melting point. This is analogous to the reversion of semiconducting gray tin to metallic white tin at 17°C when the co-ordination number makes the same change, and demonstrates that the choice between semiconducting or metallic behavior depends on co-ordination number (short-range order) rather than on the existence of long-range order.

1.4.1 Phase and Group Velocities

From the discussions in Section 1.3 it is evident that solutions of the (time-dependent) Schrödinger equation when a periodic potential is present are plane waves of the form

$$\psi = U_k(\mathbf{r}) \exp[i(\mathbf{k} \cdot \mathbf{r} - \omega_k t)] \tag{141.1}$$

Here a probability wave of angular frequency ω moves through the solid. The *long-term* probability density is of course the same in every cell, since an electron of any energy which is an eigenvalue of the wave equation can move anywhere in the crystal, even though its energy E may be lower than the peak of the periodic potential.

The phase velocity (ω/k) of the probability wave is not important. What *is* important is the velocity of the actual electron expressed as a wave packet. This is the group velocity.

$$\mathbf{v} = \nabla_{\mathbf{k}}\omega \tag{141.2}$$

and since $E = \hbar\omega$ we can alternatively write the group velocity as

$$\mathbf{v} = \frac{1}{\hbar}\nabla_{\mathbf{k}}E \tag{141.3}$$

A particular point in **k**-space with a certain energy characterizes the motion of an electron (in real space) in a straight line with uniform velocity **v**. It is interesting that the electron's behavior can be described without knowing the *absolute* value of **k**. As will be seen below, it is necessary only to know the value of **k** relative to that at a zone boundary. This leads to a useful simplification of the zone scheme.

1.4.2 The Reduced Zone

In discussing the simple one-dimensional Kronig–Penney model in Section 1.3.2, it was noted that zone boundaries occurred whenever k_x was a multiple of π/a. It is not in fact necessary to use values of k_x larger than $\pm\pi/a$ in describing any state. For suppose the wave-vector of a position *outside* the first zone is described as $(k_x + 2\pi n/a)$, where n is a (positive or negative) integer and k_x is the wave-vector of a position *inside* the first zone. Then the wave-function

$$\psi = U(x) \exp[ix(k_x + 2\pi n/a)] \tag{142.1}$$

can equally well be written as

$$\psi = U'(x)\exp(ixk_x) \tag{142.2}$$

where $U'(x)$, like $U(x)$, has the periodicity of the lattice. Eq. (142.2) is as good a Bloch function as (142.1).

This means that the electron energy $E(k)$ can be plotted as a multi-valued function of **k** within the first Brillouin zone, as indicated by the dashed curves of Fig. 14.1. Such a representation is known as that of

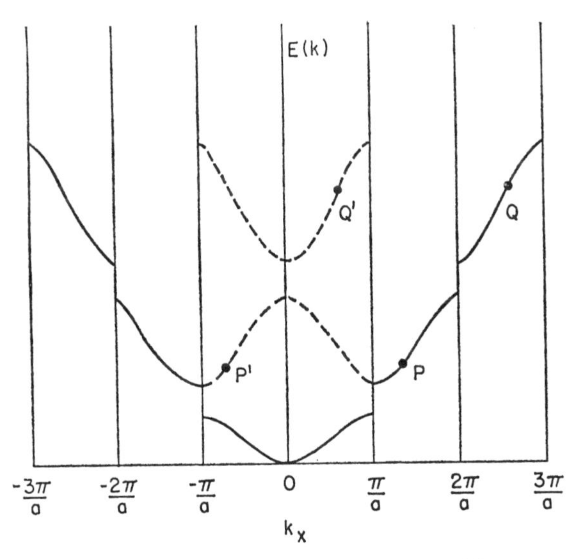

FIG. 14.1. Multi-zone and reduced zone representation of the energy–wave-vector relationship for a one-dimensional monatomic lattice.

the *reduced zone*, and the value of **k** corresponding to a whole series of possible energies is known as the *reduced wave-vector*. The point P in Fig. 14.1 becomes P' in the reduced zone, just as Q becomes Q'.

A reduced zone formalism is very useful since the mathematics is greatly eased. This is not too apparent for the hypothetical one-dimensional solid of Kronig and Penney but becomes much more obvious when the reduced zone concept is applied to multi-dimensional systems. Thus consider Fig. 14.2, which shows the first four Brillouin zones for a simple two-dimensional square lattice. Even this provides enough complexity for the points A and B in separate sections of the fourth zone to have no obvious connection. Yet the equivalent points A' and B' in the reduced zone can be seen to correspond with closely neighboring states, quite near to the zone center.

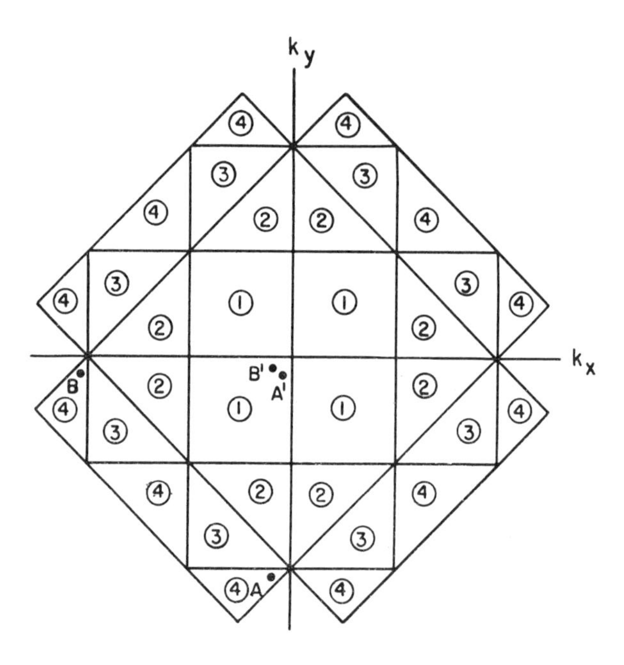

FIG. 14.2. The first four zones of a two-dimensional square lattice. The points A and B in the fourth zone appear quite remote; but when viewed as the corresponding points A' and B' of the reduced zone can be seen to be neighboring states.

The translation in **k**-space which relates equivalent points in different zones is said to be 2π times a *reciprocal lattice vector*. The establishment of the directions and magnitudes of such vectors is as follows. Consider a general (not necessarily cubic) three-dimensional lattice for which the primitive translations are $\mathbf{a}_1$, $\mathbf{a}_2$, and $\mathbf{a}_3$. These are not necessarily perpendicular to each other or of equal length. Then the *reciprocal lattice* is defined by three primitive vectors $\mathbf{b}_1$, $\mathbf{b}_2$, and $\mathbf{b}_3$ such that

$$\mathbf{a}_i \cdot \mathbf{b}_j = \delta_{ij} = \begin{cases} 1 & \text{if } i = j \\ 0 & \text{if } i \neq j \end{cases} \tag{142.3}$$

The $\mathbf{b}_j$ are given by expressions

$$b_1 = \frac{\mathbf{a}_2 \times \mathbf{a}_3}{\mathbf{a}_1 \cdot (\mathbf{a}_2 \times \mathbf{a}_3)} \tag{142.4}$$

so that $\mathbf{b}_1$ is normal to the plane of $\mathbf{a}_2$ and $\mathbf{a}_3$, and so on. A reciprocal lattice vector is then of the form

$$\mathbf{n} = n_1\mathbf{b}_1 + n_2\mathbf{b}_2 + n_3\mathbf{b}_3 \tag{142.5}$$

where n_1, n_2 and n_3 are integers. Such vectors have the convenient property that $\exp(2\pi i\mathbf{n} \cdot \mathbf{r})$ has the periodicity of the lattice; and it is this property which enables us to assert that two states in $\mathbf{k}$-space, with wave-vectors $\mathbf{k}$ and $\mathbf{k}'$ related by $\mathbf{k}' = (\mathbf{k} + 2\pi\mathbf{n})$, are essentially the same state, though they occur in different Brillouin zones.

When $\mathbf{k}$ is expressed as a sum of components k_1, k_2, k_3 along the directions of $\mathbf{b}_1$, $\mathbf{b}_2$ and $\mathbf{b}_3$, the first—or reduced— zone is the region of $\mathbf{k}$-space attainable within the limits

$$\begin{aligned} -\pi b_1 &\leqslant k_1 \leqslant \pi b_1 \\ -\pi b_2 &\leqslant k_2 \leqslant \pi b_2 \\ -\pi b_3 &\leqslant k_3 \leqslant \pi b_3 \end{aligned} \tag{142.6}$$

For crystals of hexagonal symmetry (including zinc and cadmium), the reduced zone is itself a simple hexagonal prism (see Fig. 13.4). A more complicated polyhedron is necessary with most types of lattice; thus the first zone for a F.C.C. lattice (such as copper or aluminum) in Fig. 13.3 is constrained by six 100 surfaces and eight 111 surfaces. For a more complete discussion, see (1946:**1**).

1.4.3 The Effective Mass

It has previously been shown (Eq. 141.3) that the group velocity of an electron wave-packet in space is

$$\mathbf{v} = \frac{1}{\hbar}\nabla_{\mathbf{k}}E$$

Accordingly, the acceleration in an external field is

$$\mathbf{a} = \frac{\mathrm{d}\mathbf{v}}{\mathrm{d}t} = \frac{1}{\hbar}\frac{\mathrm{d}}{\mathrm{d}t}\nabla_{\mathbf{k}}E$$

$$= \frac{1}{\hbar}\nabla_{\mathbf{k}}\left[\nabla_{\mathbf{k}}E \,.\, \frac{\mathrm{d}\mathbf{k}}{\mathrm{d}t}\right] \qquad (143.1)$$

Now if the force on the electron resulting from the external field is **F** (which is just $e\nabla V$ when no magnetic field is present), then solution of the time-dependent Schrödinger equation requires that $\mathbf{F} = -\hbar(\mathrm{d}\mathbf{k}/\mathrm{d}t)$. Substitution into (143.1) gives

$$\mathbf{a} = -\frac{1}{\hbar^2}\nabla_{\mathbf{k}}\nabla_{\mathbf{k}}E \,.\, \mathbf{F} \qquad (143.2)$$

which has components

$$a_i = -\frac{1}{\hbar^2}\sum_j \frac{\partial^2 E}{\partial k_i \partial k_j}F_j, \text{ etc.} \qquad (143.3)$$

The tensor quantity $\hbar^2\,[\partial^2 E/\partial k_i\partial k_j]^{-1}$ is known as the tensor of effective mass, since it has the dimensions of mass and is analogous with the mass required to fit Newtonian equations of motion.

In the analysis of experimental data on solids, it is often assumed that there are no non-diagonal components to this tensor; indeed it is common practice to hope that all the diagonal components will be the same, giving a scalar effective mass

$$m^* = \hbar^2/(\partial^2 E/\partial k^2) \qquad (143.4)$$

for the states of interest. This can prove to be a poor approximation for a discussion of transport phenomena, but fortunately an equivalent scalar effective mass can usually be defined for use in discussions of carrier statistics.

At the lowest energy in a band, the three principal values of the effective mass tensor are all positive, but at the very top of a band the values are all negative. [This can be seen in a one-dimensional sense in Fig. 14.1; $(\mathrm{d}^2E/\mathrm{d}k_x^2)$ is positive at the bottom of each band and negative at the top.] The particle known as a hole—the absence of an electron—accordingly behaves as though it has a *positive* effective mass $-\hbar^2[\partial^2 E/\partial k_i\partial k_j]^{-1}$ near the top of a band.

The Fermi level in a metal customarily occurs at some energy intermediate between the bottom and top of a band. For such an energy the components of effective mass may be positive and negative in different directions. Fortunately in semiconductors we are usually only concerned with levels very near to either the top or bottom of a band, where all the components are of one sign.

The variation of energy E with wave-vector $\mathbf{k}$ is determined by acceptable solutions of the Schrödinger equation for the actual crystal potential—which varies markedly from one solid to another. One feature is, however, common to two very different approximate methods, the tight binding method and the nearly free electron method.† This feature is that just above the bottom of a band (characterized by E_c and $\mathbf{k}_c$) the dependence of E on $\mathbf{k}$ is to first order of the form

$$E = E_c + \text{const}(\mathbf{k}-\mathbf{k}_c)^2 \tag{143.5}$$

Terms involving higher powers of $(\mathbf{k}-\mathbf{k}_c)$ become significant at higher energies.

From the previous definition of effective mass, it is evidently possible to rewrite Eq. (143.5) as

$$E = E_c + \frac{\hbar^2(\mathbf{k}-\mathbf{k}_c)^2}{2m_c} \tag{143.6}$$

where m_c implies the electron effective mass *for the direction of the vector* $(\mathbf{k}-\mathbf{k}_c)$. Similarly, near the top of a band (E_v, $\mathbf{k}_v$) the dependence of *electronic* energy on wave-vector is represented to a first approximation by

$$E = E_v - \frac{\hbar^2(\mathbf{k}-\mathbf{k}_v)^2}{2m_v} \tag{143.7}$$

where m_v is the (positive) hole effective mass for the given direction in $\mathbf{k}$-space.

When m_c and m_v simplify to scalar quantities for energies close to that of a band extremum, the constant energy surfaces in $\mathbf{k}$-space are spherical. Fig. 14.3 shows schematically how energy contours in the Brillouin zone might develop for a two-dimensional square lattice. For

† In the tight binding approximation, the periodic potential is assumed to be very large. For the nearly free electron approximation it is assumed that the Fourier components of the periodic potential represent a small perturbation. Kittel (1953:**2**) and Dekker (1957:**3**) examine these models in some detail. Herman (1958:**1**) gives an excellent account of the results for these models with a number of real crystal structures.

the purpose of this figure the lowest energy is assumed to occur at the zone center, and the uppermost energy at the zone corners k_x, $k_y = \pm\pi/a$. Around the zone center and around the corners the energy contours are circular, indicating isotropy of effective mass; and are parabolically spaced in accordance with the requirements of Eqs.

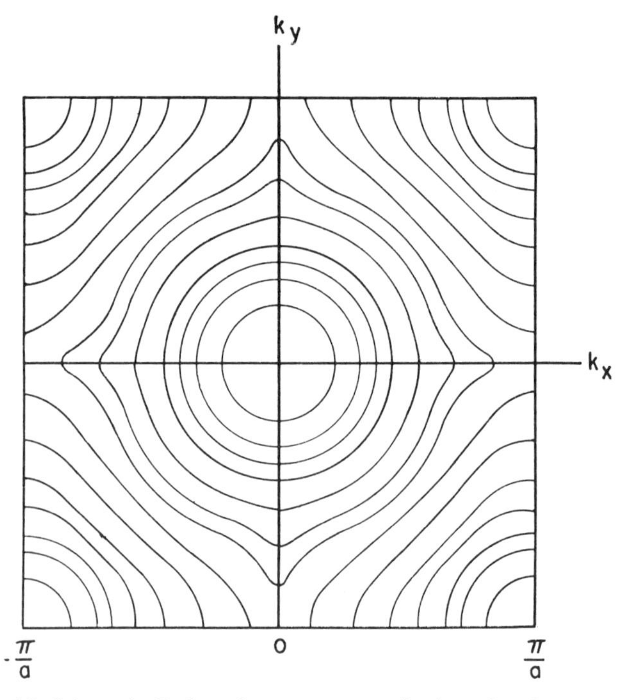

Fig. 14.3. Schematic display of energy contours in the reduced zone of a two-dimensional square lattice.

(143.6) and (143.7). (The spacing is *not* the same at the top of the band as at the bottom, since the masses m_c and m_v which characterize the two regions are by no means necessarily equal.) For intermediate energies and regions of **k**-space there is necessarily a breakdown of parabolic contour spacing and of isotropy in effective mass. As indicated previously, the manner of this breakdown depends on the periodic potential, and Fig. 14.4 shows how the energy contours are likely to be

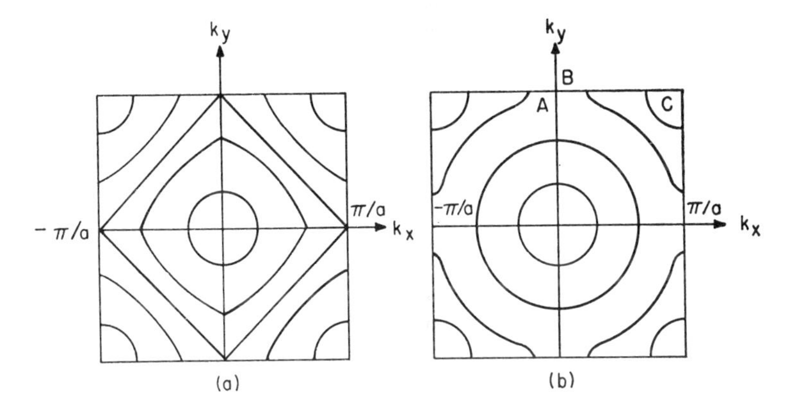

FIG. 14.4. The schematic arrangement of energy contours for a two-dimensional square lattice (a) with the tight binding approximation (b) with the nearly free electron approximation. After Dekker (1957:**3**).

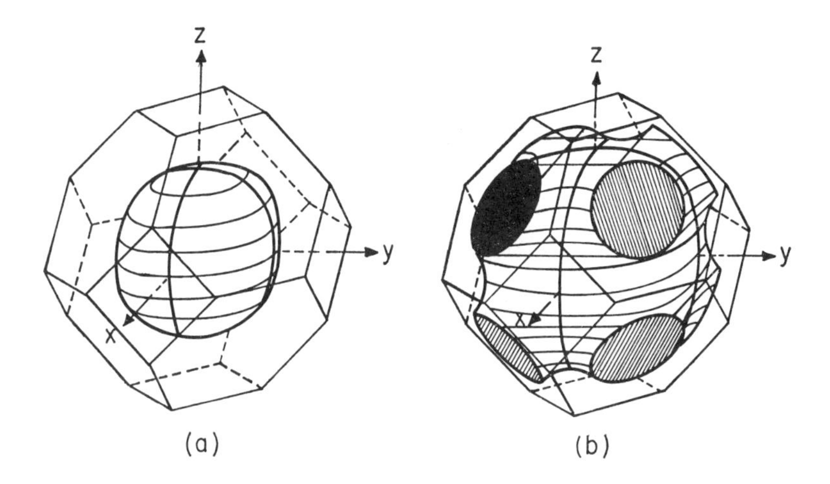

FIG. 14.5 Constant energy surfaces in the reduced zone of a face-centered cubic lattice (a) corresponding with an energy not far above the bottom of the band (b) for an energy approaching the top of the band. After Mott and Jones (1936:**1**).

distorted when the periodic potential is either very strong or rather weak.

In the limiting case of *zero* periodic potential we are left with the Sommerfeld model, and a mass m_0 is appropriate for all states. Accordingly we can expect that when the periodic potential is rather small, the effective mass at the bottom of the band will not be very far different from m_0, and that energy contours well out into the zone will bear the mark of this effective mass. These tendencies are sketched in part (b) of Fig. 14.4. Similarly, Fig. 14.5 attempts to illustrate energy contours in the three dimensional reduced zone of an F.C.C. lattice when the periodic potential is not too large.

1.4.4 The Density of States

In Sub-section 1.2.1 it was shown that the volume of **k**-space to be allowed for each electronic level is $(2\pi/L)^3$ with a cubical crystal of side L. The volume per one-electron state is half of this, $4(\pi/L)^3$, since each level can accommodate two electrons of opposite spin.† Consider two energy contour surfaces in **k**-space representing energies $\mathrm{d}E$ apart. The total volume of **k**-space lying between these two surfaces can be expressed as a surface integral.

$$\left[\int \frac{\mathrm{d}\mathbf{S}}{\nabla_{\mathbf{k}}E}\right]\mathrm{d}E$$

For unit volume of crystal this must comprise

$$\mathrm{d}n_s = \left[\int \frac{\mathrm{d}\mathbf{S}}{\nabla_{\mathbf{k}}E}\right]\frac{\mathrm{d}E}{4\pi^3} \quad \text{states} \tag{144.1}$$

The quantity $g(E) = (\mathrm{d}n_s/\mathrm{d}E)$ is the *density of states* (per unit volume of crystal) per unit energy interval, and evidently

$$g(E) = \int \frac{\mathrm{d}\mathbf{S}}{4\pi^3 \nabla_{\mathbf{k}}E} \tag{144.2}$$

The simplest situation is that of a scalar electronic effective mass,

† This statement is sometimes made in the form that the *spin degeneracy* of electronic levels is two. When we later come to consider impurity levels in semiconductors we shall find that they have a spin degeneracy which may exceed two.

when the constant energy surfaces are spheres centered on $\mathbf{k} = 0$,

$$E = E_c + \frac{\hbar^2 k^2}{2m_c} \tag{144.3}$$

Then $(\mathrm{d}E/\mathrm{d}k) = (\hbar^2 k/m_c)$ over an entire surface while $\int \mathrm{d}S = 4\pi k^2$. Application to Eq. (142.2) gives a density of states

$$g(E) = (k/\pi)^2(\mathrm{d}k/\mathrm{d}E) = 4\pi(2m_c/h^2)^{3/2}(E-E_c)^{1/2} \tag{144.4}$$

When a band covers a comparatively small range of energy:

(a) contours corresponding to successive energies are widely spaced in the Brillouin zone, i.e. $\nabla_{\mathbf{k}}E$ is small;

(b) the density of states per unit energy interval as described by Eqs. (144.2) or (144 4) is high;

(c) as a corollary of these statements the effective mass is large and the velocity (141.3) and acceleration (143.2) of an electron are small.

The common parlance for this type of situation is that electrons of large effective mass have a small mobility. Conversely, highly mobile carriers of low effective mass are to be found in a band which is spread over a wide range of energy to keep the density of states small.

In the free electron theory we obtained an expression (121.7) for the density of states which differed from Eq. (144.4) only in the use of the normal electronic mass rather than an effective mass. In Eq. (144.2), however, we have a much more powerful generalized expression for the density of states, no matter how anisotropic and convoluted the energy surfaces are.

As a simple—and practical—example, suppose that the effective mass tensor can be characterized by principal values m_x, m_y and m_z along the three orthogonal axes. A constant energy surface now satisfies

$$E - E_c = \frac{\hbar^2}{2}\left[\frac{(k_x - k_{x0})^2}{m_x} + \frac{(k_y - k_{y0})^2}{m_y} + \frac{(k_z - k_{z0})^2}{m_z}\right] \tag{144.5}$$

when the lowest energy E_c occurs at k_{x0}, k_{y0}, k_{z0}. Relative to this point in **k**-space, the energy surfaces are still parabolically spaced in any direction; but they are now ellipsoids with axes in ratios $m_x^{-1/2}:m_y^{-1/2}:m_z^{-1/2}$. Using the general principle of Eq. (144.2) or alternative simpler arguments it may be shown that the density of states is given by

$$g(E) = 4\pi(m_x m_y m_z{}^{1/2}(2/h^2)^{3/2}(E-E_c)^{1/2} \tag{144.6}$$

Now this is just of the form (144.4) if $(m_x m_y m_z)^{1/3}$ is replaced by m_c. In this case, as in many others of non-spherical energy surfaces, it is possible to describe the density of states in terms of an equivalent scalar electronic mass—the "density-of-states" effective mass. The point to note is that spherical energy surfaces [characterizing a scalar mass $m_c = (m_x m_y m_z)^{1/3}$] which describe energies δE apart capture the same volume of **k**-space as exists between the spheroidal surfaces of the same energies. This is the important thing in determining the statistical picture of a semiconductor, since the number of *electrons* within a given energy interval depends on the Fermi distribution function and the number of *states* within that interval (that is, dependent on the *volume* of **k**-space available but not affected by the distribution of this volume within the zone).

It will be understood that references made in the previous discussion to electrons at the bottom of a band are applicable, *mutatis mutandis*, to holes at the top of a band.

1.4.5 Mass Renormalization in Band Theory

In Section 1.2, electrons in a solid were considered as being free, subject only to the statistical constraint of the Fermi–Dirac distribution. This constraint did place a limit on the number of electrons which could occupy states within a given range of **k**, but **k**-space was treated as a quasi-continuum, and any solution of the simple Schrödinger equation

$$\frac{\hbar^2}{2m_0}\nabla^2\psi + E\psi = 0 \tag{145.1}$$

was regarded as acceptable.

The failure of the free electron model was attributed to the neglect of the crystal potential, and this led to a replacement of

$$-\frac{\hbar^2}{2m_0}\nabla^2$$

as the Hamiltonian operator by

$$\left[-\frac{\hbar^2}{2m_0}\nabla^2 + V(r)\right]$$

However, it was pointed out in Section 1.3 that $V(r)$ could reasonably be expected to have the periodicity of the lattice, and that the solutions of

$$\frac{\hbar^2}{2m_0}\nabla^2\psi+[E-V(r)]\psi = 0 \tag{145.2}$$

would then be the familiar Bloch functions of band theory. In the present section it has been demonstrated that many attributes of a band can be described in terms of the concept of an effective mass m^*.

Although we have not so far made the explicit statement, band theory gives back to electrons the complete freedom they had in the Sommerfeld model provided the mass is suitably renormalized. By this is meant that the wave-functions and energies of band states are the solutions and eigenvalues of the simple equation.

$$\frac{\hbar^2}{2m^*}\nabla^2\psi+E\psi = 0 \tag{145.3}$$

Eq. (145.3) differs from (145.1) only in the use of m^* rather than m_0; the value of m^* *takes into account* the periodic potential which appeared as a term in Eq. (145.2).

This assumption of free quasi-particles can even be pushed a stage further by using

$$\frac{\hbar^2}{2m^*}\nabla^2\psi+\left[E+\frac{e^2}{\kappa r}\right]\psi = 0 \tag{145.4}$$

as the equation for determining the ground state and excited states of an impurity in the lattice (1957:**2**). The procedure is not satisfactory when an orbit is so small that the concept of dielectric constant breaks down, but appears to be satisfactory in high dielectric constant materials both for impurity states and exciton states (1956:**11**).

The concepts of electrons as particles with very few restraints must undergo some adjustment when the application of an external field is considered. A conductor is not in a state of thermal equilibrium if there is any gradient of the Fermi level, as occurs when an external electric field is applied—for then energy is continuously dissipated by the consequent passage of current. Thus it is not proper to consider electric fields here. But the presence of a steady magnetic field does not constitute a violation of thermal equilibrium, and it is important to note the changes this type of field has on the distribution of states.

1.4.6 Magnetic Sub-bands

Purely from the reasoning of classical mechanics, it is to be expected that if an electron of effective mass m^* is subjected to a magnetic field H_z in the z direction, its motion in the xy plane will tend to create a circular orbit, with angular frequency

$$\omega_0 = \frac{eH_z}{m^*c} \tag{146.1}$$

This is usually referred to as the cyclotron frequency. Quantum-mechanical restrictions would be expected to take the form that the only permitted orbits would have radii corresponding with an angular momentum which was a multiple of $\hbar$. This simple reasoning is substantiated by the quantum-mechanical treatment of Landau (1930:**3**), who showed that in the presence of the magnetic field H_z, the Schrödinger equation (145.3) must be elaborated† to

$$\frac{\hbar^2}{2m^*}\nabla^2\psi - \frac{eH_z}{2m^*c}\cdot\frac{\hbar}{i}\left(x\frac{\partial}{\partial y} - y\frac{\partial}{\partial x}\right)\psi - \frac{e^2H_z^2}{8m^*c^2}(x^2+y^2)\psi + E\psi = 0 \tag{146.2}$$

Seitz (1940:**1**) demonstrates how this equation can be transformed to provide the form of a harmonic oscillator in the xy-plane. The energy levels of the system are

$$E = E_c + \frac{\hbar^2k_z^2}{2m^*} + (n+\tfrac{1}{2})\frac{e\hbar H_z}{m^*c} \tag{146.3}$$

where n is a positive integer or zero. Using Eq. (146.1), Eq. (146.3) assumes the popular form

$$E = E_c + \frac{\hbar^2k_z^2}{2m^*} + (n+\tfrac{1}{2})\hbar\omega_0 \tag{146.4}$$

The electron is free in the z direction, but for directions normal to the magnetic field is trapped in the levels of the harmonic oscillator. This affects the description of the permitted states on an energy scale *and* their locations in **k**-space.

† Landau's discussion was related in point of fact to the free electron model. The arguments of Peierls (1933:**2**) and more recently of Luttinger (1951:**9**) indicate that the same procedure may be used for electrons experiencing a periodic lattice potential if the electron mass m_0 is replaced by the effective mass m^*.

The levels for the different values of n are known as Landau levels. Since energy can vary quasi-continuously with k_z, electronic energy in the crystal is not confined to a series of *levels* in the conventional sense of the word, but to a series of *magnetic sub-bands*, each based upon one of the Landau levels. Fig. 14.6 illustrates how energy varies with

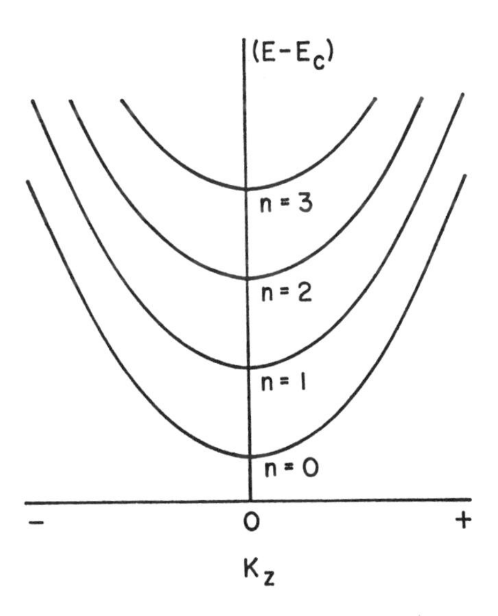

FIG. 14.6. Electron energy as a function of k_z for the first four magnetic sub-bands when a field H_z is applied in the z-direction. The base of each sub-band is at an energy $(n+\frac{1}{2})\hbar\omega_0$, where ω_0 is the cyclotron frequency (proportional to H_z).

k_z for the various sub-bands. The base of each sub-band is $(n+\frac{1}{2})\hbar\omega_0$ above E_c, thus the separation of each sub-band from the zero-field band minimum is linearly dependent on the magnetic field.

So far as the distribution of states in **k**-space is concerned, we have previously considered the field-free case for which **k**-space was uniformly filled with cells of volume $(2\pi/L)^3$, each of which could accommodate two electrons of opposing spin. This availability of all **k**-space disappears when the field H_z is applied. A given value of k_x is now compatible only with certain other values of k_y, such that

$$k_x^2+k_y^2 = \frac{(2n+1)eH_z}{c\hbar} = \frac{(2n+1)m^*\omega_0}{\hbar} \tag{146.5}$$

Upon viewing a cross-section of **k**-space in a plane normal to k_z (as in Fig. 14.7), the permissible relationships of k_x to k_y are represented by a

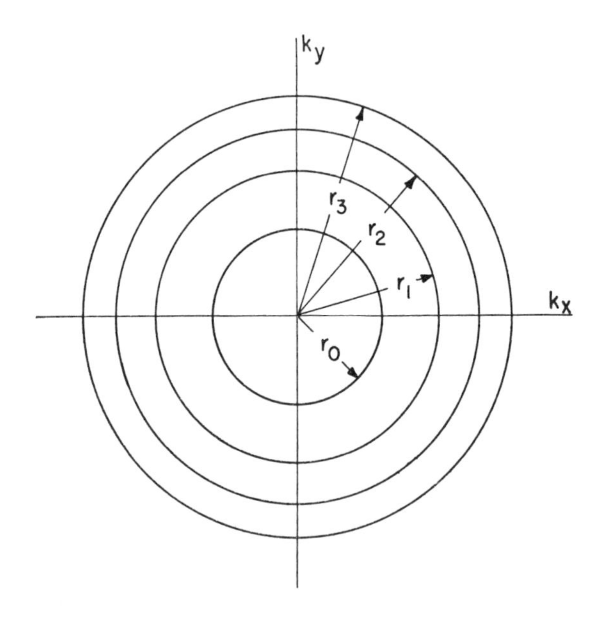

FIG. 14.7. A cross-sectional view of any k_xk_y plane in **k**-space when a magnetic field H_z is applied. The permitted states fall on circles (cross-sections of cylinders in three-dimensional **k**-space).

series of circles, with radii

$$r_n = [(2n+1)m^*\omega_0/\hbar]^{1/2} \tag{146.6}$$

Since k_z is still allowed to be quasi-continuous, all the allowed states fall on a series of coaxial cylinders in **k**-space, aligned along the axis of k_z.

This does not mean that a band has states for fewer electrons in the presence of a magnetic field than it has in the absence of the field. Each level of the two-dimensional system illustrated in Fig. 14.7 contains as many states as does an area $(2\pi m^* \omega_0/\hbar)$ in the $k_x k_y$ plane of the field-free semiconductor. What a magnetic field does do is collect up bundles of $(m^* \omega_0/\hbar)$ states (per unit volume) which had energies in the *xy* plane between $n\hbar\omega_0$ and $(n+1)\hbar\omega_0$, and impress upon each the energy $(n+\frac{1}{2})\hbar\omega_0$. This collection into bundles is illustrated schematically in Fig. 14.8. The larger the magnetic field, the more states per bundle,

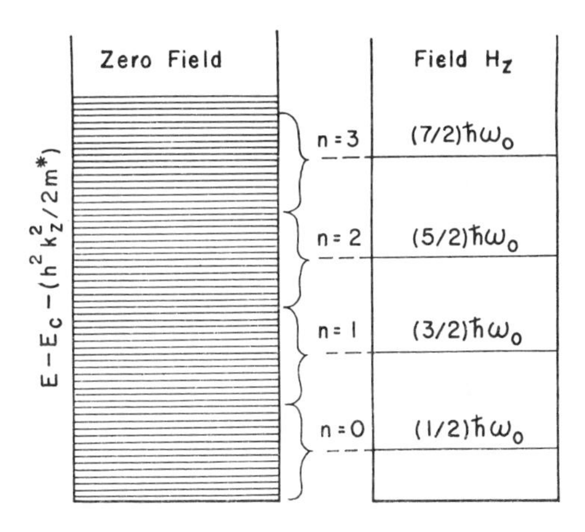

FIG. 14.8. Illustrating how the application of a magnetic field H_z causes the collection of bundles of $(m^* \omega_0/\hbar)$ states (per unit volume) from energy ranges $n\hbar\omega_0 \rightarrow (n+1)\hbar\omega_0$ into degenerate states at energies $(n+\frac{1}{2})\hbar\omega_0$.

the wider the energy range from which this bundle is drawn, and the larger the steps of energy between successive bundles for a given k_z.

Viewed over a sufficiently large range of energy or of **k**-space, the application of a magnetic field does not change the *average* density of levels—but it certainly changes the detailed distribution. Since in a semiconductor we are usually interested in the lowest lying energy states of a band, the influence of the magnetic field can be profound.

Kahn and Frederikse (1959:**7**) give a result for the density of states per unit volume and energy interval which may be expressed (allowing for electron spin degeneracy) as

$$g(E) = 2\pi\left(\frac{2m^*}{h^2}\right)^{3/2} \sum_{n=0}^{n_{\max}} \frac{\hbar\omega_0}{[E-E_c-(n+\frac{1}{2})\hbar\omega_0]^{1/2}} \tag{146.7}$$

where the summation over n extends over all positive integers for which the radical is real. When the magnetic field is very large, only a small number of terms contribute to $g(E)$ for any moderate energy. For vanishingly small H_z, the summation involves so many terms that it can be replaced by an integral, which of course gives the anticipated result,

$$g(E) = 4\pi\left(\frac{2m^*}{h^2}\right)^{3/2} \cdot (E-E_c)^{1/2}, \qquad H_z \to 0 \tag{146.8}$$

We shall return to the result (146.7) in Chapters 2 and 3 where consideration is given to the relationship of the Fermi level to a band containing a given number of electrons, and the effect of a magnetic field on impurity ionization. In a completely qualitative fashion, it can be surmised from the appearance of Fig. 14.9, with most of the

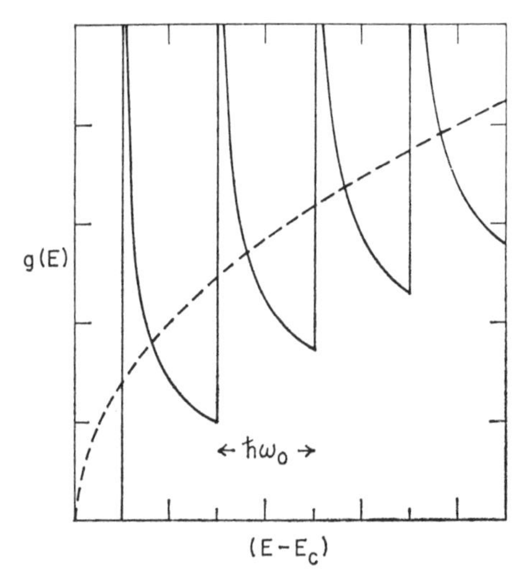

FIG. 14.9. The density of states as a function of energy above E_c. Broken curve shows the smooth function (146.8) which applies in the absence of a magnetic field. Solid curve shows the discontinuous nature of $g(E)$ when a magnetic field is applied [from Eq. (146.7)].

energy levels compressed into narrow sub-bands, that the problems of carrier statistics will depend on the relative magnitudes of $\hbar\omega_0$ and kT, and on whether the electron supply is enough to fill several sub-bands or only a small portion of one.

The preceding discussion has for simplicity been couched in terms of an isotropic effective mass. Such a simplification is not valid in many cases, for the conduction and valence bands of most semiconductors seem to proliferate with multiple extrema, band degeneracies, spin–orbit splittings and the like. However, Luttinger and Kohn (1955:**17**) have shown that the Landau procedure can be extended to cover each of these band complexities. That the creation of quantized Landau levels is still recognizable when the effective mass is anisotropic and multi-valued permits an interpretation of the vast amount of recent literature concerning cyclotron resonance experiments (e.g. 1955:**8**, 1956:**5**), oscillatory magneto-absorption (e.g. 1957:**13**, 1959:**8**, 1959:**9**), Faraday effect (1959:**10**) and other associated phenomena. In a highly degenerate semiconductor the magnetic quantization produces a tendency towards an oscillatory behavior of magnetic susceptibility, known experimentally as the de Haas–van Alphen effect (1930:**4**). This effect is very useful in providing information about the shape of the Fermi surface in a metal, even when the shape is very complicated (e.g. 1957:**14**, 1960:**2**). A very full account of progress up to 1958 in the various fields of magnetic quantization is given by Lax (1958:**2**), who demonstrates the relationships between some of the more prominent effects.

1.5 BAND SHAPES FOR SOME REPRESENTATIVE SEMICONDUCTORS §

In order to illustrate more fully the forms which can be taken by the effective mass tensor, this section indicates the state of knowledge (at the time of writing) about the shapes of conduction and valence bands in some well-known semiconductors. In the last decade it has been the general rule that, the more is known about a semiconductor, the *less* simple do its bands appear.

One of the most important features of the band structure in a semiconductor is the intrinsic gap E_i. This is the *minimum* energy separation between the valence and conduction bands. Since optical phenomena are so frequently employed in attempting to find band separations, it

§ See Preface. (Note: from this point on, the symbol (§) will serve to refer the reader to the Preface for updated information and citations of post-1960 literature.)

is desirable to emphasize the distinction between "vertical" and "non-vertical" optical transitions as used for this purpose.

Ideally one would like to have the minimum of the conduction band and the maximum of the valence band occur at the same point (or points) in the reduced zone. Such a situation is illustrated in Fig. 15.1. Since the momentum of a photon is exceedingly small, energy and momentum are conserved if an electron is raised from the valence band to a conduction band state of almost exactly the same **k**. Such a transition appears *vertical* when drawn on a figure such as Fig. 15.1, and is

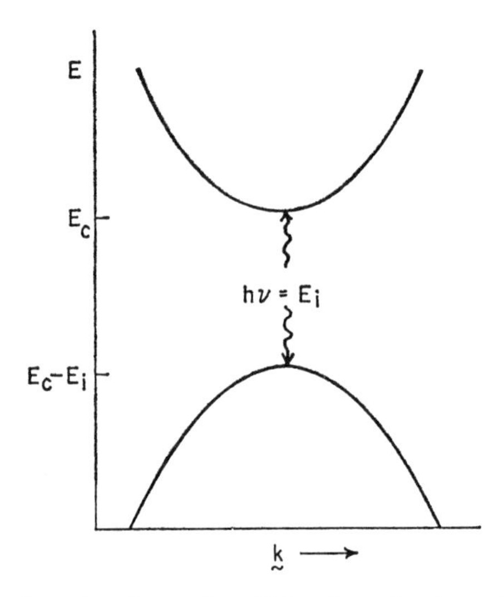

FIG. 15.1. A semiconductor for which valence band maximum and conduction band minimum are at the same point in the reduced zone, so that the least energetic optical transition is a direct or "vertical" one.

also *direct* in that the transition takes place in a single step. The least energetic photon which can induce such a transition has $h\nu = E_i$, thus the intrinsic gap can be deduced from the position of the fundamental optical absorption edge.

The form of optical absorption for $h\nu > E_i$ depends on the matrix element of the initial and final wave-functions, and this is a complete subject in itself which need not be pursued here. In practice, the position of the absorption edge may be complicated due to exciton formation (1958:**4**) but this too is a point of fine detail which lies outside the present scope. For a complete and lucid description of the theories of direct (and indirect) optical transitions, the reader is referred to the book by Smith (1959:**4**).

Indirect transitions are important when the valence band maxima and conduction band minima occur for *different* values of **k**, as illustrated by Fig. 15.2. A hole at energy $(E_c - E_i)$ and an electron at E_c

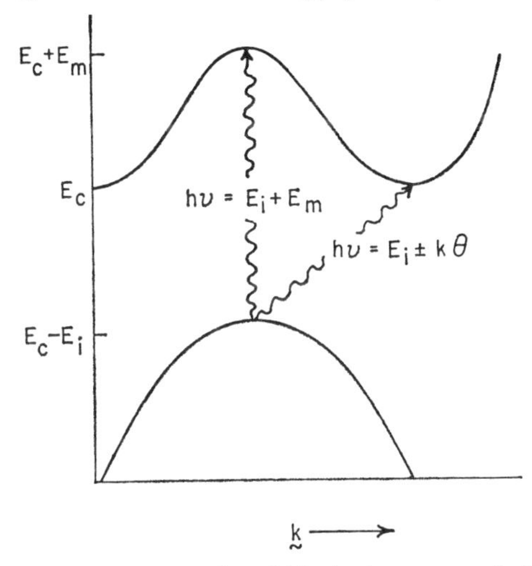

FIG. 15.2. A semiconductor for which the least energetic intrinsic optical transition is an indirect or "non-vertical" one, involving a lattice phonon.

can not be created directly by absorption of a photon for which $h\nu = E_i$, since momentum would not be conserved. Bardeen *et al.* (1956:**12**) point out that such a "non-vertical" transition can occur indirectly; that is, as a two-stage process involving the emission or absorption of a lattice phonon to make up the difference in momentum. Such a phonon inevitably has some energy $k\theta$ associated with it; thus there will be two closely spaced absorption edges (1955:**12**) corresponding with $h\nu = E_i \pm k\theta$. Since exciton effects can again produce complications, it is a delicate and involved procedure to determine the actual intrinsic gap from optical data.

Even when the intrinsic difference between conduction and valence bands does not correspond with a vertical transition, it is still of some importance to determine the *vertical* band separation also, the quantity marked as $(E_i + E_m)$ in Fig. 15.2. In thin samples the powerful absorption due to this transition can be detected above the skirts of indirect absorption. Thus in germanium, optical absorption (1955:**10**) and magneto-absorption (1957:**8**) have been used to establish the value of (E_i+E_m) for the point in **k**-space where the valence band maximum occurs.

While more and more reliance seems to be placed on optical techniques for determining interband energies, a variety of techniques has been improved and devised for exploring the $E-\mathbf{k}$ relationship within a band. Perhaps the most spectacular of these is diamagnetic or cyclotron resonance, which can measure components of the effective mass tensor from the separation of the Landau levels. The anisotropy of magnetoresistance (e.g. 1954:**6**) and of piezoresistance (e.g. 1954:**7**) provide additional valuable information. The possible forms of band anisotropy can be delineated from group theory considerations, based on the symmetry operations of the crystal lattice.

The first two semiconductors to be discussed, silicon and germanium, crystallize in the diamond structure; and the third, InSb, in the related zincblende structure. As Fig. 15.3 shows, each atom in the diamond

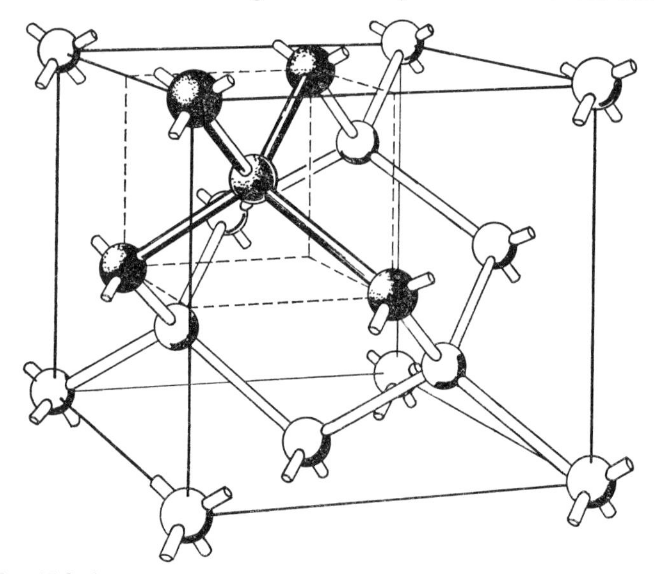

FIG. 15.3. Arrangement of atoms in the diamond structure, showing each atom with four nearest neighbors in a tetrahedral arrangement. After Shockley (1950:**1**).

structure has four nearest neighbors in a tetrahedral configuration. The only difference for the zincblende structure is that each atom has four atoms of the other chemical type as its nearest neighbors. Both of these structures consist essentially of two interpenetrating face-centered cubic lattices. Since the translational symmetry is the same as that of a F.C.C. lattice, the reduced zone is a volume bounded by six (100) faces and eight (111) faces, just as for a simple F.C.C. lattice itself. This reduced zone is illustrated in Fig. 15.4.

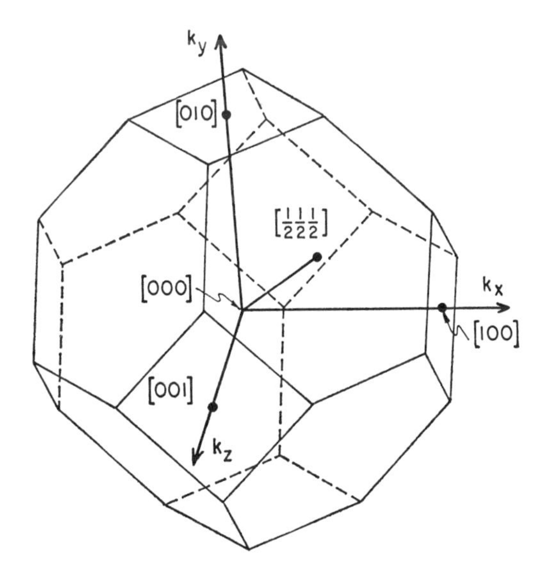

FIG. 15.4. The reduced zone for a material crystallizing in a lattice with the translational symmetry of face-centered cubic. Thus this is the reduced zone for the diamond structure. Each co-ordinate should be multiplied by $2\pi/a$ to yield the actual magnitude of the component of $\mathbf{k}$ (a is the unit cube edge).

In connection with this figure, note a point of terminology. The point on the reduced zone boundary for the positive axis of k_x has a wave-vector with components $[(2\pi/a), 0, 0]$ with respect to the zone center. (Here a is the length of the unit cube, as indicated in Fig. 15.3.) For brevity of expression, the factor $(2\pi/a)$ is often omitted, and this point described simply as [100]. In like manner, both $[\pi/a, \pi/a, \pi/a]$ and

$[\frac{1}{2}\,\frac{1}{2}\,\frac{1}{2}]$ are accepted and understood descriptions of the zone boundary in the center of the positive octant, and so on.

The Brillouin zone of Fig. 15.4 has a number of axes and planes of symmetry. If the lowest energy anywhere in the conduction band occurs at a point in **k**-space which is *not* on any of these axes or planes of symmetry, then this same low energy must occur at forty-seven other positions in the reduced zone. For a very slightly higher energy, there must be an energy contour in the form of forty-eight ellipsoidal surfaces surrounding these extrema.

Usually we can expect to find that the lowest energy *does* occur on one or more axes and planes of symmetry. The number of equivalent points in the zone is then smaller, and the energy surface surrounding each extremum is less general in shape—such as an ellipsoid of revolution.

1.5.1 The Band Structure of Silicon

Theory [notably as developed by Herman (1954:**1**, 1955:**7**) using the orthogonalized plane wave method] and experiment have been fruitful and mutually helpful in providing information about energy bands in silicon. Probably the most direct evidence comes from measurements of cyclotron resonance (1955:**8**, 1956:**5**), but useful support can be derived from other effects, such as magnetoresistance (1954:**6**) or piezoresistance (1954:**7**). All of this evidence indicates that the lowest energy for the conduction band occurs at six points in the reduced zone. These points lie on the principal cubic axes of the zone, and are about 75% of the way out from $\mathbf{k} = 0$ to the zone boundary.

An energy surface for any slightly higher energy must then comprise six ellipsoids (Fig. 15.5). From symmetry arguments these must be ellipsoids of revolution pointing along the cubic axes, characterized by a longitudinal mass m_l and two equal transverse masses m_t. The experimental evidence is that these ellipsoids are quite prolate (elongated), with $m_l \approx 0{\cdot}98\ m_0$ and $m_t \approx 0{\cdot}19\ m_0$. Thus for discussions of carrier statistics and density of states, all the ellipsoids could be replaced by a single spherical surface with a density-of-states effective mass

$$m_c = 6^{2/3} \,.\, (m_l m_t^2)^{1/3} = 1{\cdot}08 m_0 \tag{151.1}$$

The energy bands of silicon are shown in Fig. 15.6 as visualized by Herman (1954:**1**). This figure shows how energy varies with reduced wave-vector along one of the cubic axes and along a cube diagonal direction from the center of the zone. One of the six equivalent conduction band minima is clearly apparent from the deep trough part way along the [100] direction, and it can be expected that almost all phenomena involving free electrons will be associated with these

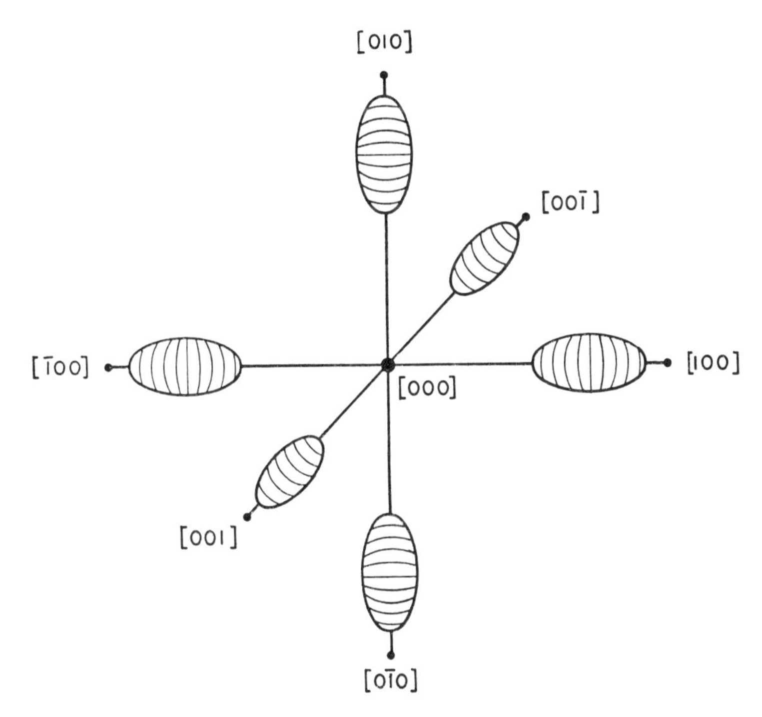

Fig. 15.5. The surface of constant energy in **k**-space for an energy just above the bottom of the conduction band in silicon. An ellipsoid of revolution pointing along one of the principal cubic axes surrounds each extremum.

portions of the zone. The figure shows that other minima do occur in the complex of conduction bands, notably at the extremities in the [111] directions, but these minima are so high in energy compared with the group of six already discussed that there can never be a noticeable number of electrons in these elevated states.

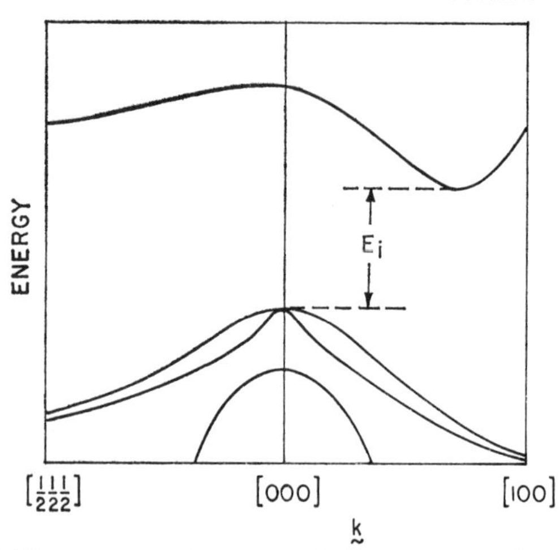

FIG. 15.6. The energy band structure of silicon as expected from the calculations of Herman (1954:**1**). The lowest conduction band minima occur at a point along each of the six [100] directions in the reduced zone. The valence bands all have a single extremum at the center of the zone (000).

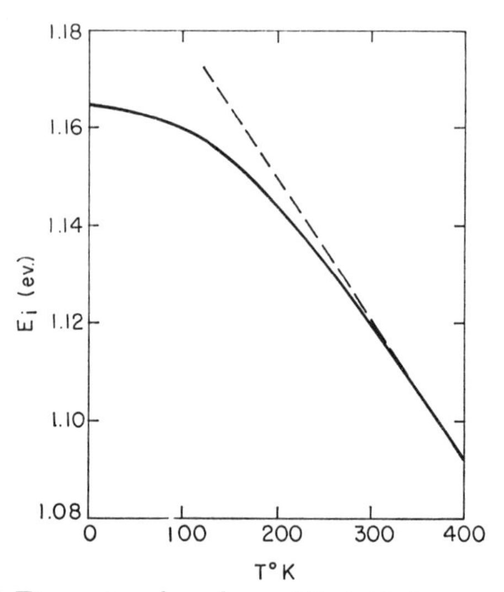

FIG. 15.7. Temperature dependence of the intrinsic energy gap in silicon, as deduced from measurements such as the optical absorption data of Macfarlane *et al.* (1958:**3**).

The energy difference between the conduction band minima and the high point of the uppermost valence bands defines the intrinsic gap. This quantity, not surprisingly, is a function of temperature. The dilatation of the lattice and the increasing strength of lattice vibrations both tend to modify the intrinsic gap as silicon is heated; the result is believed to be substantially as shown in Fig. 15.7, determined from the absorption edge for indirect (non-vertical) optical transitions.

Below the intrinsic gap lie the valence bands, repositories of free holes. Fig. 15.6 shows three valence bands, all of which have a single extremum at $\mathbf{k} = 0$. The two upper ones are degenerate at this point in the zone—that is, they have the same energy. According to the simpler forms of energy band theory, all three valence bands would be degenerate at $\mathbf{k} = 0$, but the degeneracy is partially removed by spin–orbit splitting.† The three resultant bands are known as the heavy-hole band, the light-hole band and the split-off band (the last name being self-explanatory).

Of the two upper valence bands in Fig. 15.6, the term "heavy" is applied to the one for which energy decreases least rapidly with increasing **k** in every direction. This follows from the discussion of Section 1.4.4, that if $\nabla_{\mathbf{k}}E$ is small, the density of states and the effective mass are large. The effective mass in the heavy-hole band, m_2, is some three times larger than the mass m_1 for the light-hole band with which it is degenerate at $\mathbf{k} = 0$. These masses are not isotropic, for the surfaces of constant energy are warped from truly spherical shapes in **k**-space. The energy surface for the heavy-hole band protrudes in [111] directions, while for light holes the corresponding surface for the same energy is squashed in [111] directions and protrudes in [100] directions. Fig. 15.8 indicates the intersection of the two energy surfaces with the (110) plane in **k**-space for a given energy. Dresselhaus *et al.* (1955:**8**) have developed the expression,

$$E = E_v - \frac{\hbar^2}{2m_0}\{Ak^2 \pm [B^2k^4 + C^2(k_x^2k_y^2 + k_x^2k_z^2 + k_y^2k_z^2)]^{1/2}\} \quad (151.2)$$

for the two bands, where the plus sign refers to the light-hole band and the minus sign to the heavy holes. The constants A, B and C have been

† The importance of taking account of spin–orbit interaction in energy band calculations was brought out by Elliott (1954:**5**). This phenomenon is actually the interaction between the magnetic dipole field set up by a spinning electron and the magnetic field produced by the orbital motion of the same electron.

determined from cyclotron resonance (1956:**5**) as

$$\left.\begin{aligned} A &= 4{\cdot}0 \pm 0{\cdot}1 \\ B &= 1{\cdot}1 \pm 0{\cdot}4 \\ C &= 4{\cdot}1 \pm 0{\cdot}4 \end{aligned}\right\} \quad \text{for silicon} \qquad (151.3)$$

It will be noted that the light- and heavy-hole bands of Eq. (151.2) *are* parabolic; energy decreases as the *square* of wave-vector for any

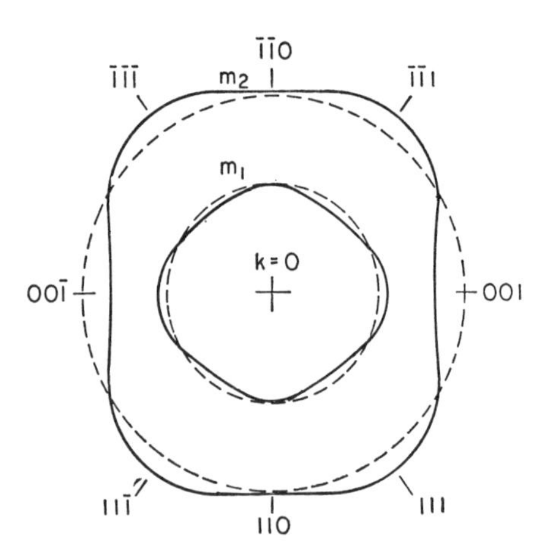

FIG. 15.8. Contours of constant energy for the two uppermost valence bands of silicon, as viewed by a cross-section of the (110) plane in **k**-space. m_1 denotes the light-hole band and m_2 the heavy holes. After Lax (1958:**2**).

direction away from the origin of **k**-space. This at least is one comforting thought, though as we shall show in a moment, parabolic behavior breaks down when **k** and $(E_v - E)$ become at all large.

Even in the region of **k**-space for which energy surfaces *are* parabolically spaced, the surfaces of Eq. (151.2) are very complicated, and it is not easy to deduce the corresponding density-of-states effective masses. Gold (1957:**4**) has demonstrated a general method for evaluating the volume of **k**-space lying within a constant energy surface, but when applied to the valence bands of silicon this method has to reckon with severe computational difficulties. A rather different approximating procedure was used by Lax and Mavroides (1955:**9**), who arrive at

$m_1 = 0{\cdot}16m_0$ and $m_2 = 0{\cdot}53m_0$ for the *density-of-states* masses of light and heavy holes. From this,

$$m_v = [m_1^{3/2} + m_2^{3/2}]^{2/3} = 0{\cdot}59m_0 \tag{151.4}$$

for the combination of upper valence bands.

The lower valence band cannot be ignored in these discussions. The energy Δ by which it is split from the other bands is quite small, possibly as small as $\sim 0{\cdot}04$ eV. This band *is* spherically symmetrical, with a mass dependent on the parameter A in Eq. (151.2),

$$E = E_v - \Delta - \frac{A\hbar^2 k^2}{2m_0} \tag{151.5}$$

so that $m_3 \approx 0{\cdot}25\, m_0$.

Eqs. (151.2) through (151.5) have validity only for a small region of **k**-space surrounding the center of the zone, i.e. only for energies quite close to the extrema. Kane (1956:**4**) has shown that the proximity of the split-off band seriously perturbs the situation, so that the bands become non-parabolic. Fig. 15.9 shows the result of Kane's perturbation calculation. In this figure, energy is plotted vs. k^2 for the

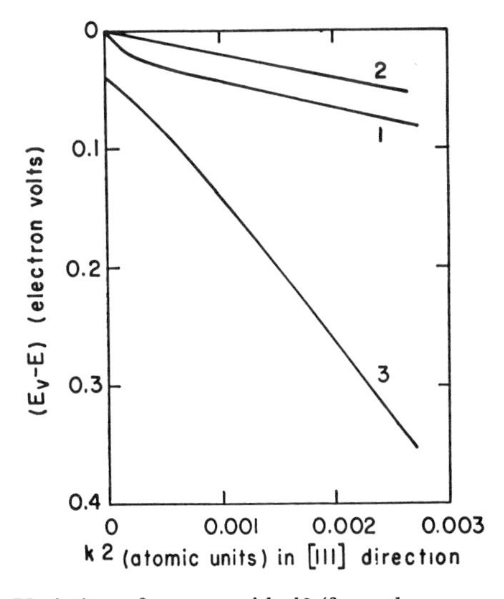

FIG. 15.9. Variation of energy with k^2 (from the zone center in a [111] direction) for the three valence bands of silicon. [After Kane (1956:**4**.)] 1 denotes the "light" holes, 2 the "heavy" holes, and 3 the split-off band.

[111] direction. Thus a parabolic band for which m^* was independent of energy would show up as a straight line in this representation. It will be noted that the "light"-hole band becomes almost as heavy as the "heavy"-hole band for energies more than ~ 0·02 eV below the valence band maximum. This means that the assumption of constant effective mass for holes in silicon is not a good one for temperatures higher than 100°K—though such an assumption is frequently made in the interests of expediency. Accurate considerations of carrier statistics must take account both of the departure from parabolic behavior of the light-hole band and the presence of free holes in the split-off band at high temperatures.

1.5.2 Germanium

There are many similarities in the semiconducting behavior of silicon and germanium, but also some differences in the band structure which make it profitable to consider Ge as another example.

It was noted for silicon that the important conduction band minima occurred at points along the [100] directions of the zone, and that another branch of the conduction band had minima much higher in electronic energy at the points equivalent to $[\frac{1}{2}\ \frac{1}{2}\ \frac{1}{2}]$. It is this latter branch of the conduction band which now becomes important—for in Ge the minima at $[\frac{1}{2}\ \frac{1}{2}\ \frac{1}{2}]$ and seven other equivalent points offer the lowest possible energy for occupancy by electrons. Part (a) of Fig. 15.10 shows the reduced zone for germanium and the positions of one opposite pair of minima. For a slightly higher energy, the constant energy surfaces have the symmetry of ellipsoids of revolution, characterized by a mass m_l towards the zone center and a transverse mass m_t. Since each minimum occurs actually on the zone boundary, only half an ellipsoid develops from an extremum. As indicated by part (b) of the figure, two facing half-ellipsoids should be regarded as *one* complete ellipsoidal energy surface, since they can be made to match by translating through a vector of the reciprocal lattice.

Thus the germanium conduction band has *four* ellipsoids, not eight. Cyclotron resonance results (1955:**8**, 1956:**5**) indicate that $m_l \approx 1{\cdot}64m_0$ and $m_t \approx 0{\cdot}082m_0$. Accordingly the set of ellipsoids can be regarded from a density-of-states point of view as being equivalent to a single spherical surface with mass

$$m_c = 4^{2/3}(m_l m_t^2)^{1/3} = 0{\cdot}56m_0 \tag{152.1}$$

Unlike the previous example of silicon, it is not possible to focus attention in germanium on just one group of conduction band minima. Other branches of the conduction band have minima also, and these

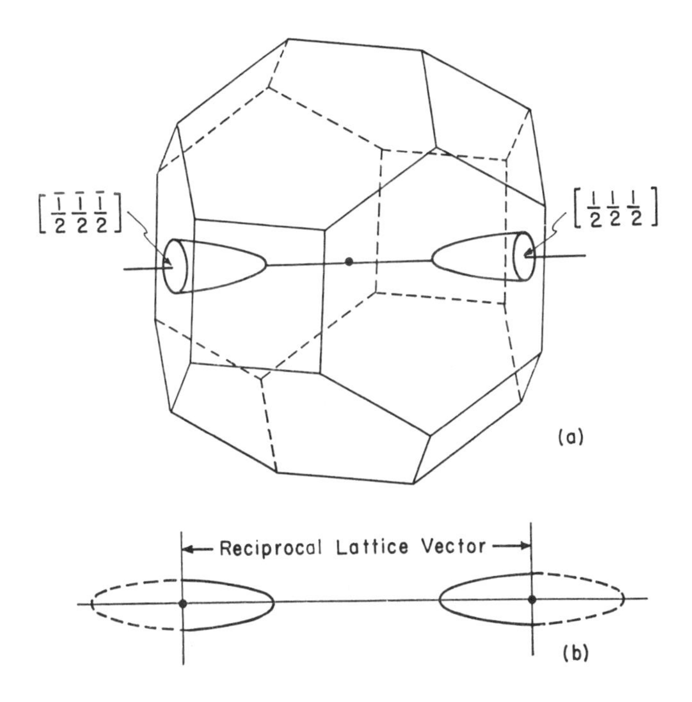

FIG. 15.10. (a) The reduced zone for germanium, showing two of the eight positions on the zone boundary where conduction band minima occur. The half-ellipsoids extending from each for an energy slightly higher than E_c are shown. (b) Showing how a pair of half-ellipsoids can be regarded as a single ellipsoid, since they match when either is translated through a reciprocal lattice vector.

at energies not very much higher. Fig. 15.11 illustrates schematically the conception (at the time of writing) of the complete conduction and valence band structure for germanium. In addition to the previously discussed minima (the principal seats of free electrons), there is a single minimum at the center of the zone [000], and six at points along the

[100] directions. It is obviously an important matter to determine the energy of these states relative to the lowest conduction band minima.

From an analysis of optical absorption (1955:**10**, 1958:**4**) and of oscillatory magneto-absorption (1957:**8**) it appears that the minimum at $\mathbf{k} = 0$ is higher than the [111] minima by 0·14 eV both at 77°K and

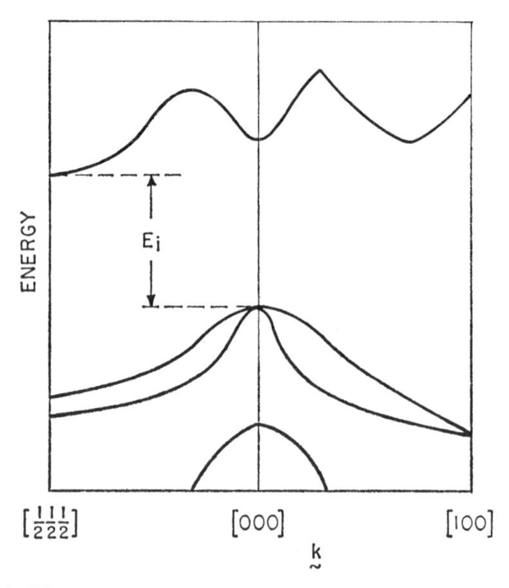

Fig. 15.11. The energy band structure for germanium as visualized by Herman (1954:**1**, 1955:**7**). There are eight conduction band minima, one at the center of each of the hexagonal faces in the reduced zone (Fig. 15.10). Thus these minima lie along the various [111] directions, and a half-ellipsoid spreads out from each as we consider progressively higher energies. The valence bands all have a single extremum at the center of the zone.

300°K. Less is known of the [100] minima, but these are likely to be comparable in energy to the [000] minimum. Thus while the [111] minima represent the lowest energy states in the conduction band, the other minima are only a few kT higher at elevated temperatures and must inevitably support an appreciable fraction of the free electron density at such temperatures. This has an effect on the Fermi level of intrinsic germanium at sufficiently high temperatures.

The highest valence bands in germanium are separated from the lowest conduction band by an intrinsic gap which is—as for silicon—a non-linear function of temperature. Fig. 15.12 shows the dependence predicated by optical measurements.

The valence band structure of germanium is qualitatively similar to that of silicon. The two upper bands, degenerate at [000], have warped

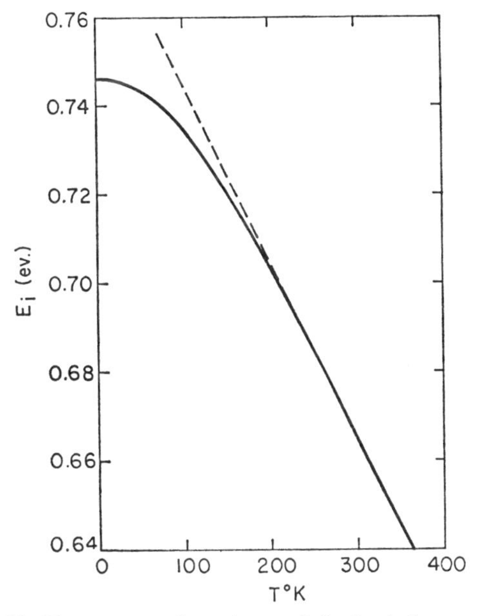

FIG. 15.12. Temperature dependence of the intrinsic energy gap in germanium, as illustrated by Smith (1959:**4**) and largely based on the optical absorption results of Macfarlane *et al.* (1957:**7**).

energy surfaces described by Eq. (151.2), but now with parameters

$$\left.\begin{aligned} A &= 13{\cdot}1 \pm 0{\cdot}4 \\ B &= 8{\cdot}3 \pm 0{\cdot}6 \\ C &= 12{\cdot}5 \pm 0{\cdot}5 \end{aligned}\right\} \qquad (152.2)$$

These bands are less severely warped than the corresponding bands of silicon, but the ratio (m_2/m_1) of "heavy"-hole mass to "light"-hole mass is considerably larger, so that only 4% of the free holes are "light" holes. Lax and Mavroides (1955:**9**) estimate that the density-of-states masses for the two bands are $m_1 = 0{\cdot}043m_0$ and $m_2 = 0{\cdot}36m_0$; from which

$$m_v = [m_1^{3/2} + m_2^{3/2}]^{2/3} = 0{\cdot}37m_0 \tag{152.3}$$

Infrared optical absorption which is attributed to transitions between the upper valence bands and the split-off band (1955:**11**) indicate that the spin–orbit splitting in germanium is much larger than in Si, amounting to some 0·3 eV. This has two simplifying effects. First, the split-off band is so low in energy that it is never likely to contain any free holes under conditions of thermal equilibrium. Second, the perturbing effect on the E–$\mathbf{k}$ dependence of the upper valence bands is not too pronounced. The perturbation calculations of Kane (1956:**4**) suggest that the light- and heavy-hole bands will be approximately parabolic (effective mass independent of energy) down to an energy $\sim$ 0·1 eV below E_v. For lower energies the "light"-hole mass does become rather larger, but not to an extent which should seriously jeopardize a simplified discussion of carrier statistics at any reasonable temperature.

1.5.3 Indium Antimonide

It has already been remarked that the zincblende lattice in which InSb and a number of other III–V compounds crystallize has the same reduced zone as the diamond and F.C.C. structures. From several points of view, we might reasonably expect the semiconducting nature of III–V compounds to show similarities with that of group IV elements —but with modifications imposed by the partially ionic nature of the bonding. This aspect has been extensively developed by Welker (1959:**5**).

Despite intensive investigation over a period of several years, some details of the InSb band structure remain in doubt at the time of writing. It does appear fairly definite that there is but a single conduction band minimum at the center of the zone. Constant energy surfaces for higher conduction band energies are spherically symmetrical (i.e. the effective mass is a scalar), but these surfaces are non-parabolically spaced to make the effective mass a sensitive function of energy. An electron mass $m_c = 0{\cdot}013m_0$ is found by cyclotron resonance (1955:**12**) for the lowest conduction band states, but values considerably larger are reported from measurements involving states of higher energy.

Kane (1957:**5**) has shown that the departure from parabolic behavior in the conduction band of InSb arises naturally from the interactions between bands—particularly since the intrinsic gap is rather small. Fig. 15.13 shows the gross features of Kane's calculation for the

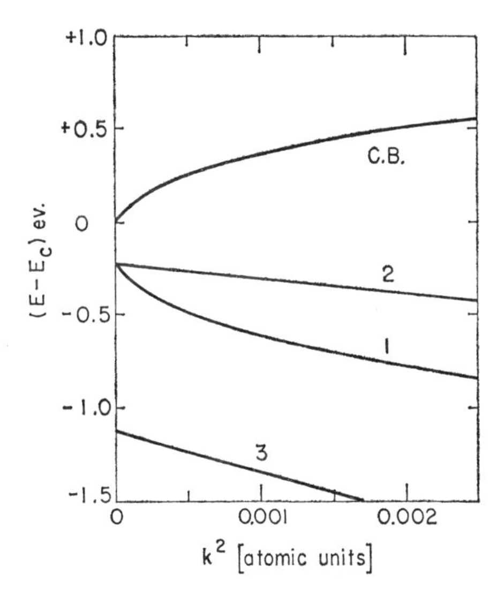

FIG. 15.13. Valence and conduction band energies for InSb as a function of k^2 in some typical direction of **k**-space, according to the calculations of Kane (1957:**5**). The curvature indicates departure from parabolic band behavior in the conduction band and light-hole band.

energy bands in InSb. There are light and heavy holes degenerate at $\mathbf{k} = 0$, and a split-off band separated from the others by such a large spin–orbit splitting that it can be ignored for all practical purposes.

The effective masses of holes in the "light" and "heavy" bands remain in doubt. The cyclotron resonance data of Dresselhaus *et al.* (1955:**12**) indicates a band of mass $0{\cdot}2m_0$, with rather ambiguous evidence of a larger mass also; but other evidence suggests that $0{\cdot}2m_0$ should be the mass of the *heavy* rather than the *light* holes. Kane's calculations lead to a possibility that the heavy-hole band may have eight shallow maxima slightly separated from $\mathbf{k} = 0$ along the [111] directions. This is not readily apparent from Fig. 15.13 but is shown in more detail by Fig. 15.14. Such a model for the heavy-hole band would conform with the interpretation of optical absorption given by Potter (1956:**6**). An alternative explanation of the optical data, given by Dumke (1957:**9**), would require the heavy-hole band to have but a

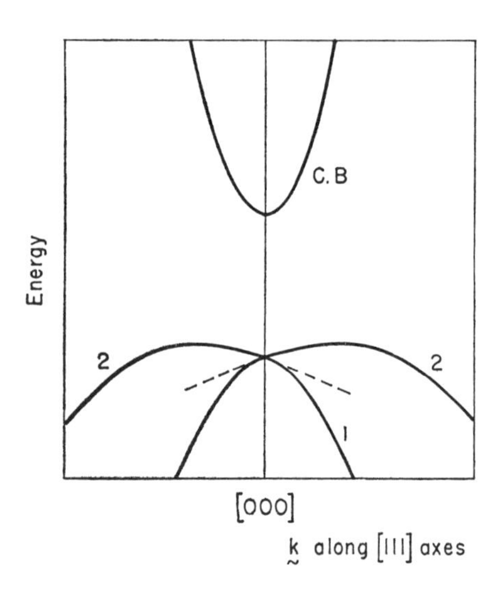

FIG. 15.14. One possibility for the details of the energy band structure of InSb near $\mathbf{k} = 000$, as described by Herman (1957:**6**) based on calculations by Kane (1957:**5**). The heavy-hole band maxima would occur only a small percentage of the way out to the zone boundary.

single maximum at [000]; and correct discussion of carrier statistics will be much simplified if this proves to be the case.

Indium antimonide provides a striking demonstration of the caution which must be used in applying optical absorption evidence to a picture of band separation. Early measurements of the fundamental absorption edge showed that this occurred at a shorter wavelength for impure n-type samples than for purer samples (1953:**10**). Burstein (1954:**10**) and Moss (1954:**11**) independently suggested the explanation of this effect, which is a result of the very small electronic effective mass. When the electron density is rather large, the Fermi level is a considerable energy above E_c, and optical transitions to the conduction band states lower than ϕ are inhibited (since these states are already completely filled). This Burstein–Moss effect is liable to occur in any material for which the majority carrier mass is rather small.

Various kinds of electrical and optical measurements suggest that at least some of the other III–V intermetallic compounds have a band structure resembling that of InSb, though with rather larger energy gaps. In general, however, it can be expected that the accretion of experimental data on both elemental and compound semiconductors will lead to the identification of *rather few* semiconductors in which conduction and valence extrema coincide in the zone, and a considerably *larger* number of semiconductors for which the extrema occur in different parts of the zone.

1.6 SOME VARIETIES OF IMPURITY CENTER (FLAW) §

Section 1.3.4 mentioned Wilson's idea of localized levels in a semiconductor, which can provide either electrons or holes for an energy expenditure smaller than E_i. The simplest kind of *donor center* has two states of charge; it is either neutral or bears a charge† of $+q$. The simplest acceptor is either neutral, or is ionized and has a charge $-q = e$.

It is sometimes useful to employ the term "flaw" suggested by Shockley and Last (1957:**21**) as a generic name for *any* permanent perturbation of the periodic crystal lattice which gives rise to localized states. The word "impurity" sometimes carries the connotation that localized states have arisen from the presence of foreign atoms. Similarly, the words "defect" or "imperfection" are often taken to imply the activities of lattice vacancies and interstitials. The term "flaw" encompasses foreign atoms, vacancies, interstitials or combinations of any of these. In the following chapters we shall sometimes follow the traditional course in speaking of *impurities*, but at times the word *flaw* is used to emphasize the generality of the discussion.

Some impurities (flaws) are, as described in the first paragraph, monovalent. Such flaws have only two possible conditions, separated by the amount q, and present but a single level which is either occupied

† q is a *positive* charge numerically equal to that of an electron and absolutely equal to that of a hole.

or not. Other kinds of flaw are multivalent, and a series of levels are presented as electrons are added or subtracted one by one.

1.6.1 Impurities in Elemental Semiconductors Such as Ge and Si

Probably the most easily appreciated example of a monovalent donor impurity in an elemental semiconductor is furnished by the picture of an arsenic atom replacing a germanium atom in the Ge lattice. Since the arsenic atom has one more electron than the germanium atom it replaces, the tetrahedral bonding arrangement leaves this extra electron rather loosely bound; it is the removal of this electron to a remote part of the crystal which constitutes single ionization of the donor. A *second* electron could be removed from the arsenic atom only by a *much larger* expenditure of energy—no less than the intrinsic gap.

Analogous to the behavior of this type of flaw there is the monovalent acceptor, such as a gallium atom in germanium. In this case there is a deficiency of one electron when the four tetrahedral bonds have to be formed, and such a situation can be envisaged as maintaining neutrality by the device of a weakly bound hole, which can be enticed away rather easily.

It may then be expected that the replacement of an atom in the germanium lattice by one of an element outside groups IIIB, IVB, and VB of the periodic table could produce a situation in which several levels might appear in the intrinsic gap, corresponding to successive stages of ionization. This is indeed the case. As an example, when zinc (the element to the left of gallium in the periodic table) is placed substitutionally in the germanium lattice, *divalent acceptors* result. Tyler and Woodbury (1956:**24**) have shown that it takes an energy $E_{a1} = 0{\cdot}03$ eV to release one hole from a zinc acceptor and that then a second hole can be freed by providing the energy $E_{a2} = 0{\cdot}09$ eV. The ratio of these energies is not too different from what might naïvely be expected by drawing an analogy between a divalent impurity and a helium atom.

In elemental semiconductors such as germanium and silicon, a host of other chemical elements provide several levels corresponding with states of successive ionization. Thus divalent acceptors are produced in germanium by addition of the transition elements manganese (1955:**25**), iron (1954:**16**), cobalt (1955:**26**), and nickel (1955:**27**). An impurity in germanium such as gold presents a fascinating problem, and the possibility that it can act either as acceptor or donor, depending on the Fermi level (1956:**25**). We shall have occasion to refer again to this "amphoteric" behavior of gold as an impurity in Ge.

Of course the behavior of a foreign atom in a lattice depends to a large extent on whether it is present substitutionally or interstitially. The transition elements mentioned above occupy interstitial positions in the germanium lattice, as do lithium and copper, whereas gold appears to be a substitutional impurity. Interstitial atoms of germanium itself provide donor levels, and germanium vacancies act as acceptors. These two forms of imperfection are readily created by fast nucleon bombardment; the results of such treatments were at one time interpreted as though each imperfection provided a single level (1951:**13**, 1951:**14**), but a more complete analysis indicates that interstitials and vacancies act as divalent donors and divalent acceptors, respectively (1957:**27**).

1.6.2 Donors and Acceptors in Compound Semiconductors

Foreign atoms and departures from lattice perfection are both very important in creating localized levels for compound semiconductors. Sometimes (but not, alas, very frequently) the kind of level engendered by the substitution of a foreign atom is what might be expected from a simple-minded valency approach. Verwey and his associates have used the "controlled valency" principle to some effect in promoting conduction in oxide semiconductors; thus it has previously been noted that an acceptor is formed when a divalent nickel atom in NiO is replaced by a monovalent lithium one (1948:**3**, 1950:**6**). Similarly, the replacement of zinc by aluminum in ZnS provides donor centers, and replacement with copper forms acceptors (1955:**28**). But in a great many cases the rules which control the type and effective valency of an impurity site are less easy to divine.

Interstitials and vacancies play a great role in compound semiconductors. Even for a compound which is completely stoichiometric, the lattice is partially disordered at high temperatures in the state of maximum entropy. One form of disorder is that of Frenkel defects (1926:**1**) whereby some atoms are in interstitial positions, leaving the same number of vacancies. The alternative form, Wagner–Schottky disorder (1931:**5**), has vacancies of two atomic species present in the proportions needed for chemical equilibrium. The relative abundance of the two forms of disorder depends on their energies of formation.

More serious still, compound semiconductors are rarely stoichiometric, and appreciable densities of interstitials or vacancies (each effective as a flaw) must be present when the proportions of the elements making up the compound deviate from the ideal ratio. This deviation can be modified by changing the vapor pressure of the more volatile component while keeping the semiconductor at a high temperature. Thus the free charge carrier densities in semiconductors such as NiO, Cu_2O and PbS can be varied over a wide range by vapor pressure adjustment (e.g. 1951:**12**, 1956:**26**, 1961:**3**).

The equilibrium distribution of electrons, holes, vacancies and interstitials is governed by a series of equations based on the law of mass action. The relationships can be very complicated, and a complete discussion would fall outside the scope of this volume.† The reader is recommended to the comprehensive review article by Kröger and Vink (1956:**27**) for an extensive analysis of the reactions between a semiconducting crystal and the vapor of one of its constituents.

The flaw levels provided by interstitials and vacancies (and more elaborate complexes of these) are still of interest to us in the chapters which follow. For lattice defects are "frozen-in" when a semiconductor is rapidly quenched from a high temperature. They also occur in material which is subjected to high-energy nucleon bombardment at temperatures low enough to inhibit annealing effects. We are interested in seeing how electronic equilibrium is obtained for these situations, even though the lattice itself is not in a condition of minimum free energy and is unable at these low temperatures to perform the atomic replacements necessary for minimizing the free energy.

† It is the purpose of the present volume to consider purely electronic adjustments in a semiconductor. This means that we are restricted to temperatures low enough for atomic migration to be negligible.

Chapter 2

THE FERMI LEVEL—ELECTRON DENSITY EQUILIBRIUM

THE concept of the Fermi level was introduced in Section 1.2.2. as a normalizing parameter for conditions of thermal equilibrium. At that time it was remarked that the probability of finding an electron in a state of energy E is

$$f(E) = \frac{1}{1+\exp\left[\dfrac{E-\phi}{kT}\right]} \tag{200.1}$$

When states are distributed over permitted ranges of energy, it is permissible to speak of the density of states $g(E)$ per unit energy interval at any energy. Then if the total electron density is n_0, there must clearly be a unique value of the parameter ϕ for each temperature which allows the condition

$$n_0 = \int_{-\infty}^{\infty} f(E) \, . \, g(E) \, . \, \mathrm{d}E \tag{200.2}$$

to be satisfied.

The simplest possible kind of band has a single energy minimum in the reduced zone, and spherical constant-energy surfaces are parabolically spaced with respect to this minimum,

$$E = E_c + \frac{\hbar^2 k^2}{2m_c} \tag{200.3}$$

The electronic effective mass m_c then has a perfectly clear meaning, and the density of states is

$$g(E) = 4\pi(2m_c/h^2)^{3/2}(E-E_c)^{1/2} \tag{200.4}$$

Of course, the parabolic spacing of Eq. (200.3) must break down beyond a certain range of **k**; then the density of states must deviate from Eq. (200.4) for *high* energies. This does not affect the evaluation of the free carrier distribution provided that Eq. (200.4) is valid up to energies at which the probability of occupancy is essentially zero (i.e. to energies a sufficient number of kT above the Fermi level).

The previous chapter indicated that the density of states can still be written in the form (200.4) even though energy surfaces be far from spherical. The only necessary condition is that energy must increase as the square of wave-vector in every direction. For example, Section 1.4.4. noted the possibility of a band with a single extremum surrounded by ellipsoidal surfaces

$$E = E_c + \tfrac{1}{2}\hbar^2\left[\frac{(k_x-k_{x0})^2}{m_x} + \frac{(k_y-k_{yo})^2}{m_y} + \frac{(k_z-k_{zo})^2}{m_z}\right] \tag{200.5}$$

and remarked that the density of states would be of the form (200.4) with $m_c = (m_x m_y m_z)^{1/3}$. It can well happen that there are $\mathcal{N}$ such minima at symmetrical points in the Brillouin zone; the equivalent density-of-states mass is then $m_c = \mathcal{N}^{2/3}(m_x m_y m_z)^{1/3}$. Similarly, if two separate bands of masses m_1 and m_2 are degenerate in energy at their extrema, the total density of states can be described in the terms of Eq. (200.4) with

$$m_c = [m_1{}^{3/2} + m_2{}^{3/2}]^{2/3} \tag{200.6}$$

The individual bands may be far from isotropic, but this too does not matter. Thus it will be recalled that the principal valence bands of silicon and germanium have appreciably warped or "dimpled" surfaces. As Gold (1957: **4**) has demonstrated, it is impossible to calculate exactly the corresponding density-of-states mass for these bands; but the difficulty is purely computational and *not* conceptual. Since E *does* vary as k^2 for every direction a density-of-states mass does exist, and by numerical methods may be approximately calculated.

Suppose a band with minimum energy E_c, for which Eq. (200.4) is a satisfactory description of the density of states up to an energy well beyond any likely Fermi level. As a result of some thermal excitation (whose nature we shall not worry about for the present), there are n_0 electrons per unit volume occupying some of the states in this band.

Then dependent on the magnitude of n_0 and on the temperature, the Fermi level ϕ may be either higher or lower than E_c. Its value is controled by the condition

$$n_0 = \int_{E_c}^{\infty} n(E) \,.\, \mathrm{d}E = \int_{E_c}^{\infty} f(E) \,.\, g(E) \,.\, \mathrm{d}E$$

$$= \int_{E_c}^{\infty} \frac{4\pi(2m_c/h^2)^{3/2}(E-E_c)^{1/2}\,\mathrm{d}E}{1+\exp\left[\dfrac{E-\phi}{kT}\right]} \qquad (200.7)$$

The upper limit of integration is unimportant provided that it lies well above all occupied states. Then it causes no error to suppose that Eq. (200.4) will hold up to infinite energy and to set $+\infty$ as the limit of the integral (200.7).

When n_0 is large and T small, the condition (200.7) can be satisfied only by a value of ϕ higher than E_c. The curve of $n(E)$ vs. energy will then resemble that shown in Fig. 20.1. Almost all states are occupied up to an energy one or two kT short of the Fermi level. This *degenerate*† kind of occupancy distribution was encountered in the earlier discussion of the free electron model. Mildly degenerate conditions often occur in semiconductors, but the degree of degeneracy is usually much smaller than that of the electron distribution in a normal metal.

When the temperature is not too low and the number of carriers not unduly large, the condition (200.7) is satisfied with $\phi < E_c$, as illustrated in Fig. 20.2. Even for the lowest energies in the band, only a minor fraction of the available states are now occupied, and almost all the occupied states lie within three or four kT of E_c. This kind of system is truly *non-degenerate* in that every electron has a full opportunity to readjust to thermal change. The term *classical* is also applied to such a carrier distribution; for if ϕ is several kT lower than E_c, the function $f(E)$ may be approximated by a classical Boltzmann factor $\exp[(\phi-E)/kT]$ for all energies within the band.

Whether the electron distribution be classical or degenerate, the condition relating the Fermi level to the electron content of a band of

† It will be recalled that the term degenerate indicates that the specific heat per electron is degenerated to a small fraction of the classical value $3k/2$.

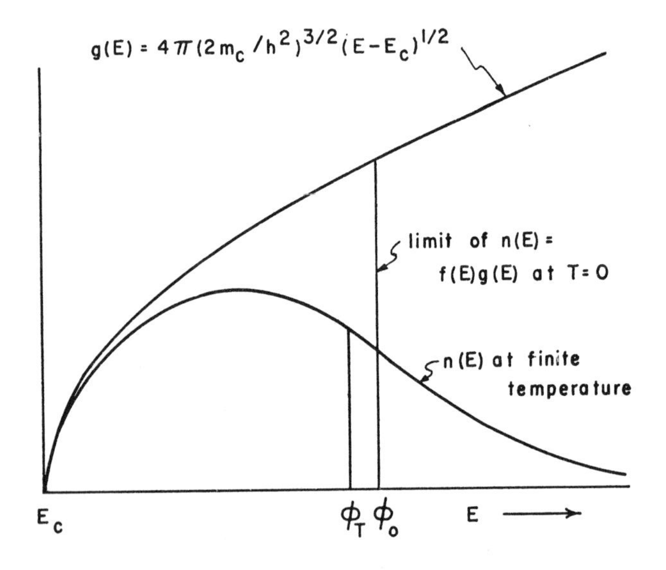

FIG. 20.1. Electron density distribution in a highly degenerate case.

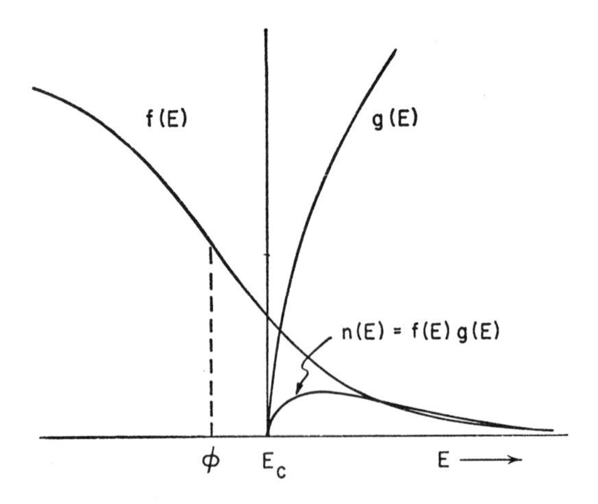

FIG. 20.2. Electron density distribution in a non-degenerate case.

standard form† is rigorously given by (200.7). The integral in this equation is a member of a well studied series.

2.1 THE FERMI–DIRAC INTEGRALS §

For further study of the integral in (200.7) it is convenient to adopt a dimensionless notation. We shall set

$$\epsilon = \left[\frac{E-E_c}{kT}\right]$$

and

$$\eta = \left[\frac{\phi-E_c}{kT}\right]$$

The choice of E_c as the origin of energy simplifies the discussion, and is perfectly legitimate since only differences of energy are important. In the new notation Eq. (200.7) becomes

$$\begin{aligned} n_0 &= 4\pi\left[\frac{2m_ckT}{h^2}\right]^{3/2}\int_0^{\infty}\frac{\epsilon^{1/2}\,.\,d\epsilon}{1+\exp(\epsilon-\eta)} \\ &= \mathcal{N}_c\mathcal{F}_{1/2}(\eta) \end{aligned} \tag{210.1}$$

where

$$\mathcal{N}_c = 2\left[\frac{2\pi m_ckT}{h^2}\right]^{3/2} \tag{210.2}$$

and $\mathcal{F}_{1/2}(\eta)$ denotes the integral

$$\mathcal{F}_{1/2}(\eta) = 2\pi^{-1/2}\int_0^{\infty}\frac{\epsilon^{1/2}\,.\,d\epsilon}{1+\exp(\epsilon-\eta)} \tag{210.3}$$

This is one of the more important members of the set of functions

$$\mathcal{F}_j(\eta) = \frac{1}{\Gamma(j+1)}\int_0^{\infty}\frac{\epsilon^j\,.\,d\epsilon}{1+\exp(\epsilon-\eta)} \tag{210.4}$$

which are collectively known as the Fermi–Dirac integrals.

† We shall frequently describe a band as being of standard form when energy increases as the square of wave-vector, so that a density-of-states mass m^* can be defined which is independent of energy above the bottom of the band.

It will readily be appreciated that finding the Fermi energy corresponding with a given electron density (or vice versa) will be greatly facilitated if $\mathscr{F}_{1/2}(\eta)$ is expressible analytically. This, alas, is not the case for a Fermi–Dirac integral of any positive order. Asymptotic expansions are available for the various orders when $\eta \gg 0$, and all $\mathscr{F}_j$ tend towards $\exp(\eta)$ when $\eta \ll 0$ ("classical" conditions) but expressions of rather limited accuracy only are available when η is fairly small (1952:**2**). The asymptotic expansions and some approaches to approximate expressions for the semidegenerate region are discussed in Appendix C. This appendix also indicates the occasions which make the integrals (210.4) important for various values of j.

Some approximate expressions for $\mathscr{F}_{1/2}(\eta)$ developed in Appendix C will be used elsewhere in this book. We are not, however, dependent on these alone, since a number of tabulations of $\mathscr{F}_j(\eta)$ for various j have been published, and all of this tabular matter is collected in Appendix B. The description in Appendix B indicates the use of these tables, including the procedures for interpolation and inverse interpolation.

2.1.1 Equivalence of Formalism for Electron and Hole Populations

It has been shown that the number of electrons in a conduction band of standard form is related to the Fermi level by

$$\begin{aligned} n_0 &= \mathscr{N}_c \mathscr{F}_{1/2}(\eta) \\ &= 2(2\pi mkT/h^2)^{3/2} \mathscr{F}_{1/2}\left[\frac{\phi - E_c}{kT}\right] \end{aligned} \tag{211.1}$$

The quantity $\mathscr{N}_c$ is sometimes referred to as the *effective density of states in the conduction band*. This term owes its origin to the fact that, for a highly *non-degenerate* carrier distribution such that $\eta \ll 0$, $\mathscr{F}_{1/2}(\eta)$ approaches the classical value

$$\exp(\eta) = \exp\left[\frac{\phi - E_c}{kT}\right]$$

This is the same as the classical limit for occupancy of a level at $E = E_c$. Thus in a classical or non-degenerate semiconductor the total number of electrons in the conduction band is the same as though there were $\mathscr{N}_c$ levels per unit volume all at the energy E_c.

Similarly, for a valence band characterized by an effective mass m_v, when the Fermi level is far above the band extremum E_v, the total number of *free holes* will be the same as though there were $\mathcal{N}_v = 2(2\pi m_v kT/h^2)^{3/2}$ levels at $E = E_v$ replacing the band.

In all other respects also, the formalism of holes in a valence band matches that of electrons in a conduction band. Thus if $f_p(E)$ denotes the probability of an electron *not* occupying a state at energy E,

$$f_p(E) = 1 - f(E) = \frac{1}{1+\exp\left[\dfrac{\phi - E}{kT}\right]} \tag{211.2}$$

When a band of mass m_v extends downwards from energy E_v, the total hole density will be

$$p_0 = \int_{-\infty}^{E_v} g(E) f_p(E) \,.\, \mathrm{d}E$$

$$= 4\pi(2m_v/h^2)^{3/2} \int_{-\infty}^{E_v} \frac{(E_v - E)^{1/2} \,.\, \mathrm{d}E}{1+\exp\left[\dfrac{\phi - E}{kT}\right]} \tag{211.3}$$

We have previously defined reduced energy with respect to the base of the conduction band

$$\epsilon = \left[\frac{E - E_c}{kT}\right]$$

For consideration of a valence band it is convenient to set

$$\epsilon_p = \left[\frac{E_v - E}{kT}\right] = -\epsilon - \epsilon_i \tag{211.4}$$

where ϵ_i is the intrinsic gap width in units of kT (and is a positive quantity). When the integral in Eq. (211.3) is made dimensionless in terms of ϵ_p, the hole density becomes

$$p_0 = \mathcal{N}_v \int_0^{\infty} \frac{(2/\sqrt{\pi})\, \epsilon_p^{1/2} \,.\, \mathrm{d}\epsilon_p}{1+\exp(\epsilon_p + \epsilon_i + \eta)}$$

$$= \mathcal{N}_v \mathcal{F}_{1/2}(-\epsilon_i - \eta) \tag{211.5}$$

which is a complete analogue of Eq. (211.1).

2.2 INTERRELATION OF FREE ELECTRON DENSITY AND FERMI LEVEL

We are now well aware that the free electron density in thermal equilibrium, n_0, can be related to the reduced Fermi energy

$$\eta = \left[\frac{\phi - E_c}{kT}\right]$$

by

$$n_0 = \mathcal{N}_c \mathscr{F}_{1/2}(\eta) \tag{220.1}$$

In this equation,

$$\mathcal{N}_c = 2\left[\frac{2\pi m_c kT}{h^2}\right]^{3/2} = 4{\cdot}829 \times 10^{15}(m_c/m_0)^{3/2}T^{3/2} \text{ cm}^{-3} \tag{220.2}$$

and the quantity $\mathscr{F}_{1/2}(\eta)$ is by now quite familiar. Evidently η must increase monotonically when temperature is lowered yet n_0 maintained constant, and similarly η must rise monotonically with n_0 at constant temperature. Fig. 22.1 shows the course of lines of constant η for the

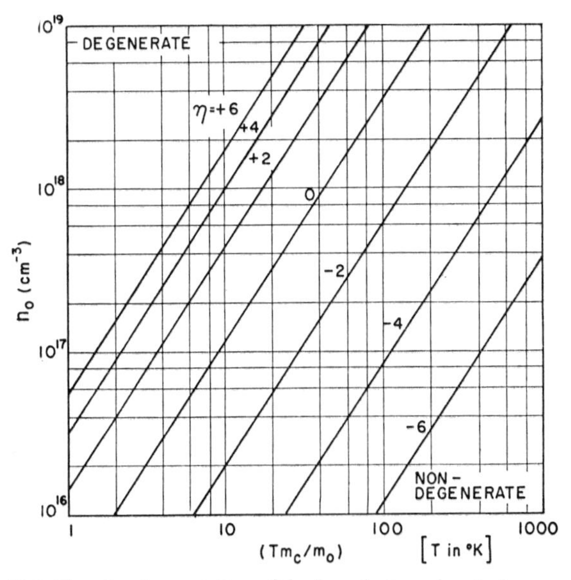

FIG. 22.1. Showing the variation of the free electron density in a conduction band with temperature and effective mass for various set values of the reduced Fermi level.

free electron density as a function of (Tm_c/m_0). A large carrier density, particularly in a band of small effective mass at low temperatures, leads inevitably to the complications of degeneracy. This figure is useful as a rapid guide in indicating whether a degenerate or non-degenerate treatment is called for in a particular situation.

When any free electrons remain in a band at 0°K, the conditions must necessarily be completely degenerate. The Fermi level ϕ_0 and electron density are then related by

$$\left.\begin{aligned} n_0 &= (8\pi/3)(2m_c/h^2)^{3/2}(\phi_o-E_c)^{3/2} \\ \text{or} \qquad \phi_0 &= E_c+(h^2/2m_c)(3n_0/8\pi)^{2/3} \end{aligned}\right\} \qquad (220.3)$$

For a finite but small temperature, the Fermi level is very close to ϕ_0, and as may readily be derived using Eq. (C3.15) of Appendix C,

$$\phi \approx \phi_0 - \frac{(\pi kT)^2}{12(\phi_0-E_c)}, \qquad kT \ll (\phi_0-E_c) \qquad (220.4)$$

The situations of Eqs. (220.3) and (220.4) are of course exactly those depicted in Fig. 20.1.

When ϕ_0 is expressed in electron-volts and n_0 in cm^{-3},

$$\phi_0 = E_c+3{\cdot}64\times 10^{-15}(m_0/m_c)n_0^{2/3} \qquad (220.5)$$

McDougall and Stoner (1938:**2**) noted that ϕ_0 can be used as a complete characterization of the carrier density at any *finite* temperature. This means that instead of quoting the carrier density n_0 at any temperature T, the same information could be conveyed by quoting T *and* the Fermi energy ϕ_0 which would be achieved by the given carrier density at 0°K [using Eq. (220.3) as the vehicle for interchange of variable]. Their procedure amounted to using

$$\left[\frac{\phi_0-E_c}{kT}\right]^{3/2} = \frac{3\pi^{1/2}}{4}\mathscr{F}_{1/2}(\eta) \qquad (220.6)$$

in order to find the value of $\eta = [(\phi-E_c)/kT]$ corresponding with a given value of $[(\phi_0-E_c)/kT]$. Table 22.1 (which is based on one of McDougall and Stoner's tables) shows the result of carrying through this procedure for various ratios of kT to (ϕ_0-E_c).

Table 22.1

Temperature T in units of $\left[\frac{k}{\phi_0-E_c}\right]$	$\left[\frac{\phi_0-E_c}{kT}\right]$	Reduced Fermi energy at temperature T, $\eta = \left[\frac{\phi-E_c}{kT}\right]$
0·05	20	19·96
0·1	10	9·916
0·2	5	4·823
0·5	2	1·486
1	1	−0·021
2	0·5	−1·231
5	0·2	−2·675
10	0·1	−3·734
20	0·05	−4·765

2.2.1 Temperature-Independent Electron Density

The successive entries of Table 22.1 may be visualized as forming a sequence of increasing temperature when conditions occur to make n_0(and ϕ_0) temperature-independent over some range. The first few entries show a close correspondence between the values in the second or third columns. This is not at all surprising, since for a given n_0 the Fermi level is very weakly temperature-dependent under conditions of strong degeneracy $[kT \ll (\phi_0-E_c)]$. Differentiating Eq. (220.4), the result is that

$$\frac{d\phi}{d(kT)} \approx -\frac{\pi^2 kT}{6(\phi_0-E_c)} \ll 1 \quad \text{if} \quad kT \ll (\phi_0-E_c) \qquad (221.1)$$

Table 22.1 shows that the Fermi level passes through E_c when T is very slightly smaller than $(\phi-E_c)/k$, and that ϕ drops much more rapidly on further warming. The manner in which this occurs, and the fact that $(d\phi/dT)$ becomes essentially constant in the high-temperature non-degenerate region can probably be brought out more effectively by a graph rather than a table. Accordingly, Fig. 22.2 shows curves which illustrate the dependence of ϕ on T (or kT) for two supposedly temperature-independent free electron densities.

The slope of such a curve is zero at $T = 0$ and becomes monotonically more negative as temperature rises. In order to appreciate the

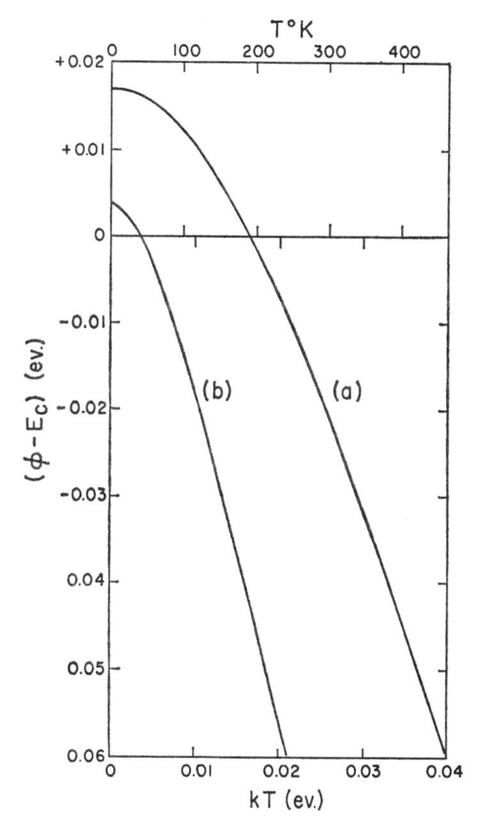

FIG. 22.2. Variation of Fermi level with temperature when the density of electrons in the conduction band is constant.

(a) For $n_0(m_0/m_c)^{3/2} = 10^{19}\text{cm}^{-3}$, $\phi_0 = 0{\cdot}0169$ eV.
(b) For $n_0(m_0/m_c)^{3/2} = 10^{18}\text{cm}^{-3}$, $\phi_0 = 0{\cdot}00364$ eV.

course taken by $(\mathrm{d}\phi/\mathrm{d}T)$, consider the following argument. If n_0 does not depend on temperature, then

$$\frac{\mathrm{d}}{\mathrm{d}T}[T^{3/2}\mathscr{F}_{1/2}(\eta)] = 0 \tag{221.2}$$

or

$$\frac{\mathrm{d}}{\mathrm{d}T}\mathscr{F}_{1/2}(\eta) = -\frac{3}{2T}\mathscr{F}_{1/2}(\eta) \tag{221.3}$$

It is more convenient to perform the differentiation with respect to another variable:

$$\frac{d}{dT}\mathscr{F}_{1/2}(\eta) = \frac{d\eta}{dT}\cdot\frac{d}{d\eta}\mathscr{F}_{1/2}(\eta) = \frac{d\eta}{dT}\cdot\mathscr{F}_{-1/2}(\eta) \qquad (221.4)$$

where of course

$$\frac{d\eta}{dT} = \frac{d}{dT}\left[\frac{\phi - E_c}{kT}\right] = \frac{1}{kT}\left[\frac{d\phi}{dT} - \frac{\phi - E_c}{kT}\right] \qquad (221.5)$$

From Eqs. (221.3)–(221.5), the Fermi level varies with kT at a rate

$$\frac{d\phi}{d(kT)} = -\left\{\frac{3}{2}\cdot\frac{\mathscr{F}_{1/2}(\eta)}{\mathscr{F}_{-1/2}(\eta)} - \eta\right\} \qquad (221.6)$$

when n_0 is invariant. For the highly degenerate conditions of low temperatures, $\mathscr{F}_{1/2}(\eta)$ and $\mathscr{F}_{-1/2}(\eta)$ must be described in the form of Eq. (C3.9); if the first term only of each series (C3.14) is retained in describing the remainder $R_j(\eta)$, it may easily be shown that Eq. (221.6) is consistent with (221.1).

When η passes through zero at a temperature $0{\cdot}99\ (\phi_0 - E_c)/k$,

$$\left[\frac{d\phi}{d(kT)}\right]_{\phi = E_c} = -\frac{3}{2}\cdot\frac{\mathscr{F}_{1/2}(0)}{\mathscr{F}_{-1/2}(0)} \qquad (221.7)$$

Using Eq. (C3.3) for expression of $\mathscr{F}_j(0)$ in terms of the zeta function,

$$\left[\frac{d\phi}{d(kT)}\right]_{\phi = E_c} = \frac{3\zeta(3/2)}{2^{3/2}\zeta(1/2)} = -1{\cdot}898 \qquad (221.8)$$

It is rather interesting that the slope of ϕ for this condition should be a universal constant, independent of carrier density. It may be verified that the two curves of Fig. 22.2 *are* parallel, with the required slope, as they pass through E_c.

At much higher temperatures, when essentially non-degenerate conditions prevail, $(n_0/N_c) = \mathscr{F}_{1/2}(\eta) \approx \mathscr{F}_{-1/2}(\eta) \approx \exp(\eta)$. Accordingly,

$$\frac{d\phi}{d(kT)} \approx -\left[\frac{3}{2} + \ln(N_c/n_0)\right], \quad \eta \ll 0 \qquad (221.9)$$

The temperature dependence of $\ln(N_c)$ will have but a mild effect on $(d\phi/dT)$; thus Eq. (221.9) confirms the visual evidence of Fig. 22.2

that under non-degenerate conditions ϕ falls more or less linearly when temperature rises yet n_0 remains unchanged.

The preceding discussion has considered how the Fermi level varies with temperature when the free carrier density remains constant over the entire range. But this is not a normal condition for a semiconductor —it is more reminiscent of a metal. As elaborated in Section 2.3, the carrier densities in an intrinsic semiconductor vary continuously with temperature. At lower temperatures such that intrinsic excitation is overshadowed by impurity effects (to be explored in Section 2.4 and in Chapter 3), the majority carrier density can be invariant with temperature only in the temperature range for which all impurity levels are ionized. This condition must normally be violated when the temperature becomes sufficiently small, since progressive cooling eventually causes all conduction and valence states to be emptied in favor of trapping impurity states.† It will depend on the ratio of the intrinsic gap width to the impurity ionization energy how wide the "exhaustion range" of constant majority density may be. In germanium dominated by shallow chemical impurities, for instance, this range extends from $\sim 350°K$ down to $\sim 40°K$ with typical localized center densities.

2.2.2 The Effect of a Magnetic Field

Section 1.4.6 described the change which occurs in the distribution of band states when a magnetic field is applied, due to the creation of sub-bands based on the Landau levels. It was shown that the density of states must be described as a summation over the contributions from the various sub-bands at any energy. The effective mass m_c in the conduction band determines the cyclotron frequency $\omega_0 = (eH_z/m_c c)$ for a magnetic field in the z-direction, and this in turn sets the splitting $\hbar\omega_0$ between Landau levels. In terms of this parameter it follows [see Eq. (146.7)] that

$$g(E) = 2\pi\left(\frac{2m_c}{h^2}\right)^{3/2} \sum_{n=0}^{n_{\max}} \frac{\hbar\omega_0}{[E - E_c - (n+\frac{1}{2})\hbar\omega_0]^{1/2}} \qquad (222.1)$$

is the density of states function for the conduction band.

† The solitary exception is the class of materials we call impurity metals, which are described in Section 3.5. Even in these materials, it is only the total number of electrons at energies $\geqslant E_c$ which remains temperature-independent, not the number of electrons in the "ordinary" conduction band states. Accordingly, the Fermi level in an impurity metal does not behave in the manner we have just described.

The mutual relationship of the free electron density n_0 and the Fermi level is expressed by

$$n_0 = \int_{E_c}^{\infty} f(E)g(E) \, . \, \mathrm{d}E \tag{222.2}$$

where $f(E)$ is still as given by Eq. (200.1). It makes no difference whether the lower limit of integration for Eq. (222.2) is written as E_c or as $(E_c+\frac{1}{2}\hbar\omega_0)$ when the magnetic field is finite, since it will be observed from Eq. (222.1) (and from Fig. 14.9) that there are no states between E_c and $(E_c+\frac{1}{2}\hbar\omega_0)$.

Substitution of Eqs. (200.1) and (222.1) into Eq. (222.2) gives us that

$$n_0 = 2\pi\left(\frac{2m_c}{h^2}\right)^{3/2} \sum_{n=0} \int_0^{\infty} \frac{\hbar\omega_0 \, . \, \mathrm{d}E}{\left[1+\exp\left(\frac{E-\phi}{kT}\right)\right]\left[E-E_c-(n+\frac{1}{2})\hbar\omega_0\right]^{1/2}} \tag{222.3}$$

By making the usual substitutions $\mathcal{N}_c = 2(2\pi m_c kT/h^2)^{3/2}$, $\epsilon = [(E-E_c)/kT]$, $\eta = [(\phi-E_c)/kT]$, and the additional one $\theta = (\hbar\omega_0/kT)$, Eq. (222.3) can be expressed more compactly as

$$n_0 = \mathcal{N}_c \sum_{n=0} \int_{(n+1/2)\theta}^{\infty} \frac{\pi^{-1/2} \, . \, \theta \, . \, \mathrm{d}\epsilon}{[1+\exp(\epsilon-\eta)][\epsilon-(n+\frac{1}{2})\theta]^{1/2}} \tag{222.4}$$

It is worth noting at the outset that Eq. (222.4) is consistent with the usual expression for vanishing magnetic field. For if H_z is very small, $\theta \ll 1$, the summation over n can be replaced by an integral,

$$n_0 = \mathcal{N}_c \int_0^{\infty}\int_0^{\infty} \frac{\pi^{-1/2}\theta \, . \, \mathrm{d}\epsilon \, . \, \mathrm{d}n}{[1+\exp(\epsilon-\eta)][\epsilon-(n+\frac{1}{2})\theta]^{1/2}}, \qquad H_z \to 0$$

$$= \mathcal{N}_c \int_0^{\infty} \frac{2\pi^{-1/2}\epsilon^{1/2} \, . \, \mathrm{d}\epsilon}{[1+\exp(\epsilon-\eta)]} = \mathcal{N}_c \mathcal{F}_{1/2}(\eta) \tag{222.5}$$

This is of course identical with the ordinary result (210.1).

When the magnetic field is large enough to provide an appreciable reorganization of the energy levels, the summation in (222.4) must be preserved. But each of the integrals in this equation can be expressed in terms of a Fermi function. Thus if we define a set of variables ξ_n by $\xi_n = [\epsilon-(n+\frac{1}{2})\theta]$, Eq. (222.4) can be expressed as

$$n_0 = \mathcal{N}_c \sum_{n=0} \int_0^\infty \frac{\theta\pi^{-1/2} \cdot \xi_n^{-1/2} \cdot \mathrm{d}\xi_n}{1+\exp[\xi_n+(n+\frac{1}{2})\theta-\eta]}$$

$$= \mathcal{N}_c \sum_{n=0}^{\infty} \theta \mathscr{F}_{-1/2}[\eta-(n+\tfrac{1}{2})\theta] \tag{222.6}$$

from our general definition of the set of functions $\mathscr{F}_j(\eta)$ (see Appendix B). The form of Eq. (222.6) is such that the application of a magnetic field always tends to *lower* the Fermi level with respect to the conduction band levels; i.e. it always tends to make conditions *less* degenerate.

This tendency can be demonstrated to hold whether the semiconductor is degenerate or non-degenerate in the absence of a field. To start with, consider the limiting case of a semiconductor in which the conduction band is strongly degenerate under zero-field conditions. The symbol η_0 will temporarily be used to indicate the reduced Fermi level for $H = 0$; then we are considering a material in which $\eta_0 \gg 0$. On application of the magnetic field, almost all states are occupied up as far as the sub-band of index $n \approx (\eta_0/\theta)$, whereas sub-bands of higher index are virtually empty. To obtain a crude approximation to the behavior of Eq. (222.6), it will be assumed that the strong degeneracy approximation for $\mathscr{F}_{-1/2}(\eta)$ (see Appendix C) can be used for *all* sub-bands of positive argument and that *no contribution at all* is made by the higher sub-bands, i.e.

$$\left.\begin{aligned} \mathscr{F}_{-1/2}[\eta-(n+\tfrac{1}{2})\theta] &\approx 2\pi^{-1/2}[\eta-(n+\tfrac{1}{2})\theta]^{1/2}, & [\eta-(n+\tfrac{1}{2})\theta] > 0 \\ \mathscr{F}_{-1/2}[\eta-(n+\tfrac{1}{2})\theta] &\approx 0, & [\eta-(n+\tfrac{1}{2})\theta] < 0 \end{aligned}\right\} \tag{222.7}$$

From Eqs. (222.6) and (222.7) we have that

$$n_0 \approx \mathcal{N}_c \sum_{n=0}^{n_{\max}} 2\pi^{-1/2}\theta[\eta-(n+\tfrac{1}{2})\theta]^{1/2}, \quad \eta \gg 0 \tag{222.8}$$

The reduced Fermi energy η for Eq. (222.8) is an oscillatory function of the magnetic field parameter θ, as illustrated by the example of

Fig. 22.3. These oscillations are quite real but the rather abrupt form of the assumption (222.7) makes them slightly more exaggerated than would be the case for an exact calculation. We have chosen to plot this figure with energy expressed relative to E_c, the conduction band minimum for $H = 0$. Since the lowest Landau level for any finite magnetic field is $\frac{1}{2}\hbar\omega_0$ *above* E_c (as indicated by the rising line in Fig. 22.3), the Fermi level relative to the *actual* conduction band base declines

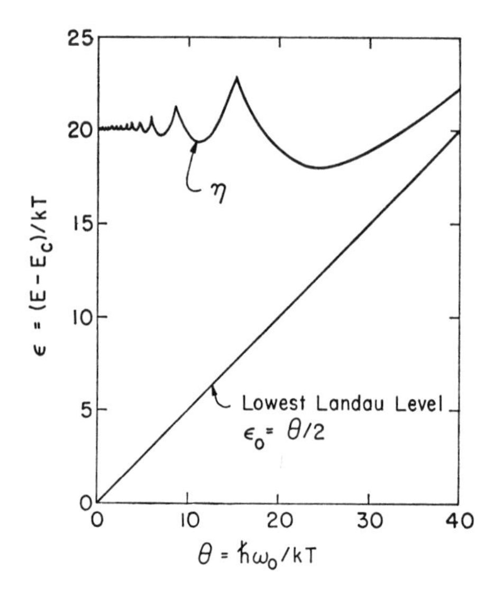

FIG. 22.3. Variation of reduced Fermi level (for a constant n_0) with the magnetic field parameter θ, when the conduction band distribution is highly degenerate ($\eta_0 = 20$) at low fields.

fairly steadily (albeit with superimposed oscillations) as H increases, precipitating a failure of the assumption of strong degeneracy.

Each maximum of η in Fig. 22.3 marks the boundary between occupancy of n or $(n-1)$ sub-bands. For the example illustrated, the only occupied states are in the *lowest* sub-band when $\theta > 15$ (and a more exact calculation confirms that this is not far from the truth).

The oscillatory result (222.8) can be graphically demonstrated in another fashion by plotting η vs. η_0 as a function of magnetic field strength. For strong degeneracy and zero field,

$$n_0 = N_c \mathscr{F}_{1/2}(\eta_0) \approx N_c \cdot \frac{4\eta_0^{3/2}}{3\pi^{1/2}}, \quad \eta_0 \gg 0 \qquad (222.9)$$

From Eqs. (222.8) and (222.9), the relationship of η to η_0 when θ has any value is

$$\sum_{n=0}^{n_{\max}} \left[(\eta/\theta) - n - \tfrac{1}{2}\right]^{1/2} = \frac{2}{3}\left[\eta_0/\theta\right]^{3/2}, \quad \eta \gg 0 \qquad (222.10)$$

Fig. 22.4 shows how (η/θ) varies with (η_0/θ) for this supposition of

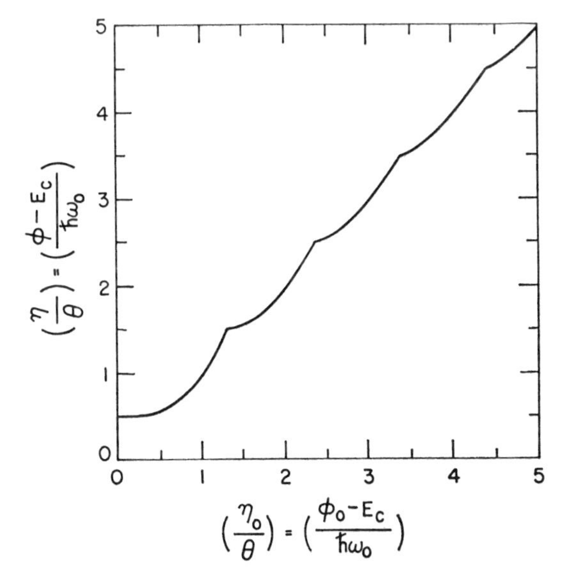

FIG. 22.4. Relation between the reduced Fermi level in a magnetic field and that for zero field. For conditions of extreme degeneracy at small fields.

strong degeneracy. This figure contains the same information as did the example of Fig. 22.3, but unlike the earlier figure is of universal character, not restricted to any particular carrier density. Whereas the abscissa of Fig. 22.3 was *proportional* to H, that of Fig. 22.4 is *inversely proportional* to H, and the strong field region is that lying to the left. It can be seen that the oscillatory character of ϕ has almost a constant period in $1/H$. As H is reduced, the difference between η and η_0 becomes progressively smaller (as had already been ascertained from the example of Fig. 22.3).

When conditions are *non-degenerate* in the absence of a magnetic field, very different approximations can be made in Eq. (222.6). Each of the Fermi integrals $\mathscr{F}_{-1/2}[\eta-(n+\frac{1}{2})\theta]$ can then be expressed (Appendix C) simply as $\exp[\eta-(n+\frac{1}{2})\theta]$. Thus Eq. (222.6) becomes

$$n_0 = \mathscr{N}_c \sum_{n=0}^{\infty} \theta \,.\, \exp[\eta-(n+\tfrac{1}{2})\theta]\,, \qquad \eta_o \ll 0 \tag{222.11}$$

$$= \mathscr{N}_c \,.\, \theta \,.\, \exp(\eta-\tfrac{1}{2}\theta) \,.\, [1+\exp(-\theta)+\exp(-2\theta)+\ldots]$$

$$= \mathscr{N}_c \exp(\eta) \,.\, \left[\frac{\theta \exp(-\frac{1}{2}\theta)}{1-\exp(-\theta)}\right]$$

$$= \mathscr{N}_c \exp(\eta) \,.\, [\tfrac{1}{2}\theta \operatorname{csch}(\tfrac{1}{2}\theta)] \tag{222.12}$$

The result is expressed in this form since $n_0 = \mathscr{N}_c \exp(\eta_0)$ is the zero-field result for a non-degenerate situation; the quantity $[\frac{1}{2}\theta \operatorname{csch}(\frac{1}{2}\theta)]$ represents the change wrought by the magnetic field. This quantity is approximately $(1-\theta^2/24)$ when θ is small, but becomes very small when $\theta \gg 1$. The effect on the equilibrium of Eq. (222.12) is that η must *increase* with θ to preserve a given value of n_0. An example of this behavior is furnished by Fig. 22.5 for a semiconductor in which $\eta_0 = -4{\cdot}6$, or $(n_0/\mathscr{N}_c) = 10^{-2}$. η rises with the magnetic field parameter θ, but never quite as fast as the lowest Landau level rises above E_c. Thus the energy separation of the lowest conduction levels and the Fermi level *widens monotonically* as magnetic field increases.

In discussing the influence of the magnetic field on the distribution of states and on the Fermi energy, it is useful to keep in mind the magnitude of field required to produce a given situation. If H is expressed in oersteds, then

$$\hbar\omega_0 \approx 1{\cdot}16\times 10^{-8}(m_0/m_c)H \,.\, \text{eV}, \tag{222.13}$$

This is only likely to be comparable with or larger than kT for bands of rather low effective mass at rather low temperatures, in view of the physical limitations on the magnetic field strength which can be maintained continuously. Thus for carriers of mass $m_c \approx 0{\cdot}2\ m_0$ at a field of ~ 5000 oersteds (as typically used in standard measurements of galvanomagnetic coefficients), $\hbar\omega_0 \approx 3\times 10^{-4}$ eV, which is smaller than kT for any temperature outside the liquid helium range.

On the other hand, for the conduction band of indium antimonide, in which $m_c \approx 0{\cdot}013m_0$, a field of 30,000 oersted will provide a Landau

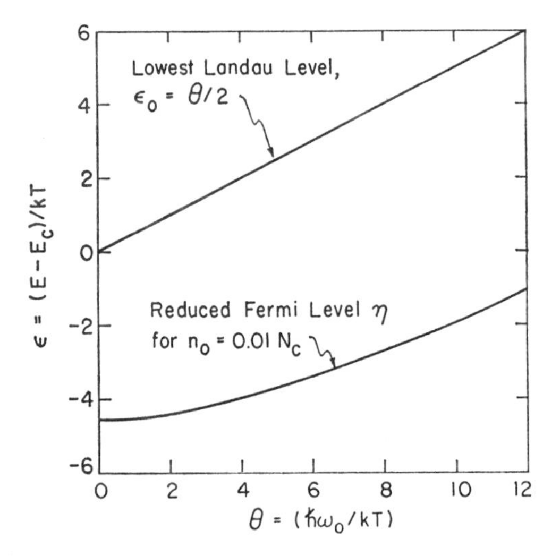

FIG. 22.5. Variation of the reduced Fermi level η with the magnetic field parameter θ when the ratio $(n_0/\mathcal{N}_c)$ remains at 0·01. η rises with θ, but still becomes progressively more separated from the lowest Landau level.

level spacing of $\hbar\omega_0 \sim 0{\cdot}027$ eV. This is a little larger than kT even for room temperature, and it is obvious that almost all free electrons will be in the lowest magnetic sub-band at low temperatures.

The condition of very large magnetic field, $\theta \gg 1$, enables us to use the first term only of the summation (222.6), viz.,

$$n_0 = \mathcal{N}_c\theta\,\mathcal{F}_{-1/2}(\eta - \tfrac{1}{2}\theta)\,, \quad \theta \gg 1 \tag{222.14}$$

whether conditions be degenerate $[(\eta - \frac{1}{2}\theta) > 0]$ or non-degenerate or of intermediate status. This simplification is, however, rarely a justifiable one.

2.3 INTRINSIC SEMICONDUCTORS §

The densities n_0 and p_0 of conduction band electrons and valence band holes in an intrinsic semiconductor depend only on the nature of these bands and the intrinsic energy gap between them. Impurities (by definition) play a negligible role.

In an intrinsic semiconductor, electrical neutrality requires that $n_0 = p_0$, a value which is usually called n_i, the subscript i denoting the intrinsic state.

A semiconductor is very sensitive to impurities at low temperatures, since carriers can often be excited from impurity levels for a small expenditure of energy. It does, however, seem reasonable that at high temperatures (when the intrinsic gap is a smaller multiple of kT), intrinsic excitation should become dominant in any semiconductor. This certainly happens in some fairly well purified semiconductors with a small intrinsic gap (such as α Sn, InSb, HgSe and Te) and in a few materials of rather larger intrinsic gap for which purification procedures are well advanced (including Ge and Si). However, in most wide gap semiconductors it is not feasible to carry purification to a point where intrinsic excitation can dominate over extrinsic excitation before either the melting point or decomposition temperature is reached. However, this is a rapidly evolving field, and the advent of new purification procedures will certainly provide us with more materials in the future which can be examined in a state of wholly intrinsic excitation.

The requirement that $n_0 = p_0 = n_i$ sets the position of the Fermi level for an intrinsic conductor. This level is the root of the equation

$$n_i = \mathcal{N}_c \mathscr{F}_{1/2}(\eta) = \mathcal{N}_v \mathscr{F}_{1/2}(-\epsilon_i - \eta) \qquad (230.1)$$

for bands of standard form, using the results (210.1) and (211.5). From symmetry considerations we might expect to find the Fermi level at $(E_c - \frac{1}{2}E_i)$, and this is just the location of $\phi_{\text{intrinsic}}$ (which will subsequently be signified as ϕ_i) at 0°K, as shown in Fig. 23.1.

2.3.1 Non-degenerate Intrinsic Semiconductors

When the intrinsic gap is a fairly large multiple of kT, and the masses m_c, m_v are not too dissimilar, n_i is small compared with both $\mathcal{N}_c$ and $\mathcal{N}_v$. The Fermi level is then considerably lower than E_c, yet considerably higher than $(E_c - E_i)$. Both of the Fermi integrals in Eq. (230.1) can be replaced by their non-degenerate limiting forms,

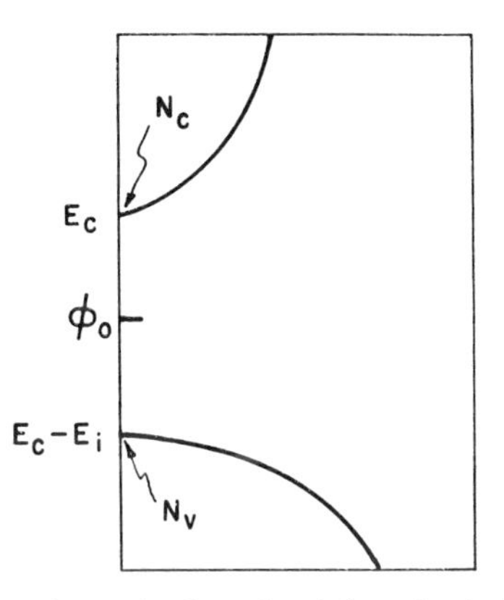

FIG. 23.1. Conduction and valence bands in an intrinsic semiconductor, with the Fermi level in the middle of the intrinsic gap at 0°K.

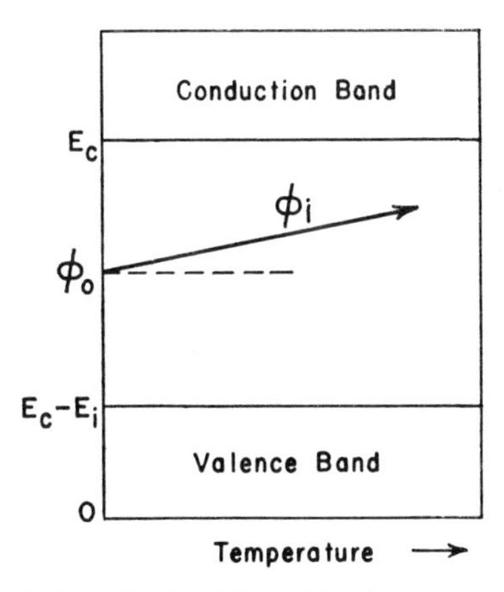

FIG. 23.2. Variation of intrinsic Fermi level with temperature if $m_c < m_v$.

so that

$$n_i = \mathcal{N}_c \exp(\eta) = \mathcal{N}_v \exp(-\epsilon_i - \eta) \tag{231.1}$$

From this, evidently

$$\exp(\eta) = (\mathcal{N}_v/\mathcal{N}_c)^{1/2}\exp(-\tfrac{1}{2}\epsilon_i) \tag{231.2}$$

or

$$\begin{aligned} \phi_i &= E_c - \tfrac{1}{2}E_i + \tfrac{1}{2}kT\ln(\mathcal{N}_v/\mathcal{N}_c) \\ &= E_c - \tfrac{1}{2}E_i + \tfrac{3}{4}kT\ln(m_v/m_c) \end{aligned} \tag{231.3}$$

On warming, the Fermi level departs from the middle of the gap at a rate dependent on the ratio of hole and electron masses, as indicated in Fig. 23.2. Only in a material for which by chance $m_c \approx m_v$ will ϕ be near the middle of the gap at very high temperatures. Extreme disparity of m_c and m_n can lead to degeneracy problems, which are examined in the next sub-section.

The intrinsic carrier density is found by re-inserting (231.2) into (231.1), yielding

$$n_i = (N_v N_c)^{1/2} \exp(-E_i/2kT) \tag{231.4}$$

When the intrinsic gap width is a rather large multiple of kT, the exponential term in Eq. (231.4) provides most of the temperature dependence for n_i [since $(N_c N_v)^{1/2}$ varies only as $T^{3/2}$]. Because of this, it is common practice to correlate experimental observations in the intrinsic range by plotting $\ln(n_i)$ vs. $1/T$. Fig. 23.3 provides an example of such a plot for intrinsic germanium. The experimental points are the observations of Morin and Maita (1954:**3**), who found that the data was best fitted by the expression

$$n_i = 1{\cdot}76 \times 10^{16} T^{3/2} \exp(-0{\cdot}785/2kT) \text{ cm}^{-3} \tag{231.5}$$

The plot of $\ln(n_i)$ vs. $1/T$ is not truly linear [because of the $T^{3/2}$ factor in Eq. (231.5)] and it is often preferred to construct a graph of $\ln(n_i/T^{3/2})$ vs. $1/T$. This is done in Fig. 23.4 for the data of Fig. 23.3, and now the relationship is accurately linear.

In comparing an experimentally derived expression such as Eq. (231.5) with Eq. (231.4), considerable care must be taken in establishing the meaning of the "intrinsic gap" deduced from the slope of $\ln(n_i/T^{3/2})$ vs. $1/T$. In the case of germanium, 0·785 eV is not the true intrinsic gap at *any* temperature. This seeming anomaly occurs because E_i is usually itself a function of temperature.

The simplest form of variation is one in which E_i changes linearly with temperature,

$$E_i = E_{i0} - \alpha T \tag{231.6}$$

Substitution into (231.4) then gives

$$(n_i/T^{3/2}) = 2\left(\frac{4\pi^2 m_c m_v k^2}{h^4}\right)^{3/4} \exp(\alpha/2k) \exp(-E_{i0}/2kT) \tag{231.7}$$

A semilogarithmic plot of $(n_i/T^{3/2})$ vs. $1/T$ for this situation still gives a linear relationship, but the slope is indicative of E_{i0}, the gap for $T = 0$, *not* the gap at the temperature of the measurements. At the same time, the intercept of such a plot is controlled by the value of α as well as by the mass ratios (m_c/m_0) and $m_v/m_0)$. If any pair of the three quantities

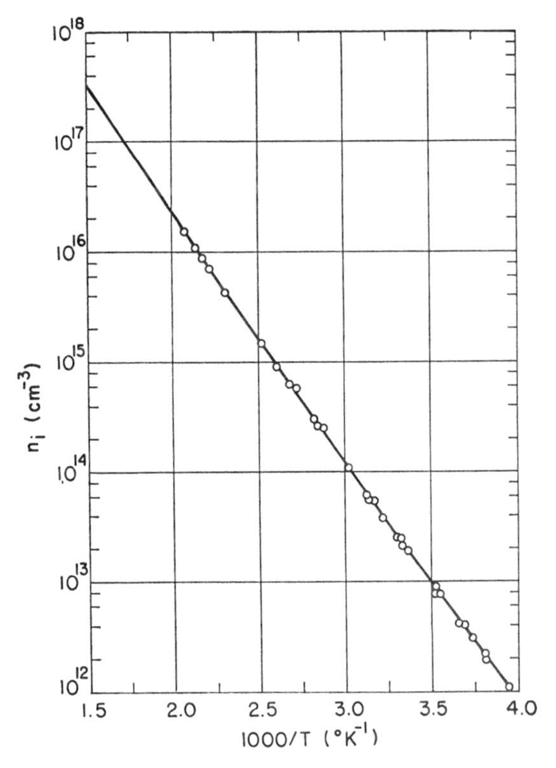

FIG. 23.3. The temperature dependence of carrier density in an intrinsic semiconductor, using the experimental data of Morin and Maita (1954:**3**) for intrinsic germanium. The curve is the expression given in Eq. (231.5).

α, (m_c/m_0), (m_v/m_0) are known, the third can be found by comparison of Eq. (231.7) with an empirical expression such as Eq. (231.5). We shall use germanium as the basis for an example of this procedure after reviewing how the intrinsic gap actually does change with temperature.

It should hardly come as a surprise to acknowledge that the temperature dependence of the intrinsic gap in a real semiconducting material will usually be more complicated than a simple linear law. If such non-linearity is pronounced, a semilogarithmic plot of $(n_i/T^{3/2})$ vs. $1/T$ will appear noticeably curved, which gives us good reason to

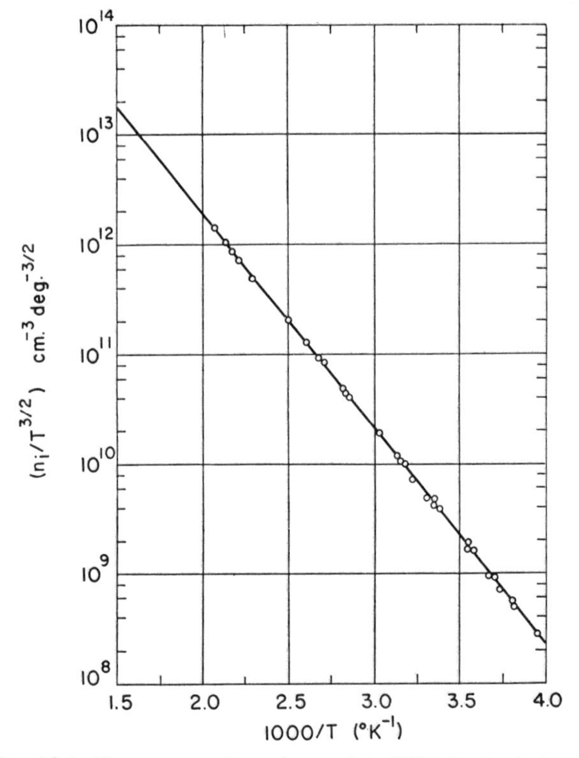

Fig. 23.4. Temperature dependence of $(n_i/T^{3/2})$ for intrinsic germanium, showing the experimental points of Morin and Maita (1954:**3**). The line gives the behavior of $1{\cdot}76 \times 10^{16} \exp(-4550/T)$. [See Eq. (231.5).]

take an active interest in the physical mechanisms giving rise to change of E_i.

The increasing amplitude of thermal vibrations as T increases will generally lead to a fall in E_i; this can be linear in T but is not necessarily so. In addition to this effect, there is a change in interatomic spacing due to thermal expansion. Depending on the character of the potential $V(r)$ in a particular material, this expansion can cause either an increase or decrease of E_i, which may be either linear or of higher power in T.

Lead sulfide provides a good example of a material in which (dE_i/dT) is far from constant. Early measurements of electrical properties on single crystals (1951:**8**) were construed as corresponding to the intrinsic state [Eq. (231.4)] with an intrinsic gap of ~1 eV. It has since been realized (1953:**7**, 1954:**8**) that the above result is seriously in error, caused by: (a) drastic temperature dependence of E_i, and (b) thermal generation of lattice imperfection donor impurities which obscured the intrinsic behavior. Some ambiguity remains concerning the true energy gap in this semiconductor; one estimate has placed it as being essentially of the form shown in Fig. 23.5. The reconciliation of Eq. (231.4) with intrinsic data is obviously far from straightforward in such a material, as it will be in any other material for which (dE_i/dT) changes over the range of measurements.

Germanium was deliberately selected as the model of Figs. 23.3 and 23.4, to be compared with Eq. (231.4), because the energy gap *can* be approximated in the form (231.6) for a wide range of temperature. The optical work of Macfarlane *et al.* (1957:**7**) indicates that $E_i \approx 0{\cdot}746$ at 0°K, and that it decreases in a highly *non-linear* fashion for temperatures up to ~150°K (see Fig. 15.10). Further warming however is characterized by a constant value of (dE_i/dT), and to a good degree of approximation we have that

$$E_i = (0{\cdot}785 - 0{\cdot}0004T) \text{ eV in Ge for } T > 200°\text{K} \qquad (231.8)$$

It is fortunate indeed that the non-linearities occur at low temperatures where intrinsic phenomena are of least interest. Germanium is usually only observable in the intrinsic state for $T \gtrsim 250$°K; then Eq. (231.8) applies, and the empirical expression (231.5) can legitimately be compared with Eq. (231.7). This is a far happier situation than the one for PbS, but in approaching a new material one should always be prepared for complexity even while hoping for simplicity!†

The coefficient of $\exp(-E_{i0}/2kT)$ in Eq. (231.7) can be expressed as $4{\cdot}83 \times 10^{15}(m_c m_v/m_0^2)^{3/4} \exp(\alpha/2k)$ cm^{-3} deg$^{-3/2}$. Comparing this with

† One complication we have overlooked for germanium is that at sufficiently high temperatures there will be some electrons in states near the [000] minimum and [100] minima of the conduction band (Section 1.5.2). This will tend to make ϕ_i rather lower and n_i rather larger than we calculate when T is higher than (say) 700°K.

the empirical equation (231·5), it is then evident that $(m_c m_v/m_0^2)^{3/4} \exp(\alpha/2k) \approx 3{\cdot}65$ for germanium, or $m_c m_v/m_0^2 \approx 0{\cdot}235$ in view of the value Eq. (231.8) provides for α. This composite effective mass ratio can be compared with the results of cyclotron resonance measurements (see Section 1.5.2). The comparison supports the assumption (based on entirely different kinds of experiment) that the germanium conduction band comprises four prolate ellipsoids rather than eight.

The cross-checking procedure of the preceding paragraph could be inverted for another semiconductor in which m_c and m_v were known, but

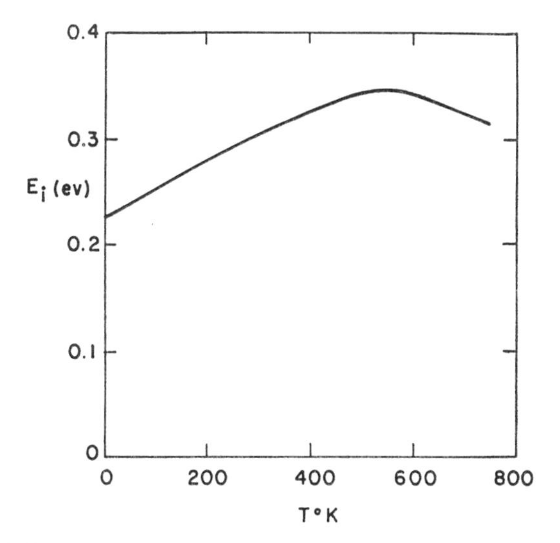

FIG. 23.5. Temperature dependence of the intrinsic gap in PbS as estimated by Smith (1954:**8**).

α unknown. It is useless, however, to attempt to deduce α from intrinsic data on a new and poorly understood semiconductor by setting m_c and m_v provisionally as equal to m_0. The result of such a dubious procedure for α is likely to be so erroneous that the only purpose served will be the demoralization of further investigations.

For temperatures which are not too high or too low, an attempt may be made to fit intrinsic data on a smaller energy gap semiconductor such as InSb by the procedure we have followed with germanium. The intrinsic gap of InSb is believed to vary non-linearly with T for low temperatures (1955:**13**) but in the higher range becomes rather more linear—as happened with Ge. Not much error would be involved in supposing

$$E_i \approx (0{\cdot}26 - 0{\cdot}00027T) \text{ eV in InSb, } T > 200°\text{K} \qquad (231.9)$$

The carrier effective masses for InSb depend on energy (see Section

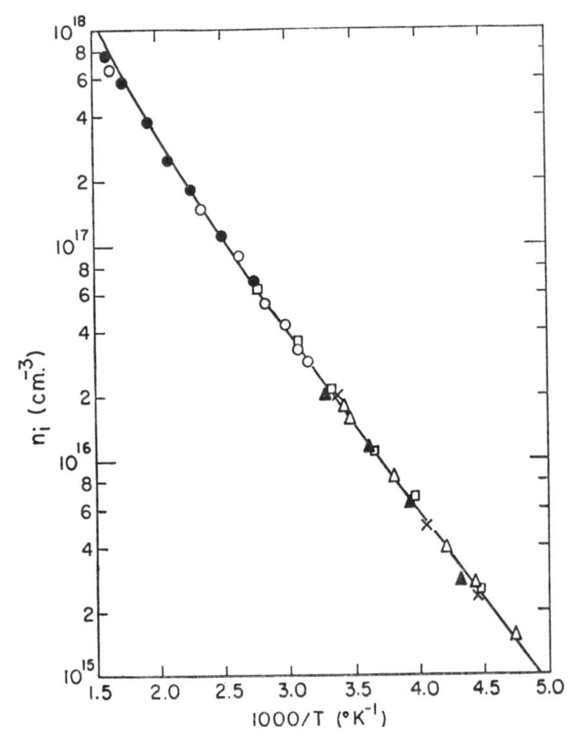

FIG. 23.6. Temperature dependence of the intrinsic carrier density in InSb. [After Hrostowski *et al.* (1955:**6**).]

1.5.3) but will not be far from $m_c \approx 0{\cdot}02\, m_0$, $m_v \approx 0{\cdot}2\, m_0$. This disparity of effective masses displaces the intrinsic Fermi level from the mid-point of the gap. When non-degenerate conditions still hold (temperature not too large),

$$\phi_i = E_c - \tfrac{1}{2}E_i + \tfrac{1}{2}kT \ln(\mathcal{N}_v/\mathcal{N}_c)$$
$$= E_c - \tfrac{1}{2}E_{i0} + \tfrac{1}{2}\alpha T + \tfrac{3}{4}kT \ln(m_v/m_c) \tag{231.10}$$

For the numerical values suggested this is

$$\phi_i = E_c - 0{\cdot}13 + 0{\cdot}000284T \text{ eV} \tag{231.11}$$

The non-degenerate intrinsic carrier density which accompanies this Fermi level should [from Eq. (231.7)] be

$$n_i \approx 3{\cdot}7 \times 10^{14} T^{3/2} \exp(-0{\cdot}26/2kT) \text{ cm}^{-3} \tag{231.12}$$

The conditions of Eqs. (231.11) and (231.12) do apply in InSb over a reasonable range of temperature. Fig. 23.6 shows the experimental data of Hrostowski *et al.* (1955:**6**) for n_i; the data over most of the temperature range follows the solid curve, which satisfies an equation whose temperature dependence is identical to Eq. (231.12). (The empirical equation has a slightly larger coefficient, but this is not surprising in view of the assumptions made.)

Note, however, that the experimental points in Fig. 23.6 fall below the solid curve at high temperatures. If we were to plot the corresponding Fermi level, this would rise at high temperatures much less rapidly than Eq. (231.11). For at these high temperatures, the conduction band is becoming degenerate.

2.3.2 Degenerate Intrinsic Semiconductors

Even for a material in which $m_c \approx m_v$, the combination of high temperature and small intrinsic gap means that the intrinsic Fermi level must be separated from each band by a painfully small multiple of kT. But this invalidates the replacement of each Fermi integral by a simple exponential, as was done in Eq. (231.1). When there is also a considerable disparity between m_c and m_v, the Fermi level remains further from the heavier carrier band (making this band less affected by degeneracy considerations), but closer (or even inside) the light carrier band. The latter band then has severe degeneracy troubles.

Such a situation occurs in InSb, which we had been considering at the close of the previous sub-section. Since $m_v \gg m_c$ it is necessary for $(\phi - E_v)$ to be considerably larger than $(E_c - \phi)$ in order to maintain the condition $n_0 = p_0 = n_i$. As the temperature is increased, the condition can be maintained only by $(E_c - \phi)$ becoming negative, presenting us with the problem of degeneracy in the conduction band.

For the non-degenerate semiconductor, both of the Fermi integrals in Eq. (230.1) were replaced by exponentials, giving Eq. (231.1) and hence the condition (231.2) for the Fermi level. Now when degeneracy must be allowed for in the conduction band (the valence band remaining non-degenerate), instead of Eq. (231.1) we should write

$$n_i = \mathcal{N}_c \mathcal{F}_{1/2}(\eta) = \mathcal{N}_v \exp(-\epsilon_i - \eta) \tag{232.1}$$

The condition for the reduced Fermi level is then

$$\exp(\eta)\mathcal{F}_{1/2}(\eta) = (m_v/m_c)^{3/2} \exp(-\epsilon_i) \tag{232.2}$$

which of course can be expressed as

$$\exp(\eta)\mathcal{F}_{1/2}(\eta) = (m_v/m_c)^{3/2} \exp(\alpha/k) \exp(-E_{i0}/kT) \tag{232.3}$$

when the intrinsic gap is of the form $(E_{i0} - \alpha T)$. The appropriate changes of terminology when $m_v \ll m_c$ and the Fermi level tends towards the valence band are obvious and will not be detailed.

Austin and McClymont (1954:**9**) have examined intrinsic data on InSb in the light of Eq. (232.3), using an approximation

$$\mathcal{F}_{1/2}(\eta) \approx \frac{\exp(\eta)}{1 + 0{\cdot}27 \exp(\eta)} \tag{232.4}$$

which is discussed in Appendix C as suitable both for non-degenerate and partially degenerate occupancy. The numerical parameters suggested for InSb can be substituted into Eq. (232.3) to yield

$$\exp(\eta) \,.\, \mathcal{F}_{1/2}(\eta) = 725 \exp(-3020/T) \tag{232.5}$$

whose solution is illustrated in Fig. 23.7. Even at 200°K the Fermi level is considerably above the middle of the gap, and it lies inside the conduction band for $T \gtrsim 440$°K. For further increases of temperature, η increases rather slowly. Fig. 23.7 is patterned on one given by Austin and McClymont, but differs in detail since they supposed rather less mass disparity.

For any semiconductor, once the intrinsic Fermi energy has been located, it is a simple matter to deduce

$$n_i = \mathcal{N}_c \mathcal{F}_{1/2}(\eta_i) \tag{232.6}$$

This is done for InSb in curve (*B*) of Fig. 23.8, using the Fermi level data of Fig. 23.7. For comparison, the original non-degenerate approximate expression (231.12) is shown in curve (*A*). Since a constant (dE_i/dT) has been supposed, the non-degenerate attempt at represent-

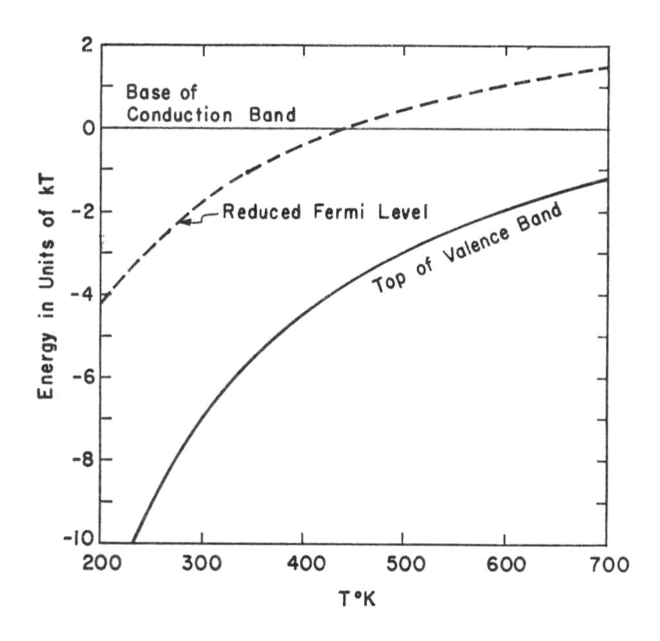

Fig. 23.7. Variation of gap energy and Fermi level (in units of kT) with temperature for intrinsic InSb if $E_i \approx (0{\cdot}26\text{–}0{\cdot}00027\ T)$ eV and $m_v \approx 10\ m_c$.

ing $\ln(n_i/T^{3/2})$ as a function of $1/T$ is linear, but it will be noted that the result of the more correct model deviates from this linearity when the Fermi level approaches and enters the conduction band.

It is easy to see that this should be so, since the number of *available and empty* band states does not increase as $T^{3/2}$ when one or other of the bands experiences degeneracy. Failure to recognize this is just one of the many pitfalls available in the interpretation of experimental data.

InSb has been used at some length as an example because it typifies a "classical" intrinsic semiconductor which becomes degenerate in one band at high temperatures. The same must happen to other small gap materials. Thus HgSe with an intrinsic gap of only 0·1 eV (1960:**3**) and gray tin with $E_i \sim 0{\cdot}08$ eV (1956:**7**) must have the Fermi level within one or two kT of one band or the other at room temperature.

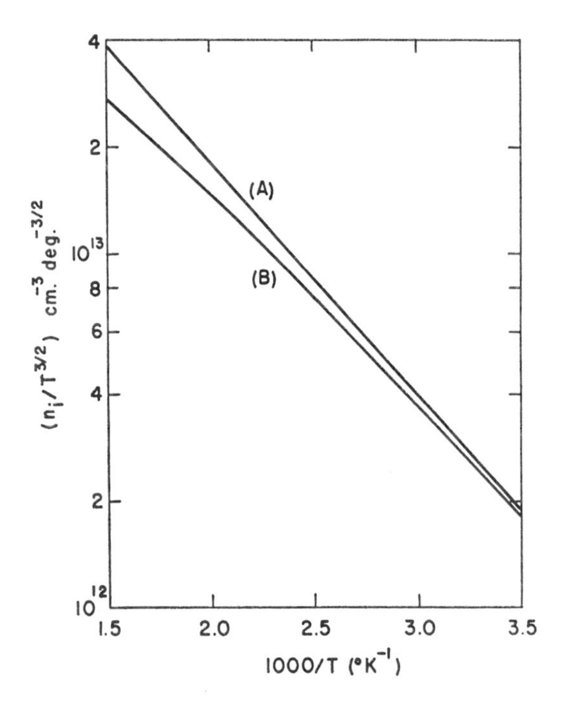

Fig. 23.8. Variation of $(n_i/T^{3/2})$ with $1/T$ for InSb if $E_i \approx (0{\cdot}26 - 0{\cdot}00027\ T)$ eV and $m_c = 0{\cdot}1\ m_v = 0{\cdot}02\ m_0$.

(*a*) Calculated from the non-degenerate expression Eq. (231.12).
(*b*) Based on Eq. (232.6) allowing for conduction band degeneracy.

For HgTe the entire gap is less than kT wide at room temperature (1955:**14**). Such an intrinsic semiconductor is necessarily semidegenerate in both bands, and must be treated with procedures similar to those employed for a semimetallic material with touching bands (e.g. graphite) or weakly overlapping bands (e.g. bismuth).

2.4 THE PRODUCT n_0p_0 AND ϕ FOR INTRINSIC AND EXTRINSIC SITUATIONS

The preceding discussions have shown that the densities of electrons and holes in the conduction and valence bands of a semiconductor can be expressed as

$$\left.\begin{aligned} n_0 &= N_c\,\mathscr{F}_{1/2}(\eta) \\ p_0 &= N_v\,\mathscr{F}_{1/2}(-\eta-\epsilon_i) \end{aligned}\right\} \tag{240.1}$$

Since the semiconductor is in thermal equilibrium it is the *same* reduced Fermi level which applies to both sections of Eq. (240.1)—thermodynamic considerations require that the same electrochemical potential should be experienced by all states. This was used in the previous section to establish a condition for η in terms of E_i and T when the semiconductor was intrinsic. It will be recalled that for the "normal" condition of a non-degenerate intrinsic semiconductor,

$$\left.\begin{aligned} n_i &= (N_vN_c)^{1/2}\exp(-E_i/2kT) \\ \phi_i &= E_c-\tfrac{1}{2}E_i = \tfrac{1}{2}kT\ln(N_v/N_c) \end{aligned}\right\} \tag{240.2}$$

but that rather less simple expressions were unavoidable if the Fermi level was rather close to one band or the other.

When impurities have an influence on the Fermi level and the carrier densities, it can be stated with complete generality that n_0 and p_0 are related to n_i by

$$\left.\begin{aligned} n_0 &= n_i[\mathscr{F}_{1/2}(\eta)/\mathscr{F}_{1/2}(\eta_i)] \\ p_0 &= n_i[\mathscr{F}_{1/2}(-\eta-\epsilon_i)/\mathscr{F}_{1/2}(-\eta_i-\epsilon_i)] \end{aligned}\right\} \tag{240.3}$$

This has a particularly simple result for a non-degenerate semiconductor, in which ϕ remains at least two or three kT from either band edge. For in non-degenerate circumstances each of the Fermi integrals in Eq. (240.3) can be replaced by an exponential factor (see Section 2.1). On making the substitutions it can readily be seen that

$$n_0p_0 = n_i^2 \tag{240.4}$$

while

$$n_0 = n_i\exp(\eta-\eta_i) \tag{240.5}$$

and

$$p_0 = n_i\exp(\eta_i-\eta) \tag{240.6}$$

These relationships for a non-degenerate semiconductor are extremely useful. From them it will be observed that, for instance, a change in impurity density which causes p_0 to be *increased* by a factor β will cause $n_0 = (n_i^2/p_0)$ to *decrease* by this factor β, while the Fermi level must move towards the valence band by an amount $kT\ln(\beta)$. Such behavior can be seen in the central portion of Fig. 24.1, which plots η as ordinate against a logarithmic scale of (p_0/n_i). The figure is based on a hypothetical semiconductor in which $(m_v/m_c) = 2{\cdot}5$ at a temperature for which $\epsilon_i = (E_i/kT) = 10$.

It will be noted in Fig. 24.1 that the linear relationship of η to $\ln(p_0/n_i)$ is disturbed when the Fermi level enters the valence band, and that the graduations of $\ln(n_0/n_i)$ become compressed as they strive to indicate the continuing truth of Eq. (240.5). The degeneracy of the valence band invalidates both Eqs. (240.4) and (240.6). Similarly,

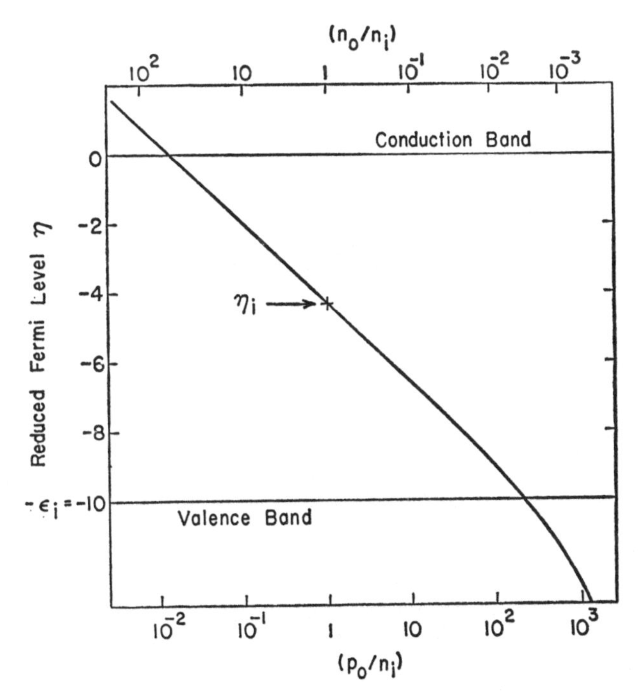

FIG. 24.1. Showing the interrelationship of (n_0/n_i) and (p_0/n_i) with the reduced Fermi level η. Example calculated for an intrinsic gap 10 kT wide; with $(m_v/m_c) = 2{\cdot}5$ so that $\eta_i \approx -4{\cdot}3$. The abscissa is a logarithmic scale in (p_0/n_i), which distorts the scale of (n_0/n_i).

when the Fermi level enters the conduction band, Eq. (240.6) remains valid [and η continues to vary linearly with $\ln(p_0/n_i)$] but Eqs. (240.4) and (240.5) are not true, so that the graduations of $\ln(n_0/n_i)$ must become swollen.

In general the expressions of Eq. (240.3) can be combined as the statement

$$\left(\frac{n_0 p_0}{n_i^2}\right) = \left[\frac{\mathscr{F}_{1/2}(\eta)\mathscr{F}_{1/2}(-\eta-\epsilon_i)}{\mathscr{F}_{1/2}(\eta_i)\mathscr{F}_{1/2}(-\eta_i-\epsilon_i)}\right] \leqslant 1 \qquad (240.7)$$

The equality sign is appropriate when ϕ is far from *both* bands.

It might seem that when ϕ is very close to one band, the minority carrier density in the other band would be so small as to render its precise value unimportant. However, it is worth remembering that when degenerate conditions obtain in the majority band, the minority density is *larger* than prescribed by Eq. (240.4), and can become relatively insensitive to the majority concentration.

Returning now to consider non-degenerate conditions, it must be observed that any difference between n_0 and p_0 for electrically neutral material is caused by the ionization of impurity states. In the next chapter considerable attention will be paid to the distribution of electrons between various kinds of impurity levels and the conduction band. Without encroaching on that discussion it can be observed that if $\mathcal{N}_r = (n_0 - p_0)$, then $\mathcal{N}_r$ is the *difference* between the densities of impurity states which have *lost* an electron and those which have *gained* an electron. The condition

$$p_0 = \left(\frac{n_i^2}{n_0}\right) = n_0 - \mathcal{N}_r \qquad (240.8)$$

leads to two simple quadratic equations for n_0 and p_0 in terms of n_i and $\mathcal{N}_r$, with solutions

$$\left.\begin{aligned} n_0 &= \tfrac{1}{2}\mathcal{N}_r[(1+4n_i^2/\mathcal{N}_r^2)^{1/2}+1] \\ p_0 &= \tfrac{1}{2}\mathcal{N}_r[(1+4n_i^2/\mathcal{N}_r^2)^{1/2}-1] \end{aligned}\right\} \qquad (240.9)$$

At low temperatures, when intrinsic excitation is rather feeble, the expressions of Eq. (240.9) simplify to

$$\left.\begin{aligned} n_0 &\approx \mathcal{N}_r + (n_i^2/\mathcal{N}_r) \\ p_0 &\approx (n_i^2/\mathcal{N}_r) \end{aligned}\right\} n_i \ll \mathcal{N}_r \qquad (240.10)$$

For a higher temperature (or smaller value of $\mathcal{N}_r$), the limiting approximation of Eq. (240.10) for almost intrinsic conditions is

$$\left.\begin{aligned} n_0 &\approx n_i+\tfrac{1}{2}\mathcal{N}_r \\ p_0 &\approx n_i-\tfrac{1}{2}\mathcal{N}_r \end{aligned}\right\} n_i \gg \mathcal{N}_r \qquad (240.11)$$

This result may at first seem a little surprising, for it indicates that when a few readily ionizable donors are added to intrinsic material, only *half* the electrons so made available enter the conduction band; the other half serve to reduce the free hole density. As $\mathcal{N}_r$ increases, the hole density becomes quite small compared with n_0, and then every additional ionized donor does indeed provide an electron for the conduction band. The contribution of impurities and of the valence band towards n_0 are equal if $n_0 = (p_0+\mathcal{N}_r) = 2p_0$. This happens when $\mathcal{N}_r = 2^{-1/2}n_i$.

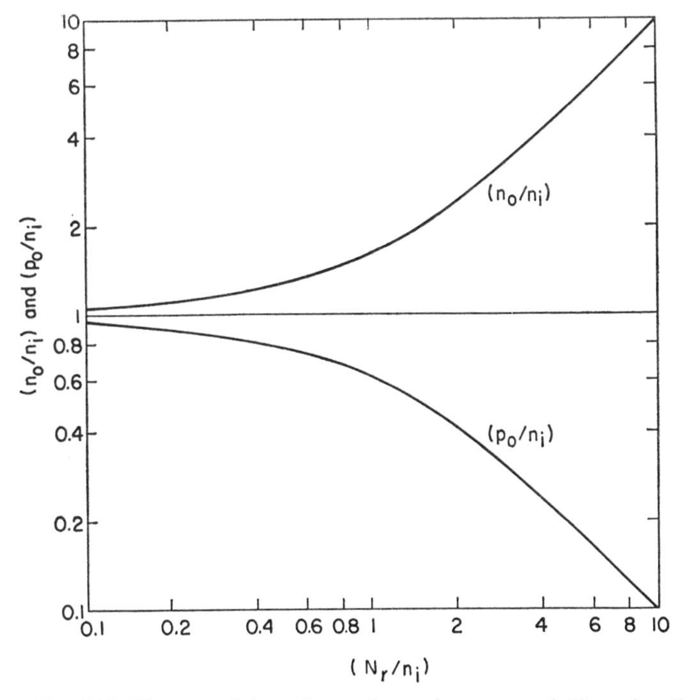

FIG. 24.2. The mutual dependence of n_0 and p_0 on n_i and $\mathcal{N}_r$, as described by Eq. (240.9) and its asymptotic forms (240.10) and (240.11).

Fig. 24.2 illustrates the solution (240.9) for the range $0 \cdot 1 \leqslant (N_r/n_i) \leqslant 10$. Beyond this range one or other of the forms (240.10) and (240.11) will be perfectly acceptable. With a simple inversion, this figure is of course equally applicable to a p-type situation.

The variations of n_0 and p_0 with temperature when $(n_0 - p_0) = N_r$ remains constant† are exemplified by the curves of Fig. 24.3. A semi-

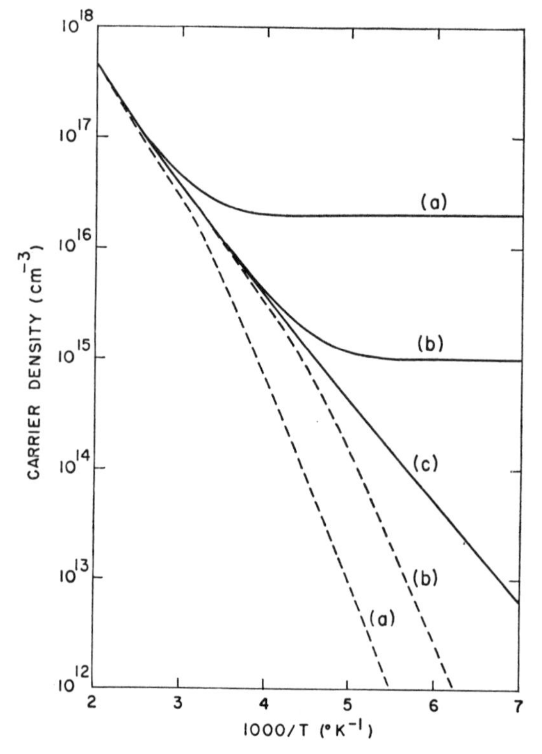

FIG. 24.3. Temperature dependence of majority electron density (solid curves) and minority hole density (broken curves) in a semiconductor for which $n_i = 1 \cdot 45 \times 10^{15} T^{3/2} \exp(-1850/T)$ cm^{-3}. [$m_c = 0 \cdot 1 m_0$, $m_v = 0 \cdot 2 m_0$, $E_i = (0 \cdot 32 - 0 \cdot 0003 T)$ eV.] (a) $N_r = 2 \times 10^{16}$ cm^{-3}, (b) $N_r = 10^{15}$ cm^{-3}, (c) $N_r = 0$ (intrinsic).

† $(n_0 - p_0)$ can only remain constant over a range of temperature if the supply of electrons from impurities is completely exhausted. This temperature interval is often referred to as the "exhaustion range" for the semiconductor.

conductor is supposed for which $m_c = 0{\cdot}1m_0$, $m_v = 0{\cdot}2m_0$ and $E_i = (0{\cdot}32\text{–}0{\cdot}0003\ T)$ eV. These parameters provide an intrinsic density

$$n_i = 1{\cdot}45 \times 10^{15} T^{3/2} \exp(-1850/T) \text{ cm}^{-3} \qquad (240.12)$$

which appears as curve (c) of the figure. The remaining curves are of n_0 and p_0 for two finite values of $\mathcal{N}_r$. At high temperatures these curves approach that of n_i in accordance with Eq. (240.10), but when the majority electron density settles towards $\mathcal{N}_r$ at lower temperatures, p_0 has the temperature dependence of n_i^2 and falls off very rapidly.

Before accepting the visual evidence of the curves in Fig. 24.3 [which are based on Eqs. (240.12) and (240.9)] we should question whether the values chosen for the parameters are compatible with the non-degenerate basis of Eqs. (240.8) and (240.9). To be on the safe side, it would be desirable to have $\eta < -2$ over the entire temperature range under consideration.

The curves of ϕ in Fig. 24.4 are for the same conditions as the correspondingly labelled curves of Fig. 24.3, and it can be seen that the condition $\eta < -2$ is indeed satisfied (except for a minor violation at the very highest temperatures). Even so, the extrinsic Fermi level does rise on cooling, and must pass through $\eta = -2$ at some low temperature *if the same value of $\mathcal{N}_r$ be maintained.* When $\eta > -2$ the condition $\mathcal{N}_r = (n_0 - p_0)$ should properly be written as a transcendental equation.

$$\mathcal{N}_r = \mathcal{N}_c \mathscr{F}_{1/2}(\eta) - \mathcal{N}_r \mathscr{F}_{1/2}(-\eta - \epsilon_i) \qquad (240.13)$$

for η, and the procedure for evaluating n_0 and p_0 is much less straightforward. [The same difficulties apply, of course, if $p_0 \gg n_0$ and $\eta < (2 - \epsilon_i)$].

For Figs. 24.3 and 24.4 it has been supposed that $\mathcal{N}_r = (n_0 - p_0)$ would remain constant over the temperature range 140–500°K. It may be queried whether this is a realistic assumption to make; the answer is that it would be most *unrealistic* in *many* semiconducting materials, but could be a good approximation in some others. For the requirement that $(n_0 - p_0)$ should not change in a certain temperature range is essentially that there should be no impurity states in the energy interval swept out by the Fermi level between the limiting temperatures. When the Fermi level passes through the energy of a set of impurity states, it must ionize or de-ionize them, changing $\mathcal{N}_r$ in the process.

Now it is possible for the exhaustion range of constant $\mathcal{N}_r$ to prevail from the intrinsic point down to a rather low temperature if the majority impurity levels are rather close to the majority carrier band, and all other impurity states are in the opposite half of the intrinsic gap. This is plausible for a semiconductor such as germanium doped with Group

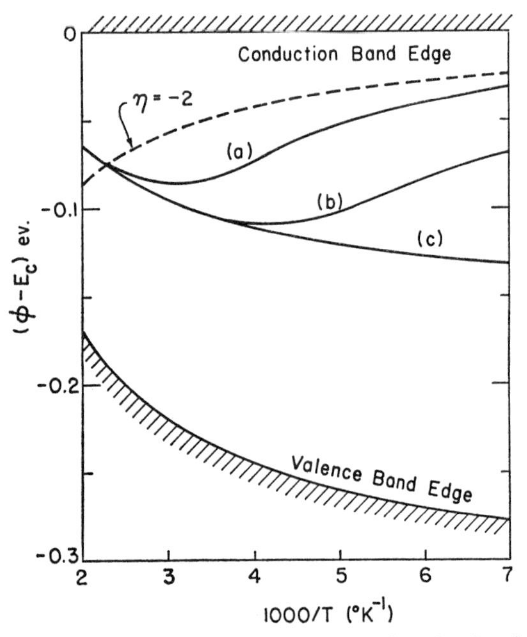

FIG. 24.4. Variation of the Fermi level with $1/T$ for the situations depicted in Fig. 24.3.

III and Group V impurities† but containing almost no other impurities (such as transition elements). On the other hand, it is suggested (1955: **15**, **16**), that some other semiconductors such as CdS and ZnS usually contain impurity states at a variety of energies all through the intrinsic

† The present author has discussed elsewhere (1958:**6**) the manner in which the Fermi level for germanium would vary with temperature for a number of values of the parameter $\mathcal{N}_r$, allowing for a temperature-dependent intrinsic gap. Except for very large values of $\mathcal{N}_r$, ϕ joins ϕ_i at high temperatures. A similar analysis could be used for other semiconductors.

gap. For such a material, exhaustion conditions of constant $\mathcal{N}_r$ could not be contrived over any temperature range.

We shall defer until the next chapter the discussions of various models for sets of impurity levels and the consequent temperature dependence of ϕ and the carrier densities.

2.5 SPATIAL FLUCTUATIONS OF CARRIER DENSITY §

In the preface to this volume it was pointed out that particular attention would not be paid to *p–n* junctions, semiconductor contacts and other systematic manifestations of inhomogeneity in a semiconducting crystal. At this point it is proposed only to comment in a qualitative fashion on two phenomena which can occur in a crystal which is—to outward appearances—macroscopically homogeneous. The two phenomena noted here have been discussed by Burgess (1956:**10**).

2.5.1 Spatial Fluctuations of the Intrinsic Gap

When two semiconductors have the same lattice, with not much disparity of lattice constant, they are often partially or wholly miscible; and the range of alloys so formed is also semiconducting. Thus semiconducting alloys in all proportions exist between silicon and germanium (1957:**11**) and between compounds such as HgSe and HgTe (1955:**14**) or CdS and ZnS (1940:**2**). Such alloys are not ordered, and there will be microscopic spatial fluctuations in the densities of two chemical species which can occupy a given kind of lattice site. We do not refer to massive variations caused by imperfect crystallization procedures, but to the minor variations required by the thermodynamic consideration of minimum energy and maximum entropy.

These variations automatically affect the electrical properties on a microscopic scale. For the example of HgSe–HgTe alloys, regions containing rather more selenium atoms will have a larger intrinsic gap than neighboring tellurium-rich regions. The degree to which this will occur depends on a number of considerations, but qualitatively it can be seen that the energies of the conduction and valence bands with respect to the intrinsic Fermi level will be *contravariant* functions of position (using the term suggested by Burgess). Such a situation is sketched in Fig. 25.1. The Fermi level is of course completely constant through any crystal in thermal equilibrium. The fluctuations of E_c and

$(E_c - E_i)$ with respect to ϕ_i create "pockets" in which electrons and holes are more numerous than elsewhere. While n_0 and p_0 are functions of position, they are everywhere equal to each other if the semiconductor is intrinsic, and electrical neutrality reigns throughout.

Such a situation does not raise any conceptual problems so far as carrier density is concerned. Whatever spatial fluctuations of E_i may

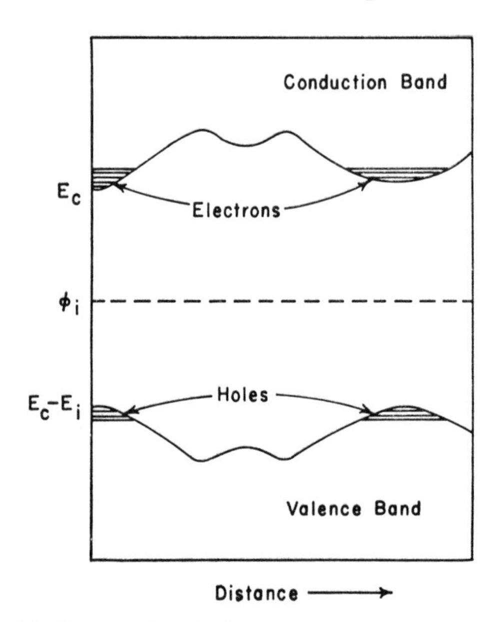

FIG. 25.1. Contravariant displacement of the energy bands with respect to the Fermi level in a disordered alloy intrinsic semiconductor.

occur, the usual expression can still be written for n_i at any point. (Great difficulties occur in attempting to interpret the transport properties of such an alloy, but we are not at present concerned with this topic!)

2.5.2 Spatial Fluctuations of Impurity Density

For this second aspect of spatial fluctuations, there are actual difficulties involved in writing down an expression for free carrier density as a function of position. Even so, it is not proposed to solve the problem, but merely to draw attention to it.

In Chapter 3, a variety of models are considered in which a semiconductor contains one or more sets of impurity levels, and the Fermi level and carrier densities consistent with these models are evaluated. Throughout that chapter the customary assumption will be made that impurity atoms are distributed evenly through the volume of the semiconductor. It is the present purpose to observe that impurities will *never*

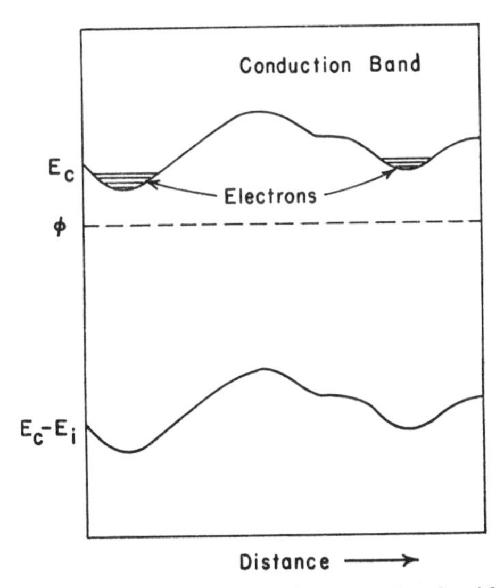

FIG. 25.2. Covariant displacement of the energy bands with respect to the Fermi level in a semiconductor with spatial fluctuations of impurity density.

be distributed *perfectly* uniformly in space, but that the discussions of Chapter 3 will overlook this additional complication.

When impurity atoms become incorporated into the lattice of a semiconductor, their spacing will sometimes be more and sometimes less than the mean value. Since some microscopic regions have more electrons to offer than others, it seems reasonable that in an *n*-type case the conduction band edge might fluctuate with respect to the Fermi level more or less as sketched in Fig. 25.2. Since the intrinsic gap is now supposed to be constant, the valence band moves *covariantly* with the conduction band. Most electrons collect in the low-lying pockets of the conduction band, and in an extreme case there might be an appreciable number of holes in areas where the valence band goes through a maximum.

The situation of Fig. 25.2 poses problems which did not occur for Fig. 25.1, in that fluctuations in the extrinsic semiconductor involve localized space charge. The regions in which $(E_c-\phi)$ is large tend to have more complete ionization of donor impurities, and since there are very few free electrons there, such regions have a positive space charge, while areas in which $(E_c-\phi)$ is small bear a net negative charge. Shockley (1949:5) in his discussion of the limiting case of a *p–n* junction, has shown that the importance of space charge effects on the spatial dependence of $(E_c-\phi)$ depends on the distance scale over which changes of impurity density occur. The form of solution depends on whether such changes occur in distances small or large compared with the Debye length, and must in general be pursued by an iterative technique. The reader is referred to Shockley's article for a more complete account of the necessary procedures.

It is natural to hope that fluctuations of impurity density will be small enough to make the maximum excursions of $(E_c-\phi)$ very small compared with kT; the semiconductor will then have properties strongly resembling those for an ideally uniform impurity distribution.

Chapter 3

SEMICONDUCTORS DOMINATED BY IMPURITY LEVELS

In Section 2.4, an allusion was made to the importance of impurity levels, in the sense that consideration was given to the relation of n_0 and p_0 when these were unequal and the Fermi level departed from the intrinsic position. It is now necessary to consider in detail just how electrons are distributed in thermal equilibrium between the bands and the various sets of levels provided by impurities.

3.1 OCCUPANCY FACTOR FOR IMPURITY LEVELS

Appendix A proves that under thermal equilibrium conditions, the probability that any state of energy E will be occupied by an electron is given by the Fermi–Dirac factor

$$f(E) = \frac{1}{1 + \exp\left[\dfrac{E-\phi}{kT}\right]} \tag{310.1}$$

In the last chapter we have seen that the application of Eq. (310.1) to the distribution of states in the permitted bands leads to expressions involving the Fermi–Dirac integrals $\mathscr{F}_j(\eta)$. It is similarly necessary to find out what fraction of impurity atoms retain their outermost electron (or acquire an additional one) when the Fermi level is at any specified energy.

Following Wilson's (1931:**2**) theory of the extrinsic semiconductive process, a rather simple approach to the problem of center occupancy was widely used during the two following decades. This approach is typified by the following argument. Consider a semiconductor containing N_d monovalent donor impurity atoms per unit volume, such that in the ground state each atom has an electron trapped at an energy E_d below the base of the conduction band (see part (a) of Fig. 13.8). It would seemingly appear that the number of states within any small range of energy centered on $(E_c - E_d)$ must be

$$\int_{E_c-E_d-\Delta}^{E_c-E_d+\Delta} g(E)\, \mathrm{d}E = N_d \tag{310.2}$$

A donor which has an electron trapped at this energy is electrically neutral; the density of these may be indicated as N_{dn}. Similarly, $N_{di} = (N_d - N_{dn})$ denotes the density of ionized donor atoms. From the formulation of Fermi–Dirac statistics it is to be expected that

$$N_{di} : N_{dn} = 1 : \exp\left[\frac{\phi + E_d - E_c}{kT}\right] \tag{310.3}$$

so that the density of *neutral* donors would be

$$N_{dn} = \frac{N_d}{1 + \exp\left[\dfrac{E_c - E_d - \phi}{kT}\right]} \tag{310.4}$$

This result looks very simple and appealing, but unfortunately represents an incorrect simplification of the matter. The factor overlooked is that of impurity level spin degeneracy, which we now consider.

3.1.1 Impurity Level Spin Degeneracy

The important consideration overlooked in the preceding discussion is that each impurity atom will usually offer *more* than one state for either the neutral or ionized configuration. This has been recognized by a few workers in the field for a considerable time (e.g. 1948:**2**), but there has been a more general awareness since the appearance of contributions by Landsberg (1952:**4**, 1953:**5**) and by Guggenheim

(1953:**6**). Using a free energy approach and the grand canonical ensemble, respectively, these authors show how spin and orbital degeneracy of bound states have an effect on the number of electrons retained by a set of impurities.

As the simplest example of this, consider a set of simple monovalent donor impurities for which all electrons save the least tightly bound are in paired valence bonds. The wave-function of the outermost electron is of purely s character, and since this is an unpaired electron, it can be trapped in two ways, with spin either up or down. Note that a donor can not trap *two* electrons, since once one electron is trapped, electrostatic forces raise the remaining spin possibility to a very high energy; nevertheless the neutral state of the impurity has a statistical weight of two compared with the ionized state. Accordingly we should replace Eq. (310.3) by

$$\mathcal{N}_{di} : \mathcal{N}_{dn} = 1 : 2 \exp\left[\frac{\phi + E_d - E_c}{kT}\right] \tag{311.1}$$

Then the density of *neutral* donors is

$$\mathcal{N}_{dn} = \frac{\mathcal{N}_d}{1 + \frac{1}{2}\exp\left[\frac{E_c - E_d - \phi}{kT}\right]} \tag{311.2}$$

For other kinds of impurity level, the coefficient of the exponential in Eq. (311.2) will differ from $\frac{1}{2}$. We may say in general that for a level at energy E_r, the probability that this level will contain an electron is

$$P(E_r) = \frac{1}{1 + \beta_r \exp\left[\frac{E_r - \phi}{kT}\right]} \tag{311.3}$$

In the current literature, the term *impurity level spin degeneracy* is applied rather indiscriminately to *either* β_r or β_r^{-1}, whichever is larger than unity. This may appear a little confusing, but should not cause undue difficulty if it is borne in mind that Eq. (311.3) refers always to the probability that a level contains an *electron* at the specified energy, *not* necessarily that the impurity is electrically neutral. For our illustrative example of simple donors, $\beta^{-1} = 2$ is the spin degeneracy, since the level can be occupied by an *electron* in two ways. When the impurity in question is an acceptor center which requires an extra electron to complete a set of paired bonds, $\beta = 2$ is the spin degeneracy —since the *absence* of this electron can be described in two ways.

When an impurity level is created by splitting off states from a conduction or valence band with multiple or degenerate extrema, β or β^{-1} will be larger than two. Thus for acceptor levels introduced by Group III impurities into a semiconductor such as germanium (with two valence bands degenerate at $\mathbf{k} = 0$), Kohn (1957:**10**) has shown that β should equal four, and this is in accord with experimental observations (e.g. 1959:**6**).

Moreover, when the impurity ground state wave-function is not spherically symmetrical, orbital degeneracy affects the statistical weights of the neutral and ionized conditions. The effect of this can be included in the quantity β, which is still loosely referred to as a "spin" degeneracy factor. For multivalent impurities which can donate or accept several electrons from successively deeper states, there will be a β_r characteristic of each state of ionization.

3.2 SEMICONDUCTORS CONTROLLED BY A SINGLE MONOVALENT DONOR SPECIES

In Chapter 2 we traced the connection between the Fermi level and the conduction band free electron density at any temperature. The previous section has further established the connection between the Fermi level and the fraction of impurity sites which retain an electron. Combining these two pieces of information, we can now see how electrons are *distributed* between impurity levels and the conduction band.

It is equally simple to study the models of either n-type or p-type semiconductors, though this section will in practice discuss primarily n-type behavior, concentrating on the conduction band. Except when especially noted, it will be assumed that the hole density p_0 is negligibly small compared with n_0 and with the densities of impurity states (i.e. we shall not discuss the transition towards intrinsic conduction at high temperatures). This is not as restrictive an assumption as it may seem, for provided that the majority of donor levels lie inside the upper half of the intrinsic gap (at least two or three kT above ϕ_i) all these impurities will become ionized before temperatures are reached at which intrinsic excitation is at all appreciable. This means that the intrinsic transition takes place from a region of temperature-independent $\mathcal{N}_r$, as described in Section 2.4.

3.2.1 TEMPERATURE DEPENDENCE OF n_0 AND ϕ FOR A SET OF SIMPLE UNCOMPENSATED DONORS

The model to be considered first is a purely academic and unrealistic one. For it is impossible to prepare a semiconductor containing only one set of impurities, with no compensating centers at all. Grave errors can result from applying this model over the complete temperature range, though it can be a reasonable approximation to the truth at temperatures which are not too low. This earliest described model of an extrinsic semiconductor (1931:**2**) is used simply because it helps to demonstrate some features which are useful in discussing more realistic models.

For this preliminary discussion, then, the model to be used is the simplified one of Fig. 32.1. There are $\mathcal{N}_d$ donor levels of spin degeneracy

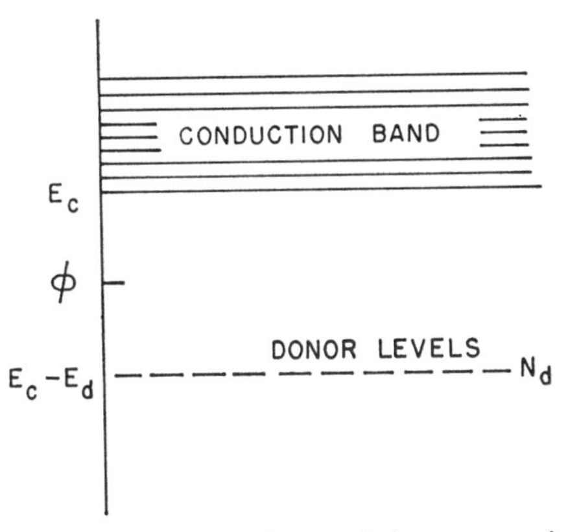

FIG. 32.1. The simplest model of an extrinsic *n*-type semiconductor.

β^{-1} per unit volume at an energy E_d below the base of the conduction band. The latter is characterized by a mass m_c and through this by the quantity $\mathcal{N}_c = 2(2\pi m_c kT/h^2)^{3/2}$. The Fermi level ϕ may be above or below either E_c or $(E_c - E_d)$.

Now the number of electrons excited in the conduction band is known to be

$$n_0 = \mathcal{N}_c \mathcal{F}_{1/2}\left(\frac{\phi - E_c}{kT}\right) \tag{321.1}$$

while from the formalism of Eq. (311.3) it is known that the number of electrons remaining in the donor levels is

$$N_{dn} = \frac{N_d}{1+\beta \exp\left[\dfrac{E_c - E_d - \phi}{kT}\right]} \tag{321.2}$$

Since electrons in the conduction band can have come only from the donor levels, the sum of the densities (321.1) and (321.2) must be N_d itself. Hence we have that

$$n_0 = N_c \mathscr{F}_{1/2}\left[\frac{\phi - E_c}{kT}\right] = \frac{N_d}{1+\beta^{-1} \exp\left[\dfrac{E_d + \phi - E_c}{kT}\right]} \tag{321.3}$$

Adopting the usual dimensionless notation, and in addition denoting (E_d/kT) as ϵ_d, the previous equation can be written

$$n_0 = N_c \mathscr{F}_{1/2}(\eta) = N_d[1+\beta^{-1} \exp(\epsilon_d + \eta)]^{-1} \tag{321.4}$$

When the donors are not too numerous, and of reasonably large ionization energy, conditions will tend to remain non-degenerate (ϕ several kT below E_c) at all temperatures. They will certainly be non-degenerate at the very lowest temperatures, for then all the electrons are withdrawn to the donor levels. As temperature rises and some electrons become excited into the conduction band, η rises; but it passes through a maximum and falls again at the high temperatures for which impurity ionization approaches completion.

When conditions are non-degenerate over the entire temperature range, the solution of Eq. (321.4) is conveniently simple. The approximation $\mathscr{F}_{1/2}(\eta) \approx \exp(\eta)$ can then be used at all temperatures. Thus substituting (n_0/N_c) for $\exp(\eta)$ on the right side of Eq. (321.4), there results a simple quadratic in n_0,

$$n_0\left[1 + \frac{n_0}{\beta N_c} \exp(\epsilon_d)\right] = N_d \tag{321.5}$$

with the solution

$$n_0 = \frac{2N_d}{1+\sqrt{[1+(4N_d/\beta N_c)\exp(\epsilon_d)]}} \tag{321.6}$$

Fig. 32.2 illustrates a typical numerical example of the temperature dependence of n_0 prescribed by Eq. (321.6). Following the usual custom, this figure plots $\ln(n_0)$ vs. $1/T$. This is done for the benefit of the low temperature "reserve" region, when few electrons are excited and Eq. (326.6) approximates to

$$n_0 \approx (\beta N_c N_d)^{1/2} \exp(-E_d/2kT), \quad \text{small } T \tag{321.7}$$

The exponential contributes most but not all of the temperature dependence in this range, as can be seen in the figure from a comparison

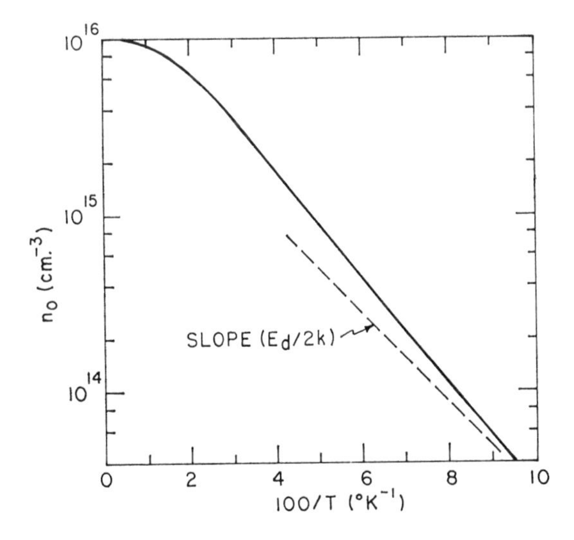

Fig. 32.2. Semilogarithmic plot of n_0 vs. $1/T$ for a set of uncompensated donors when conditions are non-degenerate at all temperatures. Calculated for $N_d = 10^{16}$ cm^{-3}, $E_d = 0{\cdot}01$ eV, $m_c = 0{\cdot}25\, m_0$, $\beta = \frac{1}{2}$.

of the straight line of slope $(E_d/2k)$ with the curve of a calculated carrier density. The discrepancy in slopes results from the $T^{3/2}$ temperature dependence of N_c.

Eq. (321.7) was originally derived by Wilson (1931:**2**) and was for a long time adopted uncritically in the interpretation of experimental data. We should note that the equation can properly be applied only if

(a) conditions are completely non-degenerate;

(b) the number of carriers n_0 excited to the conduction band is very small compared with N_d; and furthermore

(c) the number of electrons lost to compensating impurities is very small compared with n_0, i.e. $N_a \ll n_0 \ll N_d$.

We have deliberately assumed *zero* compensation for the present, and thus are safe on the last score. As will be revealed in a moment, the numerical values adopted in Fig. 32.2 are consistent with non-degeneracy at all temperatures. Before proceeding to this topic, it may be noted in passing that the carrier density of Eq. (321.6) tends to N_d at sufficiently high temperatures, producing what have previously been described as exhaustion conditions. Since at sufficiently low temperatures almost *none* of the donors are ionized, while at high temperatures they are almost *all* ionized, it is evident that ϕ tends from a position above $(E_c - E_d)$ to one below this energy on warming.

When conditions are non-degenerate, the Fermi level is always related to n_0 through

$$(\phi - E_c) = kT\eta = kT\ln(n_0/N_c) \tag{321.8}$$

Substituting for n_0 from Eq. (321.6),

$$\begin{aligned}(\phi - E_c) &= kT\eta \\ &= -kT\ln\{(N_c/2N_d) + \sqrt{[(N_c/2N_d)^2 + (N_c/\beta N_d)\exp(E_d/kT)]}\}\end{aligned} \tag{321.9}$$

Fig. 32.3 (based on the same numerical parameters as Fig. 32.2) shows how n_0, η and ϕ vary with temperature in accordance with Eq. (321.6) and (321.9).

In connection with this figure, note first the behavior of $(\phi - E_c)$, shown in part (c). At high temperatures, when essentially all the impurities are ionized, conditions approach those discussed in Section 2.2; for when T is large enough to make $\exp(E_d/kT) \ll (N_c/N_d)$, the Fermi level of Eq. (321.9) approximates to

$$\phi \approx E_c - kT\ln(N_c/N_d), \qquad \text{large } T \tag{321.10}$$

This would be true for the example of Fig. 32.3 at temperatures $> 100°$K, when at least 90% of the carriers have been excited from the donor levels.

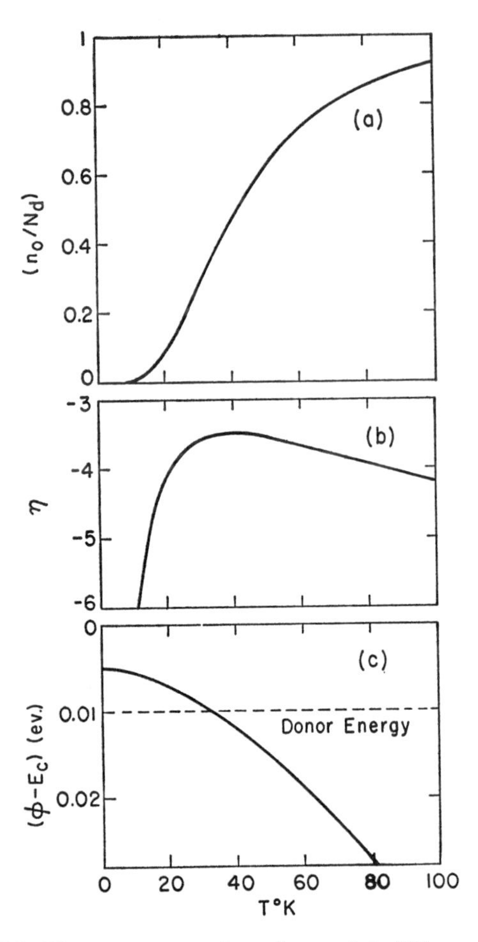

FIG. 32.3. The temperature dependence of (n_0/N_d), η and ϕ for the uncompensated donor model of Fig. 32.2.

On proceeding to lower temperatures, a progressively smaller fraction of the carriers is excited, and ϕ moves closer to the conduction band. In conformity with (321.2) ϕ must coincide with $(E_c - E_d)$ at the temperature for which $(1+\beta)^{-1}$ of the donors are neutral. In the present example, this temperature is 32°K.

When only a very small fraction of the donors are ionized, ϕ approaches the energy $(E_c - \frac{1}{2}E_d)$, but the approach is not a monotonic function of temperature. This occurs because the low temperature approximation to Eq. (321.9) is

$$\phi \approx (E_c - \tfrac{1}{2}E_d) - \tfrac{1}{2}kT \ln(N_c/\beta N_d), \qquad \text{small } T \qquad (321.11)$$

At some sufficiently small temperature T_1, N_c will be equal to βN_d; then ϕ will be higher than $(E_c - \frac{1}{2}E_d)$ for the temperature range $0 < T < T_1$. This is not readily apparent in Fig. 32.3, and so the data from 10°K downwards are shown on an expanded scale in Fig. 32.4. For the numerical example considered in these figures, $T_1 = 4{\cdot}1$°K.

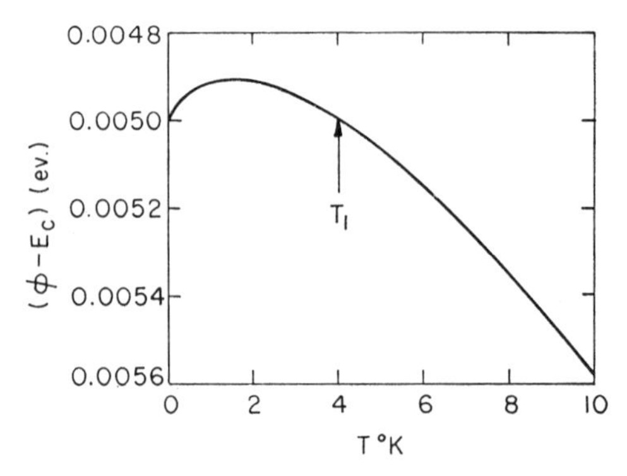

Fig. 32.4. An amplification of the low-temperature region in part (c) of Fig. 32.3, showing ϕ rising above $(E_c - \frac{1}{2} E_d)$ when the temperature is small enough to make $N_c < \beta N_d$.

Part (b) of Fig. 32.3 shows how the reduced Fermi level η varies with temperature. As already predicted, this variable passes through a maximum η_m at a temperature for which an appreciable fraction of the donors is ionized. The value of this maximum is sufficiently negative to confirm that n_0 was correctly calculated from the non-degenerate equation (321.6). It is obviously desirable to have a general procedure for determining η_{max} from parameters such as N_d, β, m_c and E_d, so that it is known in advance whether Eq. (321.6) is applicable or whether Eq. (321.4) must be solved in more general form to yield n_0 and η.

Taking η from Eq. (321.9), differentiating with respect to temperature and setting the result equal to zero, it can be shown as a result of some tedious but elementary manipulation that η will have a maximum at a temperature T_m for which $\epsilon_{dm} = (E_d/kT_m)$ satisfies the condition

$$(2\epsilon_{dm}-3)^2 \exp(\epsilon_{dm}) = 6\beta \mathcal{N}_c \epsilon_{dm}/\mathcal{N}_d \quad (321.12)$$

To employ this condition, we should like to collect everything involving temperature-dependence on one side. Since $\mathcal{N}_c$ varies as $T^{3/2}$, we can write (321.12) as

$$\mathcal{Z} = 12(2\pi m_0/h^2)^{3/2}\epsilon_{dm}^{-1/2}(2\epsilon_{dm}-3)^{-2}\exp(-\epsilon_{dm}) \quad (321.13)$$

where the quantity

$$\mathcal{Z} = \mathcal{N}_d\beta^{-1}(m_0/m_c E_d) \quad (321.14)$$

depends on the density and character of the impurities but not on temperature. When $\mathcal{N}_d$ is expressed in cm^{-3} and E_d in eV, then

$$\mathcal{Z} = 3{\cdot}6\times 10^{22}\epsilon_{dm}^{-1/2}(2\epsilon_{dm}-3)^{-2}\exp(-\epsilon_{dm})\ \mathrm{cm^{-3}\,eV^{-3/2}} \quad (321.15)$$

It is a simple matter to determine the corresponding values of $\mathcal{Z}$ and ϵ_{dm}, and their relationship is shown in Fig. 32.5. Knowledge of ϵ_{dm}

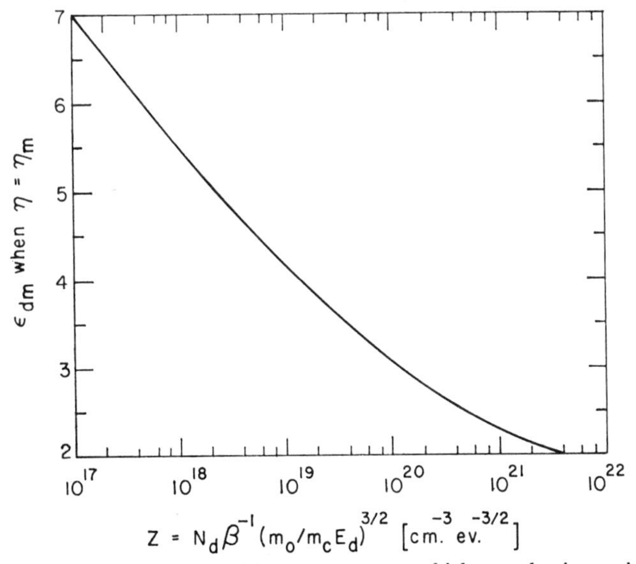

FIG. 32.5. Determination of the temperature at which η reaches its maximum value η_m, for a set of uncompensated donor levels. The ordinate is the parameter $\epsilon_{dm} = (E_d/kT_m)$ which satisfies Eq. (321.15).

means that $T_m = (E_d/k\epsilon_{dm})$ is obtained, and η_m itself can then be determined.

When Eq. (321.4) is differentiated and the condition $(\mathrm{d}\eta/\mathrm{d}T) = 0$ imposed, a simple relationship between η_m and ϵ_{dm} is obtained,

$$\eta_m = -\epsilon_{dm} + \ln\left[\frac{3\beta}{2\epsilon_{dm}-3}\right] \qquad (321.16)$$

This is valid whether conditions be degenerate or not. Combination of Eq. (321.16) with the root of Eq. (321.15) leads to the graphical relationship of η_m to $\mathcal{Z}$ shown in Fig. 32.6. Strictly speaking we should

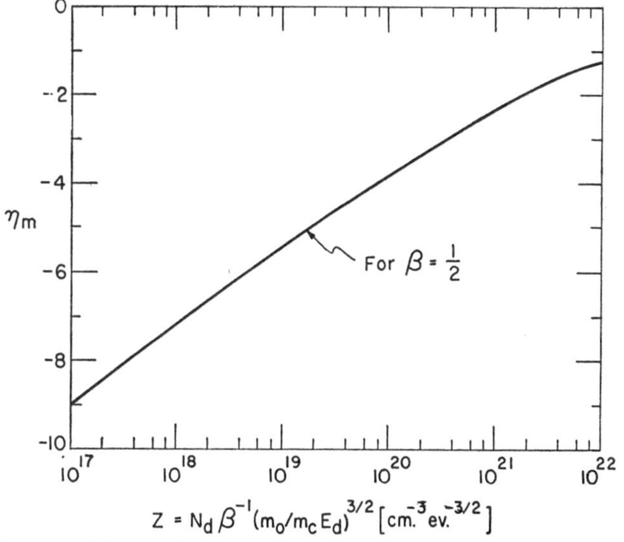

FIG. 32.6. The maximum value reached by η as a function of the density, ionization energy, etc., of a set of uncompensated donor centers. The curve shown is for $\beta = \frac{1}{2}$. With any other value, the curve should be raised by the amount $\ln(2\beta)$.

draw a family of parallel curves for various values of β; the one shown is for $\beta = \frac{1}{2}$ so that the curve for any other β would be displaced vertically by $\ln(2\beta)$.

The solution of Eq. (321.4) is less simple than we have described if the donor density is large enough to produce some conduction band degeneracy over part of the temperature range. One of the earliest and most striking discussions of the carrier statistics problem for a degenerate extrinsic semiconductor is that of Shifrin (1944:**1**). No great complication is involved provided that the maximum value of η is not much greater than unity, for then $\mathscr{F}_{1/2}(\eta)$ can be approximated by an expression of the form $[C+\exp(-\eta)]^{-1}$. As discussed in Appendix C, this kind of expression with $C \approx 0{\cdot}27$ is suitable whenever $\eta < 1{\cdot}3$. With such an approximation to the behavior of $\mathscr{F}_{1/2}(\eta)$, Eq. (321.4) becomes a quadratic in $\exp(\eta)$:

$$\mathcal{N}_c \exp(2\eta+\epsilon_d)+\beta(\mathcal{N}_c - C\mathcal{N}_d)\exp(\eta) = \beta\mathcal{N}_d, \quad \eta < 1{\cdot}3 \tag{321.17}$$

For the reduced Fermi level, the solution is

$$\exp(\eta) = \frac{2\mathcal{N}_d}{(\mathcal{N}_c - C\mathcal{N}_d)+\sqrt{[(\mathcal{N}_c - C\mathcal{N}_d)^2+4\beta^{-1}\mathcal{N}_d\mathcal{N}_c\exp(\epsilon_d)]}}, \quad \eta < 1{\cdot}3 \tag{321.18}$$

while the corresponding free electron density is

$$n_0 = \frac{2\mathcal{N}_d\mathcal{N}_c}{(\mathcal{N}_c + C\mathcal{N}_d)+\sqrt{[(\mathcal{N}_c - C\mathcal{N}_d)^2+4\beta^{-1}\mathcal{N}_d\mathcal{N}_c\exp(\epsilon_d)]}}, \quad \eta < 1{\cdot}3 \tag{321.19}$$

Considerably more difficulty is encountered if the donor density is so large that η goes through a maximum value rather larger than unity. While Appendix C does discuss approximate expressions for $\mathscr{F}_{1/2}(\eta)$ in the degenerate domain, none of these has a form which would permit a simple analytic solution for Eq. (321.4). However, it is always possible to find the mutually consistent values of ϵ_d and η. We can write (321.4) as

$$\begin{aligned}[1+\beta^{-1}\exp(\epsilon_d+\eta)]^{-1} &= \mathcal{N}_c\mathcal{N}_d^{-1}\mathscr{F}_{1/2}(\eta)\\ &= A\epsilon_d^{-3/2}\mathscr{F}_{1/2}(\eta)\end{aligned} \tag{321.20}$$

where A is a dimensionless quantity characteristic of the density and type of donor centers,

$$\begin{aligned}A &= 2(2\pi m_c E_d/h^2)^{3/2}\mathcal{N}_d^{-1}\\ &= 6\times 10^{21}(E_d m_c/m_0)^{3/2}\mathcal{N}_d^{-1} \quad \text{for} \quad \begin{cases}\mathcal{N}_d \text{ in cm}^{-3}\\ E_d \text{ in eV}\end{cases}\end{aligned} \tag{321.21}$$

Now if we denote

$$\left.\begin{aligned}x_1 &= [1+\beta^{-1}\exp(\epsilon_d+\eta)]^{-1}\\ x_2 &= [A\epsilon_d/^{-3/2}\mathscr{F}_{1/2}(\eta)]\end{aligned}\right\} \tag{321.22}$$

it will always be possible by numerical or graphical methods to find the value of η which permits the condition $x_1 = x_2$ to be satisfied for any value of ϵ_d (i.e. for any temperature). Such procedures are certainly tedious, but there is no other alternative for an exact solution.

In order to bring home the change wrought by conduction band degeneracy on the temperature dependence of n_0, Fig. 32.7 shows how n_0 and η vary with $1/T$ for a typical numerical example. The ionization energy, spin factor and effective mass ratio are all the same as for the previous example of Fig. 32.2; the only parameter changed is that N_d is now assumed to be 10^{19} cm^{-3} instead of 10^{16} cm^{-3}. It is interesting to compare the shape of the curve in Fig. 32.2 with that of part (a) in Fig. 32.7. In the former case the slope of $\ln(n_0)$ vs. $1/T$ was not very different from $(E_d/2k)$ when donor ionization was less than 10%. This is certainly not true for the example of Fig. 32.7, because the Fermi level is well above E_c until the temperature is low enough to make $n_0 < 0{\cdot}01\, N_d$. At *sufficiently* small temperatures and ionized densities, the slope does eventually approach $(E_d/2k)$, but Fig. 32.7 demonstrates how dangerous it can be to infer an impurity ionization energy from an experimental curve unless all the factors are known.

Of course, the situation for a real solid is complicated by a number of other factors as well, which must now be considered in turn.

3.2.2 The Realistic Case—Partly Compensated Impurities §

The most important respect in which the discussion of Sub-section 3.2.1 fails to represent the properties of any real extrinsic semiconductor is that semiconductors inevitably contain traces of *several kinds* of impurity. Sophistication in purification techniques may *reduce* the influence of "unwelcome" impurities, but no process can completely eradicate them.

There are several kinds of complexity which have to be considered. Thus an n-type semiconductor will usually contain significant quantities of more than one donor species. It will always contain acceptor impurities of various kinds. Some impurities may be able to provide or accept more than one electron. Moreover, electrons can be trapped by an impurity not only in ground states but also in excited states, and the spin and orbital degeneracy of any bound state may be modified by splitting occasioned by a magnetic field or by anisotropic elastic strain.

Thus the general problem for an extrinsic semiconductor is quite complicated. It is possible, as Landsberg (1958:**10**) has shown very powerfully (by the method of the grand canonical ensemble), to write

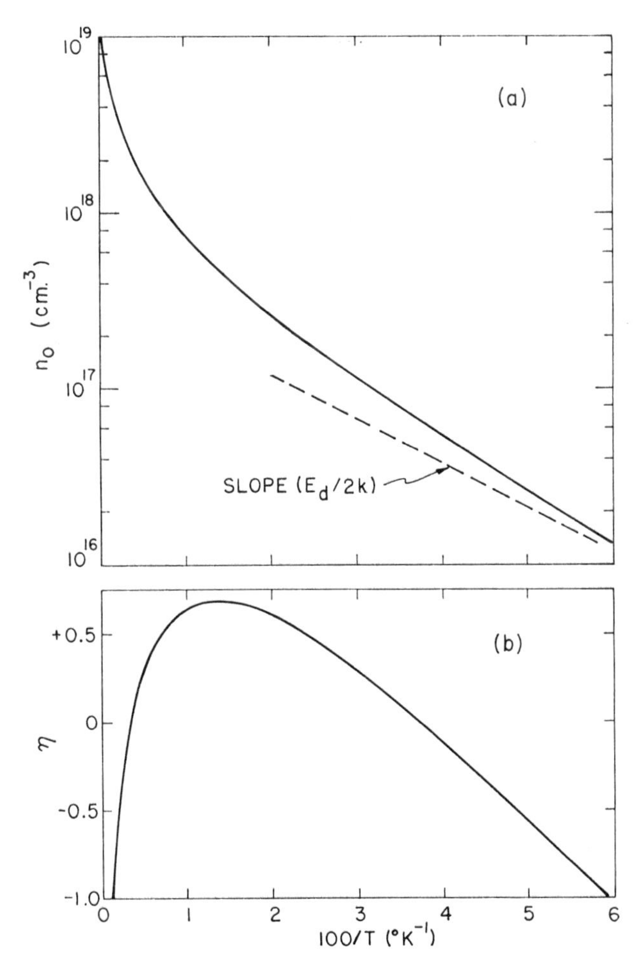

Fig. 32.7. Variation of (a) n_0 and (b) η with reciprocal temperature for a set of uncompensated donors when conditions are partially degenerate over much of the temperature range. Calculated for $N_d = 10^{19}$ cm^{-3}, $E_d = 0{\cdot}01$ eV, $m_c = 0{\cdot}25\, m_0$, $\beta = \frac{1}{2}$.

down a general expression for the electronic equilibrium in a semiconductor containing any impurity configuration; but this is *not* the same thing as a complete solution. Such a complex problem must be attacked piecemeal, by considering which complications can be relinquished in each individual case.

Accordingly, the complications of multivalent impurities are deferred to Section 3.4. Section 3.3 deals with the problem of an *n*-type semiconductor containing two species of donors at appreciably different energies in the upper half of the gap—and it will be seen at that time that each species will dominate the behavior over a different temperature range. The influence of occupied excited bound states is evaluated

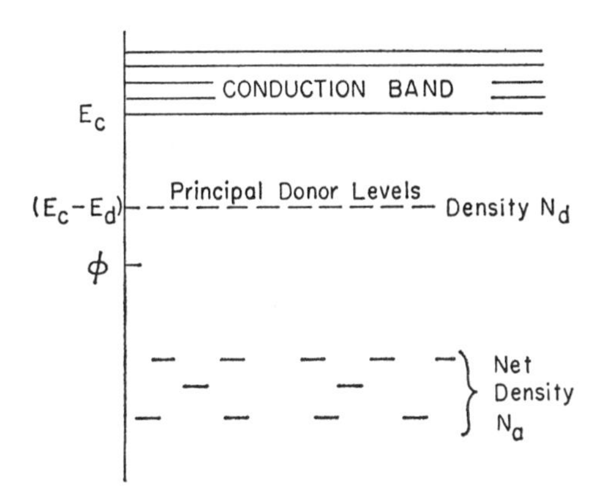

FIG. 32.8. Model of a partially compensated extrinsic *n*-type semiconductor.

in 3.2.3, but first it is fitting to come to grips with the most basic of all these problems; that an extrinsic semiconductor is always partially compensated (1935:**1**, 1939:**1**).

Consider then the situation idealized in Fig. 32.8. In addition to the principal set of donor levels, we suppose that there are appreciable concentrations of several other impurity species, whose levels lie further from the conduction band. The Fermi level ϕ will presumably lie well above the energies of all these other kinds of impurity state for all temperatures of interest.

If this is the case, all *donor* states among them will retain their electrons; that is, they will be electrically neutral. Thus their density will have no bearing on the solution of our problem. All *acceptors*, however, will acquire extra electrons as consistent with their position below the Fermi level. How many acceptors there are of each type is unimportant; the only thing which matters is the *total* density of electrons required to satisfy the needs of these acceptors, a density which will be denoted as N_a.

Now since these N_a electrons occupying compensating states have had to come from the principal donors, there remains only a density $(N_d - N_a)$ of electrons which can be distributed between the donor levels at $(E_c - E_d)$ and the conduction band. The fraction of ionized donors now varies from (N_a/N_d) at low temperatures to unity at high temperatures, and the free electron density can not become larger than $(N_a - N_d)$ until the falling Fermi level reaches (*a*) another set of impurity states, or (*b*) its intrinsic position.

Since the number of ionized donors is equal to $(n_o + N_a)$ and also to $(N_d - N_{dn})$ [see Eq. (321.2)], we have for a partially compensated semiconductor that

$$n_0 + N_a = N_d[1 + \beta^{-1} \exp(\epsilon_d + \eta)]^{-1} \tag{322.1}$$

When the degree of degeneracy is not known, and n_0 can safely be related to η only by using $n_0 = N_c \mathscr{F}_{1/2}(\eta)$, we can still write

$$[1 + \beta^{-1} \exp(\epsilon_d + \eta)]^{-1} = [A \epsilon_d^{-3/2} \,.\, \mathscr{F}_{1/2}(\eta) - (N_a/N_d)] \tag{322.2}$$

where $A = [2(2\pi m_c E_d/h^2)^{3/2}/N_d]$ is the dimensionless quantity previously introduced in Eq. (321.20). It was noted for the uncompensated situations of Sub-section 3.2.1 that pairs of values for η and ϵ_d could always be found which would make the two sides of Eq. (321.20) equal. Obviously the same kind of procedure will hold good for the partially compensated case of Eq. (322.2).

Eq. (322.1) reduces to a quadratic in $\exp(\eta)$ provided that $\eta \leqslant +1{\cdot}3$, so that $(n_0/N_c) = \mathscr{F}_{1/2}(\eta)$ can be approximated by $[C + \exp(-\eta)]^{-1}$, as described in Appendix C.

When this expression is substituted into Eq. (322.1), some elementary manipulation leads to

$$\exp(2\eta) + \exp(\eta)\left\{\frac{N_a + \beta \exp(-\epsilon_d)[N_c - C(N_d - N_a)]}{N_c + CN_a}\right\}$$

$$= \frac{\beta(N_d - N_a)\exp(-\epsilon_d)}{(N_c + CN_a)}, \quad \eta \leqslant +1{\cdot}3 \tag{322.3}$$

This has the solution

$$\exp(\eta) = \frac{2(\mathcal{N}_d - \mathcal{N}_a)}{[\mathcal{N}_c - C(\mathcal{N}_d - \mathcal{N}_a) + \beta^{-1}\mathcal{N}_a \exp(\epsilon_d)] + \sqrt{\{[\mathcal{N}_c - C(\mathcal{N}_d - \mathcal{N}_a) + \beta^{-1}\mathcal{N}_a \exp(\epsilon_d)]^2 + 4\beta^{-1}(\mathcal{N}_c + C\mathcal{N}_a)(\mathcal{N}_d - \mathcal{N}_a)\exp(\epsilon_d)\}}} \tag{322.4}$$

for $\exp(\eta)$ and

$$n_0 = \frac{2\mathcal{N}_c(\mathcal{N}_d - \mathcal{N}_a)}{[\mathcal{N}_c + C(\mathcal{N}_d - \mathcal{N}_a) + \beta^{-1}\mathcal{N}_a \exp(\epsilon_d)] + \sqrt{\{[\mathcal{N}_c - C(\mathcal{N}_d - \mathcal{N}_a) + \beta^{-1}\mathcal{N}_a \exp(\epsilon_d)]^2 + 4\beta^{-1}(\mathcal{N}_c + C\mathcal{N}_a)(\mathcal{N}_d - \mathcal{N}_a)\exp(\epsilon_d)\}}} \tag{322.5}$$

for the corresponding free electron density.

These expressions are considerably simplified when the Fermi level is several kT below the conduction band, so that $\mathscr{F}_{1/2}(\eta) \approx \exp(\eta)$ and

$$n_0 = \frac{2(\mathcal{N}_d - \mathcal{N}_a)}{[1 + (\mathcal{N}_a/\beta\mathcal{N}_c)\exp(\epsilon_d)] + \sqrt{\{[1 + (\mathcal{N}_a/\beta\mathcal{N}_c)\exp(\epsilon_d)]^2 + (4/\beta\mathcal{N}_c)(\mathcal{N}_d - \mathcal{N}_a)\exp(\epsilon_d)\}}} \tag{322.6}$$

The value of $\exp(\eta)$ is then of course $(n_0/\mathcal{N}_c)$.

A comparison with the equations of Sub-section 3.2.1 shows that Eqs. (322.4), (322.5) and (322.6) reduce to the forms of Eqs. (321.18), (321.19) and (321.6) when the density of compensating centers tends towards zero. But at low temperatures even a very small acceptor density has a considerable effect on n_0 and η. This effect is of the same general character for any degree of conduction band degeneracy, thus the remarks we shall make about the non-degenerate case would apply with little modification to more strongly doped material.

Compare then Eqs. (322.6) and (321.6). The denominator of each is equal to 2 at high temperatures when the donor ionization is complete. On considering progressively lower temperatures, the quantities $(4/\beta\mathcal{N}_c)(\mathcal{N}_d - \mathcal{N}_a)\exp(\epsilon_d)$ and $(\mathcal{N}_a/\beta\mathcal{N}_c)\exp(\epsilon_d)$ become comparable with and then larger than unity. When the degree of compensation is very small ($\mathcal{N}_a \ll \mathcal{N}_d$), it is possible to find a temperature range for which $\mathcal{N}_a \ll n_0 \ll \mathcal{N}_d$. This condition is equivalent to the statement $(\mathcal{N}_a/\beta\mathcal{N}_c)\exp(\epsilon_d) \ll 1 \ll (4\mathcal{N}_d/\beta\mathcal{N}_c)\exp(\epsilon_d)$; when such a temperature range exists, the carrier density approximates to

$$n_0 \approx (\beta \mathcal{N}_c \mathcal{N}_d)^{1/2} \exp(-E_d/2kT), \qquad \mathcal{N}_a \ll n_0 \ll \mathcal{N}_d \quad (322.7)$$

which is of course just the same as Eq. (321.7). A moment's reflection will confirm that it is entirely reasonable for n_0 not to depend in any material fashion on the density of compensating impurities when this density is much smaller than n_0.

Such a situation cannot be maintained indefinitely on progressive cooling. Eventually n_0 must approach, and then become smaller than, the density $\mathcal{N}_a$. This happens when the two terms $(\mathcal{N}_a/\beta\mathcal{N}_c)\exp(\epsilon_d)$ assume the dominant role in the denominator of Eq. (322.6). At sufficiently low temperatures then,

$$n_0 \approx \beta \mathcal{N}_c \left[\frac{\mathcal{N}_d - \mathcal{N}_a}{\mathcal{N}_a}\right] \exp(-E_d/kT), \qquad n_0 \ll \mathcal{N}_a < \mathcal{N}_d \quad (322.8)$$

The dependence of $\ln(n_0)$ on $1/T$ is twice as large for this temperature range as in the range of Eq. (322.7).

When the degree of compensation is rather large, there is no range of temperature for which Eq. (322.7) has any validity; on cooling from the exhaustion range, the carrier density decreases rather rapidly and soon conforms with Eq. (322.8).

Fig. 32.9 provides a semilogarithmic plot of n_0 vs. $1/T$ for a semiconductor containing donors and rather fewer acceptors. As with the previous example of Figs. 32.2–32.4, a model is adopted of donors 0·01 eV below a conduction band, when $\beta = \frac{1}{2}$ and $m_c = 0{\cdot}25\, m_0$. The four curves of Fig. 32.9 correspond with different degrees of compensation, but for simplicity it is assumed that $(\mathcal{N}_d - \mathcal{N}_a)$ is 10^{16} cm^{-3} for each case. Curve (i) corresponds with $\mathcal{N}_a = 0$, and is identical with the curve of Fig. 32.2. Curve (ii) is for $\mathcal{N}_a = 10^{14}$ cm^{-3} (about 1% compensation), curve (iii) for $\mathcal{N}_a = 10^{15}$ cm^{-3} (about 9% compensation) and curve (iv) for $\mathcal{N}_a = 10^{16}$ cm^{-3} (50% compensation). In the cases of curves (ii) and (iii), it will be seen that n_0 is reasonably close to the zero-compensation curve until the temperature is low enough for $\mathcal{N}_a$ to become comparable with n_0. The slope then increases and reaches a limiting value of $\sim (E_d/k)$ at the lower temperatures, when Eq. (322.8) applies. The compensation is so large for curve (iv) that

$$n_0 \approx \frac{(\mathcal{N}_d - \mathcal{N}_a)}{1 + (\mathcal{N}_a/\beta\mathcal{N}_c)\exp(\epsilon_d)} \quad \text{heavy compensation} \qquad (322.9)$$

is a reasonable approximation to the truth at all temperatures.

The Fermi level corresponding with Eq. (322.6):

$$(\phi - E_c) = kT\eta = kT\ln(n_0/N_c)$$
$$= kT\ln\left\{\frac{2\beta(N_d - N_a)}{[\beta N_c + N_a\exp(\epsilon_d)] + \sqrt{\{[\beta N_c + N_a\exp(\epsilon_d)]^2 + 4\beta N_c(N_d - N_a)\exp(\epsilon_d)\}}}\right\}$$

(322.10)

is not given by a particularly simple expression. From what has been said about the behavior of n_0, Eq. (322.10) obviously must become

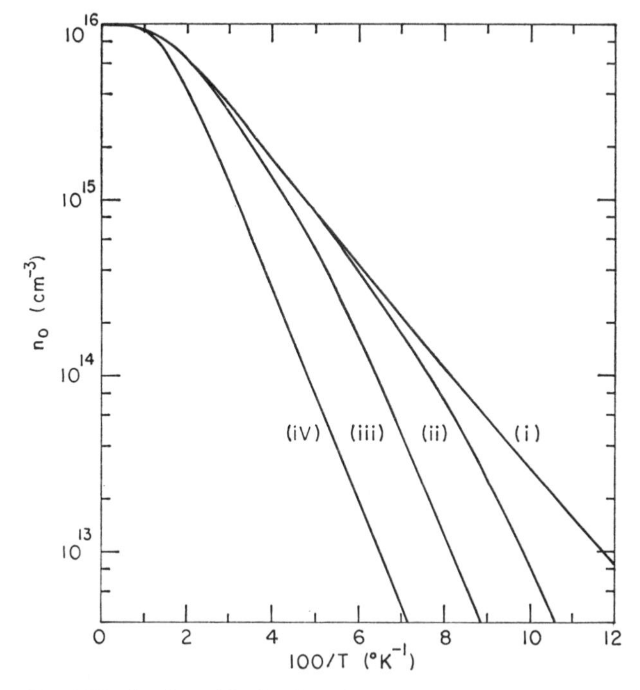

FIG. 32.9. Semilogarithmic plot of n_0 vs. $1/T$ for a set of partially compensated donors under non-degenerate conditions. For simplicity it is assumed that $(N_d - N_a) = 10^{16}$ cm^{-3} in each case, with $E_d = 0{\cdot}01$ eV, $m_c = 0{\cdot}25m_0$, $\beta = \frac{1}{2}$. (i) For $N_a = 0$, i.e. zero compensation. This is identical with the model of Figs. 32.2–32.4. (ii) For $N_a = 10^{14}$ cm^{-3}. (iii) $N_a = 10^{15}$ cm^{-3}. (iv) $N_a = 10^{16}$ cm^{-3}.

essentially equivalent to (321.9) whenever $n_0 \gg \mathcal{N}_a$. When the temperature is low enough and the compensation severe enough for $\mathcal{N}_a$ to be larger than n_0, Eq. (322.10) reduces to

$$\phi = E_c - E_d + kT \ln\left[\frac{\beta(\mathcal{N}_d - \mathcal{N}_a)}{\mathcal{N}_a}\right], \qquad n_0 \ll \mathcal{N}_a \qquad (322.11)$$

Such behavior is evident in curves (ii), (iii) and (iv) in part (b) of Fig. 32.10. It will be noted that the Fermi level starts from the

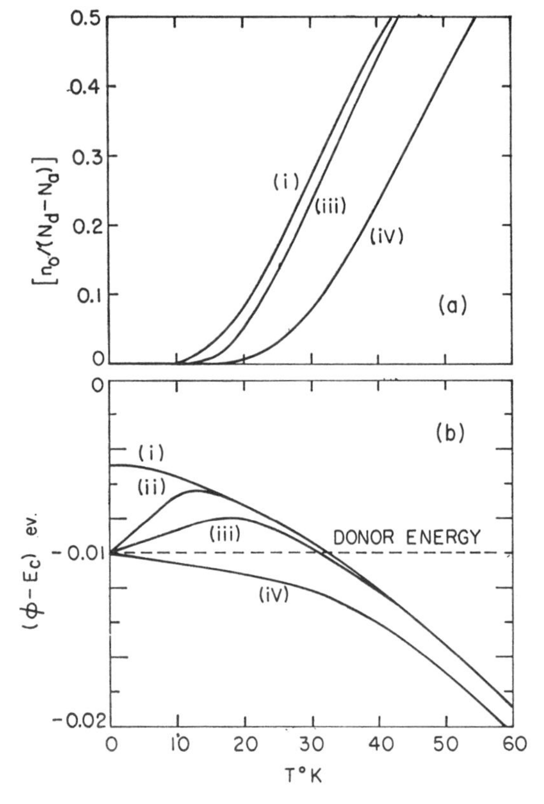

FIG. 32.10. The temperature dependence of $[n_0/(\mathcal{N}_d - \mathcal{N}_a)]$ and ϕ for the four numerical cases of Fig. 32.9. The curve for (ii) is not shown in part (a) since it lies extremely close to that of (i).

donor energy at $T = 0°K$; this must always happen no matter how small the fractional compensation, since if there are *any* compensating impurities *at all*, the principal donors are less than 100% occupied at $T = 0$. This means that the Fermi level must differ from the donor level by a finite multiple of kT as $T \to 0$, and must coincide with $(E_c - E_d)$ at absolute zero itself.

Whether the Fermi level rises or falls as T increases from absolute zero depends on whether $[\beta(N_d - N_a)/N_a]$ is larger or smaller than unity. In Fig. 32.10, the former is true of curves (ii) and (iii) and the latter of curve (iv). As T increases further, the Fermi level curves for samples of the same $(N_d - N_a)$ but different N_a eventually coincide. This process has reached completion for the situations characterized by curves (i), (ii) and (iii) in Fig. 32.10, but the Fermi level for the most heavily compensated sample will not join with the others until a temperature of some 150°K is reached.

It is customary to plot $\ln(n_0)$ vs. $1/T$ in discussing the temperature dependence of carrier density, but other forms of presentation are sometimes useful. As an example, we may note from the curves in part (a) of Fig. 32.10 that the addition of compensating centers moves the curve of n_0 vs. T bodily to the right, by an amount which is approximately proportional to $[N_a/(N_d - N_a)]$. The curve corresponding with case (ii) could not be drawn since it is almost indistinguishable from the zero-compensation curve (*i*) at all temperatures.

The reader may perhaps be wondering at this point how all the preceding information can be used in the analysis of experimental data, when the given information consists of values of n_0 for various temperatures. One of the most popular approaches starts from Eq. (322.1), rearranged to read

$$\frac{\exp(\eta)(n_0 + N_a)}{(N_d - N_a - n_0)} = \beta \exp(-\epsilon_d) \tag{322.12}$$

When n_0 is not large enough at any temperature to provoke the complications of degeneracy, $\exp(\eta) = n_0/N_c$, and

$$\frac{n_0(n_0 + N_a)}{(N_d - N_a - n_0)} = \beta N_c \exp(-E_d/kT) \tag{322.13}$$

The task now is to find values for N_a and N_d which will permit the two sides of (322.13) to be equal at all temperatures.

This does not require many experimental points if E_d, β, and m_c are known, but this is not generally the case. It is not possible to isolate β *and* m_c, only the combination $\beta m_c^{3/2}$ from use of (322.13). Thus if m_c is known, β can be determined, and vice versa. Suppose for instance that the effective mass for the conduction band is known. Referring to the curves of Fig. 32.9, $(N_d - N_a)$ can be estimated from the limit of n_0 in the exhaustion range. A reasonable approximation to E_d can be obtained from the slope of $\ln(n_0)$ vs. $1/T$ in the low temperature range, and (N_a/β) from the value of n_0 at any temperature in this range [using Eq. (322.8)]. The method of least squares can then be applied to Eq. (322.13) to find the values of the parameters which give the best fit over the entire temperature range.

As with all the preceding discussion, methods applicable to the relationships of donors to the conduction band can be adopted in their entirety for p-type semiconductors with majority acceptors above the valence band. The counterpart of Eq. (322.13) for a non-degenerate p-type semiconductor is

$$\frac{p_0(p_0 + N_d)}{(N_a - N_d - p_0)} = \left(\frac{N_v}{\beta}\right) \exp(-E_a/kT) \qquad (322.14)$$

where the spin degeneracy β of the acceptors is in general larger than unity.

Fig. 32.11 provides an example of experimental results (derived from Hall coefficient measurements) fitted by means of Eq. (322.14). The sample is one of a series the present author once investigated (1959:**6**), composed of germanium doped with indium acceptors and partially compensated with antimony. For the combination of the two valence bands of germanium, the density-of-states effective mass is known (1955:**9**) to be $m_v = 0{\cdot}37\, m_0$. The results could be fitted in the most satisfactory fashion by using the numerical values noted in the figure caption for N_a, N_d, E_a and β. It will be observed that this fit is obtained with β equal to 4. The more conventional choice for simple acceptors of $\beta = 2$ (combined with a different value of N_d to satisfy the low temperature data) led to an appreciably less satisfactory fit over the range 20–50°K. That an acceptor should offer four states above the double valence band of germanium was in fact predicted by Kohn (1957:**10**).

Before congratulating ourselves prematurely that experimental data can be reliably handled using Eqs. (322.13) or (322.14), it must be observed that these equations are not entirely correct. Next we have to see how they can be generalized to take account of excited states.

3.2.3 The Influence of Excited States

An isolated hydrogen atom consists of an electron moving under the influence of a proton. The ground state of this system, the $1s$ state, has a spin degeneracy of 2, and an energy of some 13·6 eV is required to ionize the atom. But there are also many possible excited states of this

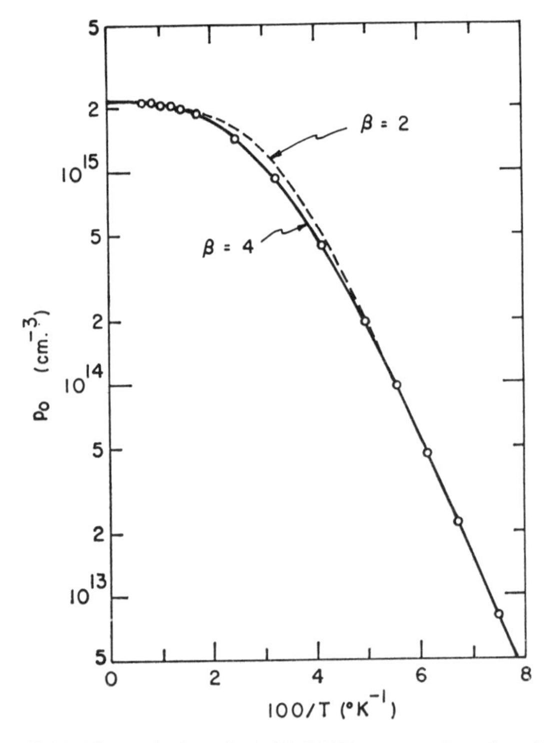

Fig. 32.11. The variation of p_0 with $1/T$ for germanium doped with indium and compensated with antimony (1959:**6**), fitted to satisfy Eq. (322.14) when an effective mass $m_c = 0{\cdot}37\ m_0$ is used for the valence band. The optimum fit is for $N_a = 2{\cdot}66 \times 10^{15}$ cm^{-3}, $N_d = 0{\cdot}48 \times 10^{15}$ cm^{-3}, $E_a = 0{\cdot}01025$ eV and $\beta = 4$.

atom, the eight $2s$ and $2p$ states, the eighteen $3s$, $3p$ and $3d$ states, and so on. It is dangerous to press too far for the analogy between a hydrogen atom and a monovalent impurity center, but such analogies are useful in reminding us that a donor impurity is electrically neutral whether it has an electron bound in the ground state at $(E_c - E_d)$ or in an excited state rather closer to the conduction band. The importance of excited states was remarked by Shifrin (1944:**1**), but allowance for them in discussions of impurity level—conduction band equilibrium has only become popular in recent years (1955:**20**, 1956:**14**).

Rather than the model of Fig. 32.8, we should then accept Fig. 32.12 as the picture of a partly compensated n-type semiconductor. We

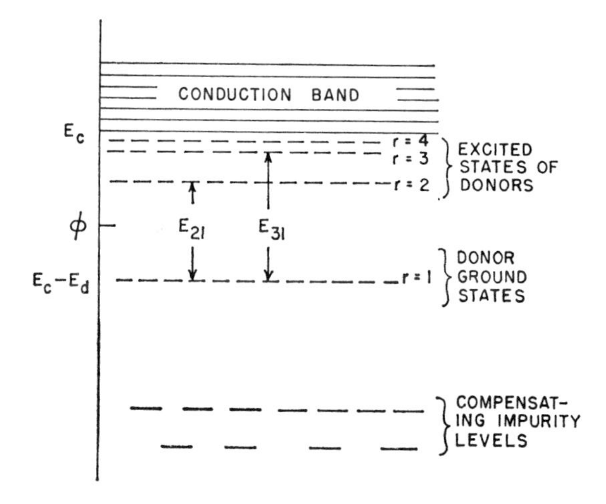

Fig. 32.12. Model of a partly compensated n-type semiconductor including the excited states of the principal donors.

denote by the symbol 1 the lowest, or ground level of the principal donors; this state has a spin degeneracy of β_1^{-1}. Groups of excited states in general have different degeneracy factors, say β_r^{-1}, and lie at energies $E_{r1} = kT\epsilon_{r1}$ above the ground states.

A donor is capable of binding an electron in one of the β_r^{-1} states at energy $(E_c - E_d + E_{r1})$ only if it does not have an electron already bound in any other state, either at the same level or a different one. If we denote the density of donors with electrons trapped at the rth level by N_{dnr}, then

$$N_{dnr} = \frac{\{N_d - \sum_{s \neq r} N_{dns}\}}{1 + \beta_r \exp(-\eta - \epsilon_d + \epsilon_{r1})} \tag{323.1}$$

The summation extends over all levels except the rth. Now the numerator on the right can be written

$$\begin{aligned} \{N_d - \sum_{s \neq r} N_{dns}\} &= N_d + N_{dnr} - \sum_{\text{all } s} N_{dns} \\ &= (N_d - N_{dn}) + N_{dnr} \\ &= (N_{di} + N_{dnr}) \end{aligned} \tag{323.2}$$

Placing this expression in the numerator of Eq. (323.1), we arrive at a relationship which might have been expected all along for the ratio of N_{dnr} to the ionized donor density:

$$\frac{N_{dnr}}{N_{di}} = \beta_r^{-1} \exp(\eta + \epsilon_d - \epsilon_{r1}) \tag{323.3}$$

This is of course exactly the kind of relationship laid down in Eq. (311.1) when only the ground states were being considered.

The total density of neutral donors is given by summing N_{dnr} over all r:

$$N_{dn} = N_{di} \sum_{r=1}^{\infty} \beta_r^{-1} \exp(\eta + \epsilon_d - \epsilon_{r1}) \tag{323.4}$$

Since $(N_{dn} + N_{di})$ is just N_d itself, (Eq. 323.4) leads to a pair of equations

$$\left.\begin{aligned} N_{dn} &= \frac{N_d \sum_{r=1}^{\infty} \beta_r^{-1} \exp(\eta + \epsilon_d - \epsilon_{r1})}{1 + \sum_{r=1}^{\infty} \beta_r^{-1} \exp(\eta + \epsilon_d - \epsilon_{r1})} \\ N_{di} &= \frac{N_d}{1 + \sum_{r=1}^{\infty} \beta_r^{-1} \exp(\eta + \epsilon_d - \epsilon_{r1})} \end{aligned}\right\} \tag{323.5}$$

which are of completely general validity. Whatever the energies and spin degeneracies of excited states, their influence can be calculated.

Let us return now to consider Fig. 32.12, and the distribution of electrons between the conduction band, all states of the donors, and any compensating impurities. N_{di} must (in the absence of any free valence band holes) be equal to the sum of n_0 and N_a. Then

$$n_0 = N_c\mathcal{F}_{1/2}(\eta) = \frac{N_d}{1+\sum_{r=1}^{\infty}\beta_r^{-1}\exp(\eta+\epsilon_d-\epsilon_{r1})} - N_a \quad (323.6)$$

When free electrons are not unduly numerous, so that the Fermi level lies below the conduction band, the non-degenerate approximation $\exp(\eta)\approx(n_0/N_c)$ can be substituted into the denominator of Eq. (323.6):

$$n_0+N_a = \frac{N_d}{1+(n_0/N_c)\sum_{r=1}^{\infty}\beta_r^{-1}\exp(\epsilon_d-\epsilon_{r1})} \quad (323.7)$$

Rearranging Eq. (323.7) in the manner employed previously, the quadratic equation for n_0 can be given in the form

$$\frac{n_0(n_0+N_a)}{(N_d-N_a-n_0)} = \frac{N_c}{\sum_{r=1}^{\infty}\beta_r^{-1}\exp(\epsilon_d-\epsilon_{r1})}$$

$$= \frac{(\beta_1N_c)\exp(-\epsilon_d)}{1+\sum_{r=2}^{\infty}(\beta_1/\beta_r)\exp(-\epsilon_{r1})} \quad (323.8)$$

As with Eq. (322.13), from which Eq. (323.8) differs only in the additional presence of the summation over excited states, the right-hand side depends on the character of the impurities and on the temperature, but not on the donor or acceptor densities. This makes the form of Eqs. (322.13) and (323.8) convenient for the treatment of experimental data when it is known that the conduction band density is small enough at all temperatures for $N_c\exp(\eta)$ to be a good approximation for $\mathcal{F}_{1/2}(\eta)$.

For compactness, we may denote

$$\sum_{r=2}^{\infty}(\beta_1/\beta_r)\exp(-\epsilon_{r1})$$

by the symbol F, so that

$$\frac{n_0(n_0+N_a)}{(N_d-N_a-n_0)} = \frac{\beta_1 N_c \exp(-\epsilon_d)}{1+F} \tag{323.9}$$

Since F is a function of temperature, the temperature dependence of n_0 will be slightly different from that predicted by (322.13), and if the data are analyzed on the basis of Eq. (322.13) rather than Eq. (323.9), it may look as though the energy E_d were slightly temperature-dependent (1957:**16**). It will depend to a major extent on the distribution of excited states in energy whether their occupancy can affect the equilibrium of Eq. (323.9). When there are some excited states with energies rather close to that of the ground states, F may become comparable with or even larger than unity in certain temperature ranges.

Certainly at low enough temperatures, $F \ll 1$, and Eqs. (322.13) and (323.9) will coincide. All neutral donors then hold an electron in the lowest possible energy state. Similarly at very high temperatures the Fermi level is well below all states of the donors, and $n_0 \approx (N_d-N_a)$. It is for intermediate temperatures that the value of F can have a maximum effect on n_0.

Let us suppose initially that an electron bound by a donor ion can be described perfectly by Eq. (145.4), the effective mass equation. Temporarily neglecting all the complications which have been superimposed on the simple Bohr model of a hydrogen atom, we may suppose that the ground and excited states of a donor resemble those of the original Bohr atom, renormalized by the effective mass and dielectric constant. This is the model in which s, p, d, etc., states of a given shell all have the same energy. Then $(\beta_1/\beta_r) = r^2$ and $E_{r1} = E_d(1-r^{-2})$. In terms of such a simple model,

$$F = 4\exp(-3\epsilon_d/4)+9\exp(-8\epsilon_d/9)+16\exp(-15\epsilon_d/16)+\ldots \tag{323.10}$$

As Shifrin (1944:**1**) remarks, it is only necessary to consider the first few terms of such a series since for a finite donor density the wave-functions for the higher excited states will overlap quite strongly and these states will form part of the conduction band.

As an illustrative numerical example of the effect produced by excited state occupancy when F has the form (323.10), consider a semiconductor with donor levels $E_d = 0{\cdot}01$ eV below the conduction band when $(N_d-N_a) = 10N_a = 10^{16}\ \text{cm}^{-3}$ and $m_c = 0{\cdot}25\ m_0$. This was the example previously used as curve (iii) in Figs. 32.9 and 32.10. The broken curve in Fig. 32.13 is identical with curve (iii) of Fig. 32.9, and the solid line shows the variation of n_0 with $1/T$ when excited states are taken into account by using Eqs. (323.9) and (323.10). For this example, the excited states have quite a considerable effect between 20°K and the exhaustion range. It would be possible crudely to fit the behavior of the solid curve in Fig. 32.13 by using Eq. (322.13), but only with seriously erroneous values of β and $\mathcal{N}_a$.

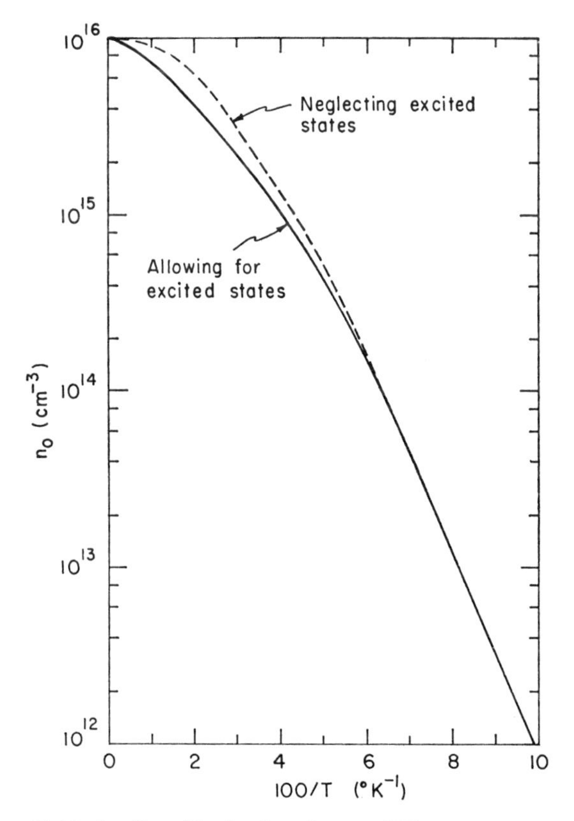

FIG. 32.13. Semilogarithmic plot of n_0 vs. $1/T$ for an n-type model with $\mathcal{N}_d = 1{\cdot}1 \times 10^{16}$ cm^{-3}, $\mathcal{N}_a = 10^{15}$ cm^{-3}, $E_d = 0{\cdot}01$ eV, $m_c = 0{\cdot}25 m_0$. The broken curve is identical with curve (iii) of Fig. 32.9. The solid curve shows the change resulting from taking into account occupancy of hydrogenic excited states.

We are then immediately faced with the question: how trustworthy is the analysis applied to the experimental data in Fig. 32.11? For excited states of the indium acceptors were not allowed for in those calculations. This is the kind of question which must be asked on an individual basis for each type of impurity in each semiconductor, since the effective mass equation has to be modified in accordance with the band structure peculiarities of a semiconductor. The energy spacings and degeneracies of excited states usually bear little relation to a hydrogenic spectrum. In the case of Group III acceptors in germanium, the calculations of Schechter (1955:**23**, 1956:**20**) suggest that the $2p$ states are split into several components, most of which are too close to the valence band to affect the carrier density–temperature relationship to any extent. Incidentally, the designation of these states as $2p$ is rather confusing, since there is no direct connection with the hydrogen energy scheme.

At any rate, for p-type germanium with Group III acceptors, it would seem to be justifiable to ignore the excited states. Similar simplifications are permissible for silicon containing these same types of acceptor. Infrared absorption measurements (e.g. 1956:**17**, 1958:**20**) and the calculations of Kohn and Luttinger (1955:**22**, 1957:**10**) indicate that the excited states are not close enough to the ground state to have much effect. In the extreme case of indium acceptors in silicon, the optical measurements of Newman (1956:**19**) indicate that the ground state binding energy is ten times larger than that of the first excited state.

For semiconductors such as germanium and silicon, description of acceptor states in terms of an effective mass equation is complicated by the existence of two valence bands, the light- and heavy-hole bands, degenerate at $\mathbf{k} = 0$.

Complexities of a different kind occur in considering donor states for these semiconductors, because the conduction band has multiple minima and the impurity wave functions are appropriate combinations of contributions from each minimum (1954:**13**, 1955:**17**, 1957:**10**). One possibility which emerges from this theoretical work is that the $1s$ states—the deepest lying states of the system—can themselves be split into two factions. This is the topic of the next sub-section.

3.2.4 Impurity Ground State Split in the Crystal Field

It is not surprising that theoretical studies of donor states in semiconductors should have concentrated on silicon and germanium, since the conduction band shapes of these semiconductors are known so well. Work on silicon is particularly profitable because the energies of optical transitions fall in a convenient spectral range. The left column in Fig. 32.14 shows the spacings of levels for phosphorus donors determined

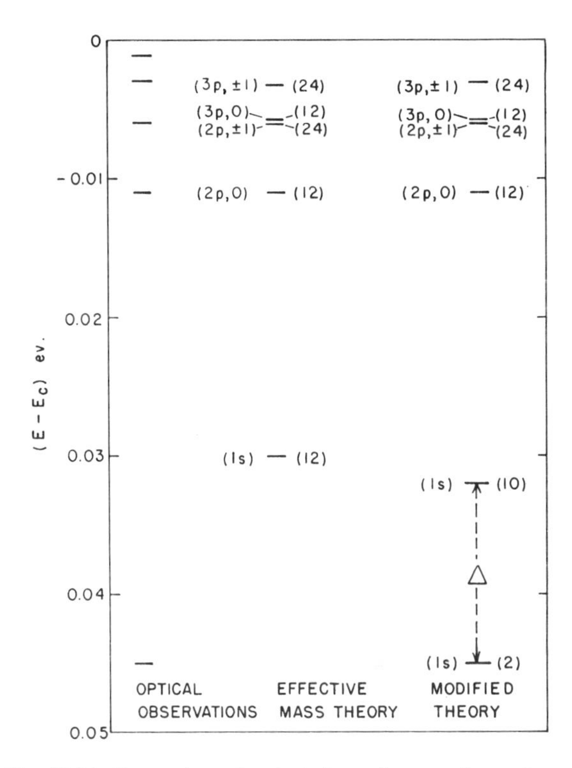

FIG. 32.14. Comparison of optical absorption experimental results (1956:**18**) with theoretical term schemes for phosphorus donors in silicon. The figure in parentheses at the right of each term is β^{-1}, the total state degeneracy (including spin).

optically by Picus *et al.* (1956:**18**). Comparison with the center column shows that the excited states agree well with the term scheme obtained from effective mass theory. But theory predicts a ground state much shallower than the energy found in practice for any Group V donor.

This discrepancy is now believed to be a result of the composition of the ground state wave-functions, influenced by the six equivalent conduction band minima. The $1s$ level is compounded of six states, each with a spin degeneracy of 2, or twelve states in all. Two of these states have wave-functions which do not vanish at the donor nucleus (completely symmetrical states) whereas the wave-functions of the other ten do vanish at this point. The two completely symmetrical states of the representation A_1 will be affected much more by a breakdown of the effective mass equation (145.4) than the others, and accordingly lie at a considerably lower energy than the remaining $1s$ states. This revised theoretical picture is shown at the right in Fig. 32.14. (Actually, group theory shows that the upper ten $1s$ states may be split again into $4+6$ states, but such splitting will presumably be rather small compared with the energy difference Δ between the two lowest $1s$ states and their erstwhile companions.)

Optical identification of the upper $1s$ states will be very difficult. For transitions between the two sets of $1s$ states are obviously forbidden. At the low temperatures required to obtain narrow optical line widths, it will be almost impossible to maintain enough electrons in the upper levels to make a transition into a $2p$ or $3p$ state detectable.

For this reason, Long and Myers (1959:**13**) used an electrical method in measuring the energy difference Δ. As illustrated in Fig. 32.15, they measured the temperature dependence of free electron density (by deduction from the Hall coefficient), and found the value of Δ which permitted the optimum fit to

$$\frac{n_0(n_0+N_a)}{(N_d-N_a-n_0)} = \frac{N_c \exp(-E_d/kT)}{2+10\exp(-\Delta/kT)+\sum_{r=2}^{\infty}\beta_r^{-1}\exp(-E_{r1}/kT)} \tag{324.1}$$

which is an obvious adaptation of Eq. (323.8). For phosphorus donors in silicon they determined Δ as $(0{\cdot}010 \pm 0{\cdot}0002)$ eV. Similar procedures should be applicable to other types of donor.

By now it should be discouragingly clear that the determination of densities and energies of bound states is by no means a simple matter. Unless a great deal of information is available about the band structure and other features of a semiconductor, we can not know whether a simple analysis is permissible. Yet if a simple analysis is carried out—say on the lines of Eq. (322.13)—when it is inappropriate, the numerical values deduced may be seriously in error. With most semiconductors, our state of ignorance at the time of writing is so profound that it would be unwarrantably pretentious to attempt more than a simple semi-quantitative analysis. Accordingly, while we have considered excited

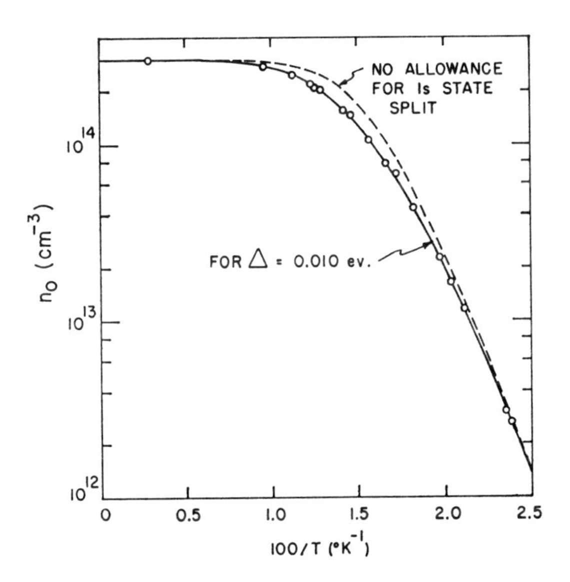

FIG. 32.15. Variation of n_0 with $1/T$ for silicon containing partly compensated phosphorus donors in silicon, according to measurements of Long and Myers (1959:**13**). Calculated curves are for $N_d = 6{\cdot}9 \times 10^{14}$ cm^{-3}, $N_a = 3{\cdot}8 \times 10^{14}$ cm^{-3}, $E_d = 0{\cdot}0435$ eV.

states and split ground states with due seriousness in these two sub-sections, it will not be fruitful to consider them in connection with all the remaining models of this chapter.

3.2.5 IMPURITY STATES SPLIT BY ANISOTROPIC ELASTIC STRAIN

The complexities of impurity wave-functions and energy levels considered so far result only from the complicated form of the periodic potential in any real solid. It should now be noted—rather briefly—that deformation of the crystal lattice will have further effects on impurity states.

A simple isotropic elastic strain should not affect the structure of impurity states in most materials, for this should be equivalent to the effects of thermal expansion and contraction on the lattice. (Even this will not be true for an anisotropic semiconductor such as tellurium, which has a negative compressibility along the *c*-axis (1954:**14**), so that hydrostatic pressure alters the bond angles.) But in any semiconductor, an anisotropic elastic strain will perturb the edges of the bands (1950:**7**). This in turn will modify impurity state wave-functions. That impurity states would be affected by strain was first pointed out

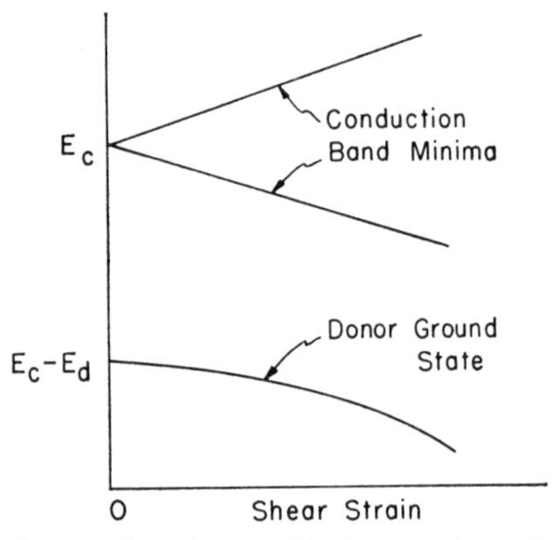

FIG. 32.16. Suggested variation with shear strain of the conduction band edges and donor ground state energy for Group V donors in silicon, according to Kohn (1957:**10**).

by Price (1956:**21**) and the implications for donor and acceptor states in Ge and Si are discussed by Kohn (1957:**10**).

Kohn remarks that a shear strain will split each conduction band in Si into two branches, with energy linearly dependent on the magnitude of the shear. On the other hand, the first-order shift of the donor ground state vanishes, and the main effect is the second-order one, as sketched in Fig. 32.16.

Measurements of the conductivity of *n*-type germanium at low temperatures under uniaxial strain have been reported by Fritzsche (1959:**14**) (1960:**6**). With antimony doped germanium, the principal effect is the inhibition of impurity conduction parallel to the strain. Strikingly different behavior is exhibited with arsenic donors (1961:**2**) due to the much larger valley-orbit splitting.

3.2.6 Effect of a Magnetic Field on Impurity States

In previous chapters it has been seen that the application of a magnetic field splits the conduction and valence bands into series of sub-bands founded on Landau levels. By analogy, it may be expected that a magnetic field will also influence the energies of bound impurity states.

Yafet *et al.* (1956:**22**) have calculated this influence for the model of a hydrogenic ground state, when the effective mass m_c is isotropic.

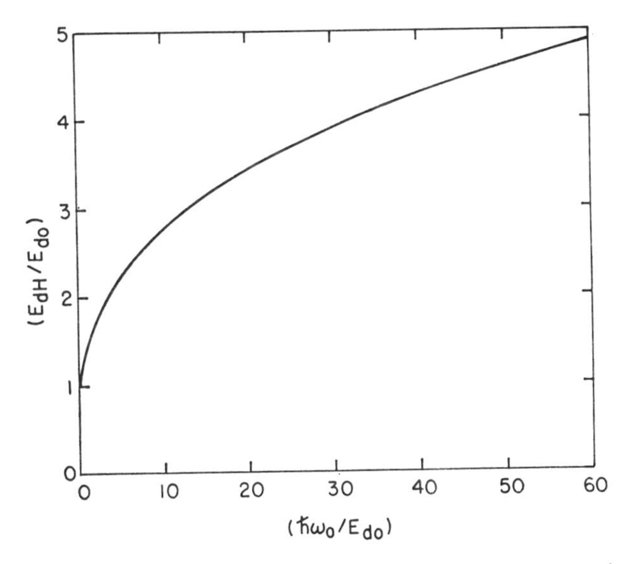

Fig. 32.17. Variation of donor ionization energy with magnetic field strength, after the calculations of Yafet *et al.* (1956:**22**).

As we already know, the lowest conduction states are at an energy $\frac{1}{2}\hbar\omega_0$ above E_c in the presence of a magnetic field (see Sub-sections 1.4.6 and 2.2.2). The donor ground state also moves towards higher energy with magnetic field, but at a rather slower rate, so that the effective donor ionization energy E_{dH} is larger than its value E_{d0} for zero field. The essential result of the variational calculation of Yafet *et al.* is shown in Fig. 32.17. It will be noted that E_{dH} changes with field most rapidly when the dimensionless parameter $(\hbar\omega_0/E_{d0})$ is still small; but appreciable increases in E_d still correspond with rather large magnetic fields for most materials. As an example, with group V donors in germanium, $\hbar\omega_0$ does not exceed E_{d0} for magnetic fields less than 10^5 oersteds.

The model used by Yafet *et al.* indicates that the impurity wave function becomes restricted to a smaller volume when a magnetic field is applied. This shrinking occurs mainly in directions normal to the field, but also to some extent along the field direction. The overall effect is that of transforming a rather large spherically symmetrical wave-function into a very small cigar shape. Such constriction of the orbit for a bound electron necessarily means that the effective mass approximation must become less tenable as the field increases; thus the high field region of Fig. 32.17 should be regarded as highly tentative.

Experiments are reported by Keyes and Sladek (1956:**23**) on the variation of n_0 with magnetic field for *n*-type InSb, in support of the calculations just mentioned. The carrier density certainly decreased with increasing H, though this was probably due in large measure to the magnetic break-up of a nascent impurity band (Section 3.5).

3.2.7 Some Comments in Summary

At this point we should take stock of the degree of complexity likely in an actual semiconductor. Except for material under rather severe strain or in a very large magnetic field, the complications of Sub-sections 3.2.5 and 3.2.6 can usually be neglected. Whether the statistical description is complicated by the influence of excited states or a split ground level as in Sub-sections 3.2.3 and 3.2.4 depends very much on the individual impurity and semiconductor; however, there is reason to believe that many systems will be essentially free from such complications.

This brings us to the discussion of Sub-sections 3.2.1 and 3.2.2. The apparently unrealistic case of Sub-section 3.2.1 was discussed in some detail for several reasons. One good reason is that it provides the simplest introduction to the ideas involved. Another is that some of the information can be applied to partly compensated semiconductors.

For instance, Figs. 32.5 and 32.6 indicate the maximum value of η and the temperature for which it occurs as functions of the parameter $\mathcal{Z}$. Now in a partly compensated semiconductor, the behavior of η is quite different at very low temperatures; but by the time ionization has proceeded far enough to take η through a maximum, the Fermi level for a given $(N_d - N_a)$ is almost independent of the actual degree of compensation (see Fig. 32.10). Thus even for a partly compensated semiconductor, η_m and T_m can be found with reasonable accuracy using Figs. 32.5 and 32.6, substituting $(N_d - N_a)$ into Z. This gives a good indication of the range of η which will be encountered and shows whether a solution must be effected with Eq. (322.2) or with the simpler non-degenerate forms of Eq. (322.6) and (322.12).

The uncertain effects of compensation discourage the use of other simple graphical aids for determining n_0 and ϕ as functions of temperature when N_d, E_d, etc., are known. In a previous discussion of the interrelationships of carrier populations in bands and impurity levels (1952:**3**) the present author used a number of graphical aids, based on the uses to which Eq. (321.4) had been put by Landsberg *et al.* (1951:**5**) and by Lehovec and Kedesdy (1951:**15**). But such curves must be replaced by families of curves for different degrees of compensation, and by families of families if excited states are to be allowed for. This removes the essential basis of graphical methods, that of simplifying the task of calculation.

3.3 SEMICONDUCTORS DOMINATED BY SEVERAL LOCALIZED LEVELS

Throughout Section 3.2 we considered the dynamics of situations dominated by a single species of monovalent donor. Other impurity levels were acknowledged only for their effect on compensation. Such a viewpoint is justifiable when the Fermi level is either far above or far below all other kinds of impurity level; but these conditions cannot necessarily be maintained over a wide range of temperature. Now it is necessary to consider more general models.

3.3.1 Several Independent Types of Monovalent Donor

The simplest kind of generalization is indicated by the model of Fig. 33.1. Two entirely independent species of monovalent donor are supposed, which present levels for electron occupancy at characteristic energies below the conduction band. There must also be some assorted compensating acceptor levels, which accommodate N_a trapped electrons per unit volume. Only $(N_{d1}+N_{d2}-N_a)$ electrons remain for distribution between the two sets of donors and the conduction band.

Two completely different forms of behavior will exist depending on whether N_a is larger or smaller than N_{d1}. If $N_a > N_{d1}$, the upper donor levels will be completely denuded of electrons at 0°K and the Fermi level will be locked to the energy (E_c-E_{d2}). As temperature rises some electrons will be excited to the conduction band and ϕ will readjust itself in an appropriate manner. At sufficiently high temperatures, ϕ will be several kT lower than (E_c-E_{d2}), and n_0 will approach

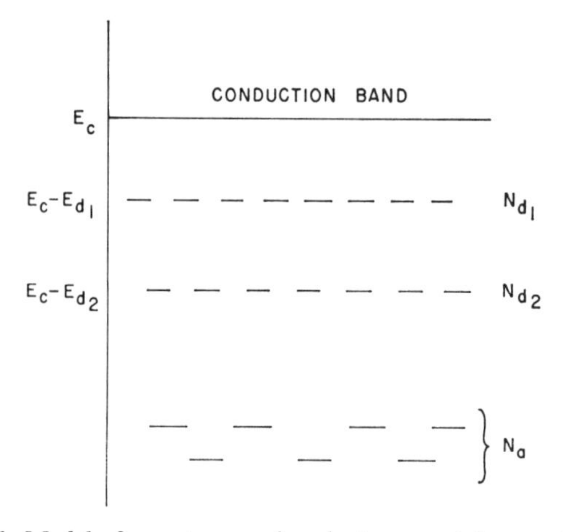

FIG. 33.1. Model of an n-type semiconductor containing two independent kinds of donors at different energies, and assorted low lying compensating centers. The temperature variation of n_0 depends on whether N_a is larger than or smaller than N_{d1}.

its limiting value of $(N_{d1}+N_{d2}-N_a)$. Note that unless the two donor binding energies are very similar, the Fermi level will always be many kT below the upper donor levels, and these will remain empty at all temperatures. This situation is really entirely equivalent to the one we have considered throughout Section 3.2, for a semiconductor dominated by the *single species* of N_{d2} donors with an *effective* compensating density of (N_a-N_{d1}) states.

On the other hand, if $N_a < N_{d1}$, at absolute zero the lower donors will be completely full and the upper donors will contain $(N_{d1}-N_a)$

electrons. The Fermi level at 0°K then coincides with the energy $(E_c - E_{d1})$. As temperatures rises, the upper donors offer their electrons to the conduction band, and ϕ must move below $(E_c - E_{d1})$ as this supply becomes exhausted. On further warming, no appreciable increase of n_0 is possible until ϕ has dropped almost to the energy $(E_c - E_{d2})$; the second set of donors then begins to lose electrons and at

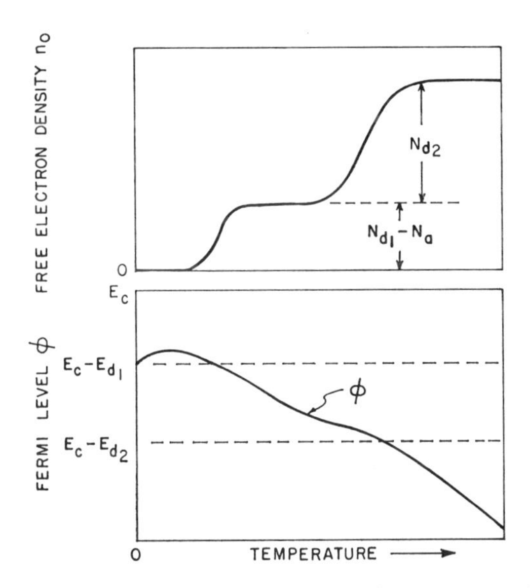

FIG. 33.2. Schematic change of n_0 and ϕ with temperature when the upper set of two donor species is incompletely compensated.

sufficiently high temperatures n_0 saturates at $(N_{d1} + N_{d2} - N_a)$ while ϕ drops more rapidly in accordance with

$$\phi = E_c - kT \ln\left[\frac{N_c}{N_{d1} + N_{d2} - N_a}\right] \quad \text{high } T \tag{331.1}$$

This kind of behavior is shown schematically in Fig. 33.2. The extension to three or more independent kinds of impurity is obvious.

The preceding description can be readily expressed in mathematical form. Suppose that there are M species of monovalent donor impurities, and that the jth class is of density N_{dj}, ground state binding energy

E_{dj}, etc. The number of ionized donors in this class may, from Eq. (323.5), be written as

$$(N_{dj})_{\text{ion}} = \frac{N_{dj}}{1+\beta_j^{-1}[1+F_j]\exp(\eta+\epsilon_{dj})} \tag{331.2}$$

where the quantity F_j indicates the influence of any excited states, as previously discussed. The sum of all ionized donors is equal to the conduction band electron density plus all electrons in compensating acceptors. Thus

$$[N_a+n_0] = [N_a+N_c\mathscr{F}_{1/2}(\eta)] = \sum_{j=1}^{M}\frac{N_{dj}}{1+\beta_j^{-1}[1+F_j]\exp(\eta+\epsilon_{dj})} \tag{331.3}$$

When the Fermi level is at least several kT below the conduction band, so that $\mathscr{F}_{1/2}(\eta)$ can be replaced by $\exp(\eta)$, Eq. (331.3) is an equation of order $(M+1)$ in either n_0 or $\exp(\eta)$.

Such an equation is by no means simple to solve in the general case, but there is one saving feature. For any temperature we choose to specify, the ground state energies of *most* classes of impurity will be either *well above* or *well below* the Fermi level; in the former case $(N_{dj})_{\text{ion}} = N_{dj}$ and in the latter $(N_{dj})_{\text{ion}} = 0$. Thus there will not usually be more than one or two classes of donor for which $(N_{dj})_{\text{ion}}$ lies between its extreme values, and Eq. (33.13) will be either a quadratic or a cubic in $\exp(\eta)$. For the example we sketched in Fig. 33.2, the two levels were so far apart in energy that ionization of one set of levels reached completion before it became at all appreciable in the other set. Separate quadratic equations can then be obtained from Eq. (331.3) to cover the various temperature ranges. Solution of a cubic equation is only necessary when two energy states are rather close in energy, and even then only for the temperature range in which ϕ progresses through those levels.

3.3.2 Electron Distribution over a Set of Multivalent Flaws

It was remarked in Section 1.6 that flaws often have the capacity to donate or accept more than one electron. When a set of multivalent centers is the dominant one in determining the electronic equilibrium, it is necessary to give a generalized discussion of the distribution over available states.

This subject has received attention in recent years from Landsberg (1956:**14**, 1958:**10**), and from Shockley and Last (1957:**21**), while Champness (1956:**8**) has discussed the particular case of divalent donors. The equations can be formulated from a direct statistical approach, by the use of the grand canonical ensemble, or from free energy considerations. The reader is referred to the literature references just cited for elaborations of the various points of view.

Some of the attributes of this problem are indicated for divalent donors by Fig. 33.3. When the Fermi level is sufficiently high, as in

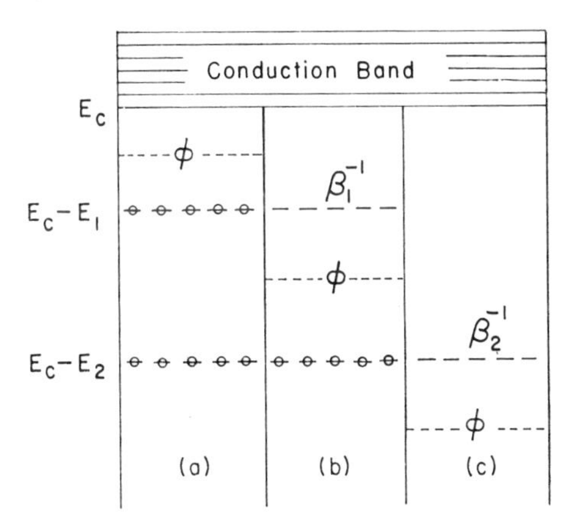

FIG. 33.3. The conventional way of indicating the energy states for divalent donors, indicating (a) the neutral condition, (b) the singly ionized condition, (c) the doubly ionized condition.

part (a) of the figure, each donor is electrically neutral, and holds two fairly weakly bound electrons with a *total* binding energy of (E_1+E_2). Now the two electrons will probably have rather similar orbits and binding energies; the significance of marking the two separate energies E_1 and E_2 is that the *center* must receive an energy E_1 to ionize it singly, and in the singly ionized state the second electron is held with energy E_2. This is the equilibrium condition when $E_1 < (E_c-\phi) < E_2$ as in part (*b*) of Fig. 33.3. A singly ionized divalent donor offers empty states at (E_c-E_1) with a statistical weight of β_1^{-1}.

When the Fermi level is lower again, the donors are doubly ionized and β_2^{-1} states per donor are offered at the energy (E_c-E_2). This situation is shown in part (*c*) of Fig. 33.3. Note that no available states are now shown at the upper level, since these states do not come into existence until a single electron has been recaptured. As soon as this first electron *is* captured, a second electron can be received only into one of the upper states which develop at this point.

In general, for each stage of ionization there will be not only a ground state but also a series of excited states into which an electron can be received. However, as Shockley and Last (1957:**21**) point out, it is not proper to construe the placement of an electron at the energy $(E_c - E_1)$ as a valid excited state of the singly ionized configuration. This is a meaningless state of affairs; the excited states for the condition of single ionization will usually be quite different.

Landsberg (1956:**14**, 1958:**10**) has provided a very compact derivation for the total number of electrons *retained* by a set of $\mathcal{N}$ centers, through differentiation of the grand partition function for the system, including allowance for excited states (which we shall not consider further). For our purposes, mindful of the amphoteric centers to be discussed in the next sub-section, we prefer to consider the numbers $\mathcal{N}_j$ of centers each of which has already *lost j* electrons. Thus $\mathcal{N}_0$ centers are neutral, $\mathcal{N}_1$ have lost one electron and present β_1^{-1} levels at energy $(E_c - E_1)$, and so on. If the centers are of valency M with respect to the crystal, then

$$\frac{\mathcal{N}_j}{\mathcal{N}} = \frac{\beta_j \exp(-\epsilon_j - j\eta)}{1 + \sum_{k=1}^{M} \beta_k \exp(-\epsilon_k - k\eta)} \tag{332.1}$$

The total number of electrons lost from the impurities is

$$\sum_{j=1}^{M} j\mathcal{N}_j$$

and this must equal the number in the conduction band and in any compensating levels. Thus

$$n_0 = N_c \mathcal{F}_{1/2}(\eta) = -\mathcal{N}_a + \sum_{j=1}^{M} j\mathcal{N}_j \tag{332.2}$$

When conditions are non-degenerate, Eqs. (332.1) and (332.2) lead to an equation of order $(M+1)$ for n_0 or $\exp(\eta)$. Thus Champness

(1956:**8**) obtained a cubic equation for the divalent case, which he solved for a numerical example of zero compensation.

This problem is not too dissimilar from that of several kinds of independent donors present in identical amounts [see Eq. (331.3)] when the energy levels are well separated. Shockley and Last (1957:**21**) have discussed the problem of two separate donors treated as a composite flaw.

As with any other of the systems considered so far, the extent of compensation will determine which level of a multivalent donor will house the Fermi level at low temperatures. For divalent donors, if the amount

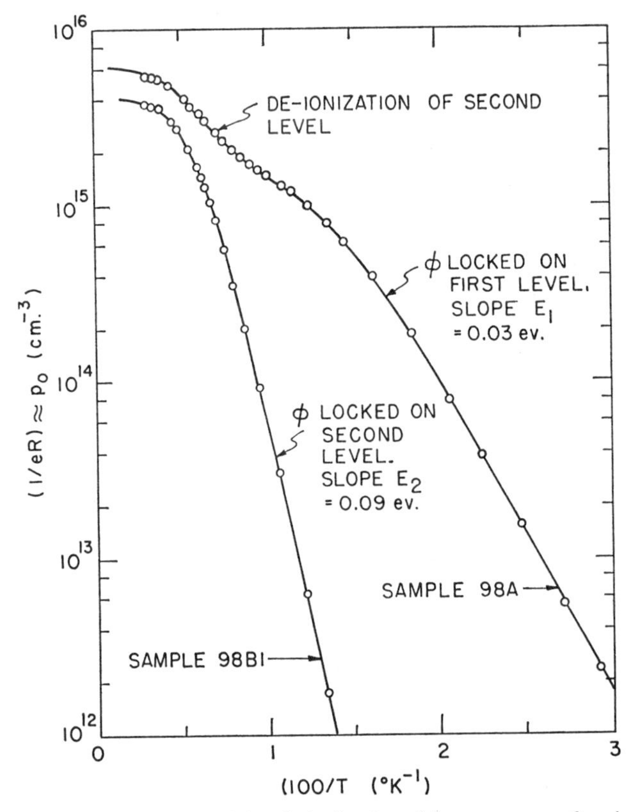

FIG. 33.4. Variation of free hole density with temperature for zinc-doped germanium crystals of Woodbury and Tyler (1956:**24**).

of compensation is rather small, the Fermi level will lock on to $(E_c - E_1)$ at low temperatures and

$$n_0 \approx \beta_1 \mathcal{N}_c \left(\frac{\mathcal{N} - \mathcal{N}_a}{\mathcal{N}_a} \right) \exp(-E_1/kT) \quad \begin{cases} \text{low temp.} \\ \mathcal{N}_a < \mathcal{N} \end{cases} \tag{332.3}$$

As temperature rises, the first stage of ionization becomes complete, and $n_0 \approx (\mathcal{N} - \mathcal{N}_a)$. Further heating drives the Fermi level down towards and beyond the second ionization energy, and an additional $\mathcal{N}$ electrons are added to the conduction band in the course of this process.

On the other hand, if $\mathcal{N} < \mathcal{N}_a < 2\mathcal{N}$, the saturation free electron density is $(2\mathcal{N} - \mathcal{N}_a)$, which is smaller than $\mathcal{N}_a$. A drop in n_0 occurs as soon as the temperature is low enough for ϕ to approach $(E_c - E_2)$, and on further cooling the Fermi level locks to this energy and provides an $\exp(-E_2/kT)$ temperature dependence for n_0.

These two forms of behavior are illustrated in Fig. 33.4, which is based on experimental data of Tyler and Woodbury (1956:**24**). The impurities in these samples are actually acceptors (zinc in germanium), but as has been emphasized previously, donor and acceptor situations are always formally equivalent. For sample 98A, cooling first changes all the zinc acceptors from double to single ionization, then the Fermi level approaches and locks on to the first ionization level. The second sample evidently has a donor density slightly in excess of the zinc concentration, and the low-temperature distribution still has many doubly charged zinc atoms.

3.3.3 Amphoteric Impurities

Some unusual kinds of impurity can act as either donor or acceptor, depending on the Fermi level. [This is true, for instance, of gold in germanium (1956:**25**).] By an amphoteric impurity we mean one which is most likely to be electrically neutral when the Fermi level lies at some energy E_0 *within* the intrinsic gap. At some lower Fermi energy the impurity is likely to lose an electron—the attribute of a donor. Perhaps more stages of donor ionization will occur before ϕ drops as low as $(E_c - E_i)$. But also, the center is likely to *add* one or more electrons when ϕ has an energy higher than E_0 yet still below E_c; this constitutes single or multiple acceptor action.

For gold in germanium, a single donor level is rather close to the valence band and there are three successive stages of acceptor ionization before the Fermi level enters the conduction band. Fig. 33.5 indicates the intrinsic gap width of germanium at room temperature and the positions of the four levels, after Dunlap (1957:**28**). The right-hand

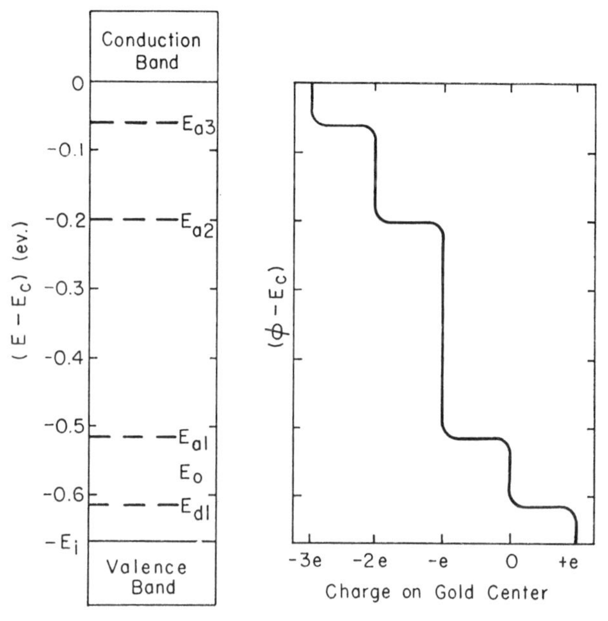

FIG. 33.5. The energy levels of the amphoteric impurity gold in germanium showing how the charge per atom will depend on the Fermi level at low temperatures.

portion of this figure shows how the charge per gold center should vary with the Fermi level at a rather low temperature (such that kT is small compared with the spacing of levels).

The statistical approach to amphoteric impurities is the same as for more conventional multivalent impurities, since it is still legitimate to use the result

$$\frac{\mathcal{N}_{r-1}}{\mathcal{N}_r} = \frac{\beta_r}{\beta_{r-1}} \exp(\eta + \epsilon_r) \tag{333.1}$$

[compare for instance with Eq. (311.1)] where now r may be either positive, zero, or negative.

3.4 THE INFLUENCE OF LATTICE DEFECTS

In addition to the impurity levels provided by foreign atoms, there are often localized levels provided in semiconductors by lattice defects such as vacancies and interstitials. This section comments very briefly on two facets of the problem.

3.4.1 Non-stoichiometric Compounds

When a semiconducting compound is maintained at a high temperature, there will be a tendency for the ratio of the elements present to change from that of the pure stoichiometric compound. The amount by which it changes depends on a number of parameters, including the pressure at which vapor of the most volatile component is maintained around the sample, and the temperature of the treatment. It was indicated in 1.6.2 that a very complete description of this electronic–ionic equilibration is given by Kröger and Vink (1956:**27**). See also the discussion by Brebrick (1961:**3**).

At any rate, when a compound is rapidly cooled to a much lower temperature, a number of lattice defects are "frozen-in" (1939:**1**) and their density will have an influence on the low-temperature electronic equilibrium. As one of the two principal choices, we may suppose these defects to be lattice vacancies and that their habit is of acceptors.

It should perhaps be remarked that vacancies can also be introduced into an elemental semiconductor such as germanium by strenuous heat treatment, and frozen-in by sudden cooling. The true vacancy effect in germanium is very small and is often masked by the influence of chemical contaminants such as copper (1952:**5**, 1952:**6**); but by careful exclusion of contaminants, effects which are probably due to vacancy acceptors can be seen (1953:**11**, 1953:**12**). The vacancy concentrations which can be produced in compounds such as oxides or sulphides are frequently several orders of magnitude larger.

If the semiconductor contains N_d monovalent chemical donors at an energy $(E_c - E_d)$, and is now confronted with N_A vacancy acceptors at energy $(E_c - E_A)$, the electronic equilibrium is described by

$$[n_0 - p_0] = (N_d)_{\text{ion}} - (N_A)_{\text{ion}} \tag{341.1}$$

The left side of the equation includes p_0 since the vacancy levels may well be closer to the valence band than the conduction band. Assuming that the Fermi level will not be closer than $2kT$ from either band, we have

$$[\mathcal{N}_c \exp(\eta) - \mathcal{N}_v \exp(-\eta - \epsilon_i)] = \frac{\mathcal{N}_d}{1 + \beta_d^{-1} \exp(\eta + \epsilon_d)} - \frac{\mathcal{N}_A}{1 + \beta_A \exp(-\eta - \epsilon_A)} \tag{341.2}$$

This is a quartic in $\exp(\eta)$, but it can always be reduced to an equation of lower order. As was seen in the previous discussions of compensation, if the donors lie in the upper half of the gap, p_0 can be dropped and

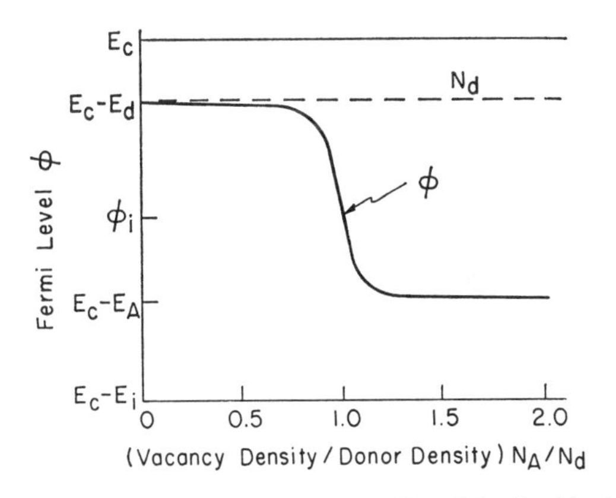

FIG. 34.1. Variation of low temperature Fermi level with the density of "frozen-in" vacancy acceptors if the semiconductor originally has $\mathcal{N}_d$ chemical donors.

$(\mathcal{N}_A)_{\text{ion}}$ simplified to just $\mathcal{N}_A$ when the vacancy density is not as large as $\mathcal{N}_d$. When the non-stoichiometry is sufficient to make $\mathcal{N}_A > \mathcal{N}_d$, the low temperature Fermi level switches to $(E_c - E_A)$ and other terms can be simplified. Fig. 34.1 shows how ϕ will vary with the ratio $(\mathcal{N}_A/\mathcal{N}_d)$ for a rather low temperature. The semiconductor is essentially intrinsic when $\mathcal{N}_A = \mathcal{N}_d$ if the two sets of levels are several kT above and below ϕ_i respectively.

For vacancy acceptors which can accept more than one electron, the course of ϕ with the ratio $(\mathcal{N}_A/\mathcal{N}_d)$ will be more or less as indicated in Fig. 34.2. Judgment of a high temperature equilibration process must be quite careful if enough vacancies are to be introduced to compensate the donors yet not so many that the Fermi level locks to the lower acceptor level.

3.4.2 Irradiation Effects

Exposure of a semiconductor to thermal neutrons leads to transmutation of some of the host atoms, often providing new kinds of chemical donors and acceptors. This is *not* the problem of immediate concern

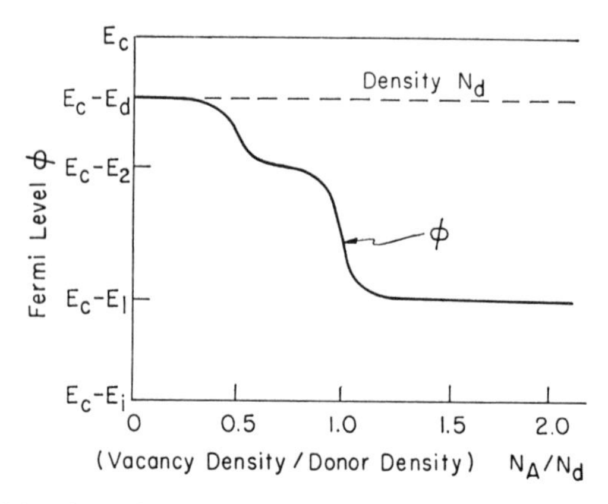

Fig. 34.2. The variation of ϕ with $(\mathcal{N}_A/\mathcal{N}_d)$ at low temperatures if each vacancy can accept two electrons, at energies (E_c-E_1) and (E_c-E_2).

here. Instead, consider a semiconductor already containing densities of shallow donor and acceptor states $\mathcal{N}_d$, $\mathcal{N}_a$, which are almost completely ionized at room temperature. (This is a reasonable assumption for semiconductors such as germanium, silicon, tellurium, InSb, PbS, and many more.) When such a semiconductor is bombarded with *fast* nucleons (energy more than say 20 eV and perhaps up to several MeV), Frenkel defects are introduced, equal densities of interstitials and vacancies. It is reasonable to suppose that irradiation has produced $\mathcal{N}$ donor levels at some energy E_D below the conduction band and an *equal number* of acceptor levels at energy (E_c-E_A). The electronic equilibrium is now given by

$$[n_0 - p_0] = (\mathcal{N}_d - \mathcal{N}_a) + \\ + \frac{\mathcal{N}}{1 + \beta_D^{-1} \exp(\eta + \epsilon_D)} - \frac{\mathcal{N}}{1 + \beta_A \exp(-\eta - \epsilon_A)} \tag{342.1}$$

The model characterized by this equation has been discussed by James and Lehman (1951:**14**) and has some rather interesting features. Consider a semiconductor which is n-type to start with, $\mathcal{N}_d > \mathcal{N}_a$, and suppose that both sets of defect levels are well below the conduction band. Then (342.1) simplifies to

$$n_0 \approx (\mathcal{N}_d - \mathcal{N}_a) - \mathcal{N} \tag{342.2}$$

for which situation

$$\phi \approx E_c - kT \ln \left[\frac{N_c}{\mathcal{N}_d - \mathcal{N}_a - \mathcal{N}} \right] \tag{342.3}$$

The fall of ϕ with increasing $\mathcal{N}$ is at first very gradual, but as $\mathcal{N}$ approaches $(\mathcal{N}_d - \mathcal{N}_a)$ this fall becomes cataclysmic. This can be appreciated most readily from viewing Fig. 34.3, which is based on a model James and Lehman use for germanium.

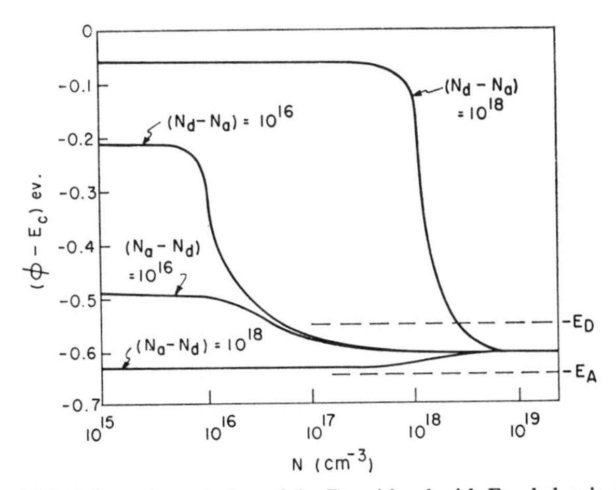

Fig. 34.3. Schematic variation of the Fermi level with Frenkel pair density for a semiconductor similar to germanium. From the model of James and Lehman (1951:**14**).

When $\mathcal{N}$ becomes large compared with $|\mathcal{N}_d - \mathcal{N}_a|$, the last two terms of Eq. (342.1) are essentially equal, and the Fermi level adopts an energy intermediate between $(E_c - E_D)$ and $(E_c - E_A)$. By equating these two terms,

$$\phi = E_c - \tfrac{1}{2}(E_D + E_A) + \tfrac{1}{2}kT \ln(\beta_D \beta_A) \qquad (342.4)$$

The change of Fermi level is less dramatic for material which was originally p-type, but a break in the behavior of ϕ still occurs when $\mathcal{N}$ exceeds $(\mathcal{N}_a - \mathcal{N}_d)$. Whether ϕ rises or falls as a result of heavy irradiation depends on the energies E_D, E_A, and on the original value of $(\mathcal{N}_a - \mathcal{N}_d)$.

For a material in which the defect levels straddle the intrinsic Fermi level ϕ_i, irradiation will tend to make either n-type or p-type material virtually intrinsic, a situation which may be the case for silicon (1951:**13**).

As experimental evidence on irradiation effects is accumulated (e.g. 1957:**27**), it appears likely that the simple model of Fig. 34.3 is inadequate for any semiconductor. Vacancies and interstitials themselves are likely to present more than one level of ionization, and in compounds there are four or more possible types of defect. It is fruitful to consider the more elaborate models which can be envisaged only in relation to experimental data on actual materials.

3.5 IMPURITY BANDS AND THE BEHAVIOR OF AN IMPURITY METAL

When impurity levels are separated by a finite energy from the conduction or valence bands, it is impossible to maintain a finite carrier density in either of the principal bands down to 0°K. However, when impurity atoms are very numerous—and hence rather closely spaced—they tend to interact with each other. As the impurity density is increased, the impurity ionization energy E_d or E_a becomes smaller, and above a critical density—characteristic of the host lattice and the impurity type—disappears completely. Shifrin (1944:**1**) forecast that this should always occur. Experimental evidence of the attenuation and final disappearance of the ionization energy is well exemplified by the classic paper of Pearson and Bardeen (1949:**4**) on silicon doped with phosphorus or boron. Their experimental result for boron acceptors is indicated in Fig. 35.1, and the curve joining the points for samples with different acceptor densities is given by

$$E_a = [0{\cdot}084 - 4{\cdot}3 \times 10^{-8} \mathcal{N}_a{}^{1/3}]\,\mathrm{eV} \tag{350.1}$$

Pearson and Bardeen noted that if the ionization energy is reduced by overlap between impurity wave-functions, this should be inversely proportional to the average distance between an ionized impurity and

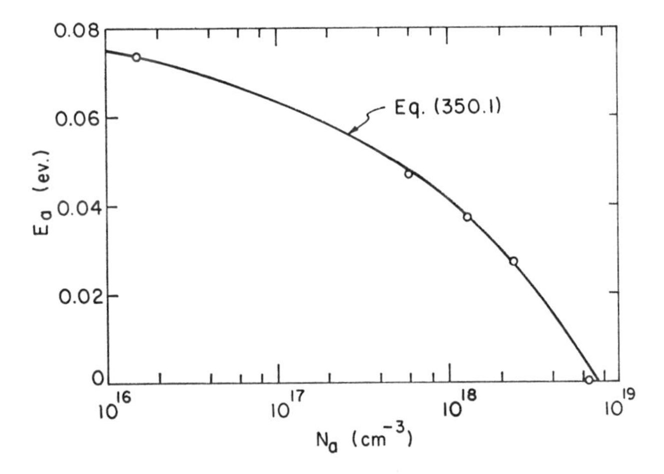

Fig. 35.1. Variation of boron acceptor ionization energy with acceptor concentration, according to the measurements of Pearson and Bardeen (1949:**4**).

a free carrier. This at first sight seems to support the presence of a term proportional to $\mathcal{N}_a{}^{1/3}$ in Eq. (350.1). Further reflection destroys this illusion: if Coulomb interactions provide the seat for the reduction of ionization energy, the reduction should depend not on the *total* impurity density but only on those which are *ionized* in the temperature range of interest. Taking this more rigorous approach, Castellan and Seitz (1951:**6**) were unable to account for the effects seen in silicon. More recently, Debye and Conwell (1954:**2**) have been able to fit the ionization energy for arsenic donors in germanium by an expression.

$$E_d = [0{\cdot}0125 - 2{\cdot}35 \times 10^{-8} (\mathcal{N}_{di})^{1/3}]\,\mathrm{eV} \tag{350.2}$$

(see Fig. 35.2) where $\mathcal{N}_{di}$ denotes the density of donors which are ionized at the low temperatures for which E_d can be measured. Not much reliable experimental information is available for impurities in other semiconductors.

Our theoretical understanding of the manner in which impurity ionization energies depend on density is still incomplete. Pincherle (1951:**7**) has shown that part of the effect can come from the screening

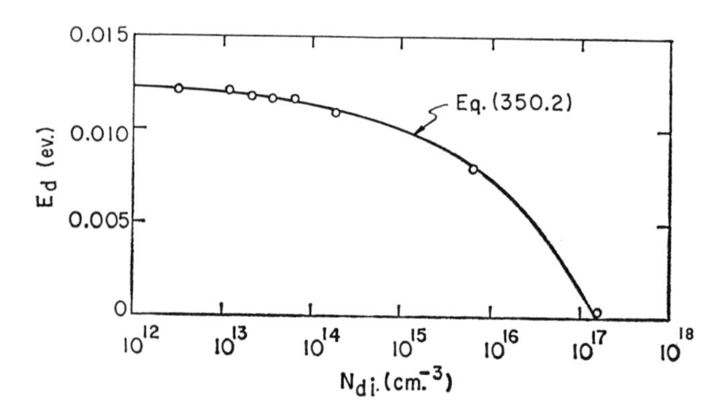

FIG. 35.2. The ionization energy for arsenic donors in Ge, as a function of the average density $\mathcal{N}_{di}$ of *ionized* donors in the temperature range used for fitting. The experimental points are the data of Debye and Conwell (1954:**2**).

of the field around an ion by free carriers. Mott (1956:**3**) has presented some arguments from which one would expect an *abrupt* change from finite to zero E_d at a critical impurity density. Landsberg (1960:**1**) makes semi-quantitative estimates of how such a transition might be affected by statistical spatial fluctuations in impurity density.

At any rate, when donor impurities become sufficiently numerous, they can no longer be described in terms of discrete localized levels below the conduction band. Instead they form an *impurity band* of non-localized states situated at the energy E_c, the base of the conduction band. (For low lying acceptor levels the corresponding impurity band is of course at the very top of the valence band.) The system of an impurity band contiguous to one of the principal bands gives us *impurity–*

metallic behavior. The term impurity metal is used since the number of carriers in non-localized states is then constant throughout the extrinsic temperature range, just as a metal has a temperature-independent electron density.

From a strict point of view, impurity states should not be regarded as entirely additional to the Bloch states of conduction and valence bands. As Brooks (1955:**5**) remarks, impurity levels usually represent states split off from the main bands. Thus when co-operation between donors leads to the formation of an impurity band joined to the conduction band, the conduction band is perhaps no more than getting its own states back again!

There is, however, more to the picture than this. Certainly if the donor density is *very* large (say large compared with 10^{20} cm^{-3}), the density of states function Eq. (144.4) will be appreciably affected by the provision of donor states, and the impurity band will be spread over a considerable range of energy. However, if the donor density is only slightly larger than the critical value required for impurity–metallic behavior (say $\sim 10^{18}$ cm^{-3}), $g(E)$ for the conduction band will be but little affected, whereas the impurity band will consist essentially of $\beta^{-1}N_d$ non-localized states all in the immediate neighborhood of the energy E_c. It is this concept of a "weak" impurity metal which is considered first.

3.5.1 Weak Impurity Metals

It will be noted that the number of states in the impurity band is described as $\beta^{-1}N_d$, not just as N_d. We have to make an adjustment to a slight change of conception with regard to impurity spin degeneracy. For previous sections have considered separate non-interacting impurities; each had β^{-1} wave-functions describing a possible ground state of the system, but only one of these could be occupied at a time. This restriction is no longer true for an impurity *band*; the wave-functions are sufficiently non-localized so that more than one electron can occupy states derived from a given impurity atom. (The simple matter of electron supply will ensure, however, that the $N_d\beta^{-1}$ impurity states contain *less than* N_d electrons.)

Suppose that in addition to the donors, there is a smaller density N_a of assorted acceptor impurities, each of which can (and will) take the opportunity to acquire an extra electron. All compensating acceptors will be ionized, since their levels fall well below the anticipated Fermi energy. Then there are $(N_d - N_a)$ electrons per unit volume to be distributed over the conduction band states and the $\beta^{-1}N_d$ impurity band states. If the latter are all at E_c, the equation expressing neutrality is

$$(N_d - N_a) = N_c \mathscr{F}_{1/2}\left(\frac{\phi - E_c}{kT}\right) + \beta^{-1}N_d f(E_c) \tag{351.1}$$

where $f(E_c)$ denotes the usual Fermi occupancy factor $\{1+\exp(\epsilon-\eta)\}^{-1}$ or $\{1+\exp[(E-\phi)/kT]\}^{-1}$ for the energy E_c.

Since the effective density of conduction band states varies as $T^{3/2}$, the term in Eq. (351:**1**) containing N_c must become negligibly small at a sufficiently low temperature. This means that all the available electron supply is in the impurity band and none in the conduction band at $T = 0$. At temperatures sufficiently small for this to be essentially the case, Eq. (351.1) is linear in $\exp(\eta)$, viz.

$$(N_d - N_a)[1+\exp(\eta)] = \beta^{-1}N_d \exp(\eta), \qquad T \to 0 \tag{351.2}$$

Thus the Fermi energy and its reduced version tend at low temperatures towards

$$\left.\begin{aligned} \eta &= \ln\left[\frac{N_d - N_a}{N_d(\beta^{-1}-1)+N_a}\right] \\ \phi &= E_c + kT\ln\left[\frac{N_d - N_a}{N_d(\beta^{-1}-1)+N_a}\right] \end{aligned}\right\} \quad T \to 0 \tag{351.3}$$

In the particular case of no compensation and simple donors (for which $\beta^{-1} = 2$), the logarithmic term in Eq. (351.3) is zero, and ϕ is at the energy E_c for any temperature low enough to keep almost all the electrons out of the "conventional" conduction band states. When β^{-1} is larger, or when there is any appreciable compensation, $(d\phi/dT)$ has a finite negative value even at the lowest temperatures. Thus for $\beta^{-1} = 2$ and $(N_a/N_d) = 0{\cdot}2$, we have $(d\phi/dT) = -0{\cdot}4k$ at 0°K.

In any event, ϕ will fall more rapidly at high temperatures than at low, since an appreciable number of the ordinary conduction band states become accessible for occupancy. The Fermi level must then be found by solving Eq. (351.1). Note that since η will necessarily be negative, one of the approximate expressions developed in Appendix C can be substituted for $\mathscr{F}_{1/2}(\eta)$ without serious loss of accuracy. In order to make Eq. (351.1) no higher than quadratic in $\exp(\eta)$, we may use

$$\mathscr{F}_{1/2}(\eta) \approx \frac{\exp(\eta)}{1+C\exp(\eta)} \tag{351.4}$$

knowing that the error will be less than $\pm 3\%$ for any negative value of η if $C = 0{\cdot}27$.

Employing the form (351.4), we can write Eq. (351.1) as the quadratic

$$\exp(2\eta)[\mathcal{N}_c + C\mathcal{N}_d(\beta^{-1}-1) + C\mathcal{N}_a] +$$
$$+\exp(\eta)[\mathcal{N}_c + \mathcal{N}_d(\beta^{-1}-1-C) + \mathcal{N}_a(1+C)] - (\mathcal{N}_d - \mathcal{N}_a) = 0 \tag{351.5}$$

whose solution for $\exp(\eta)$ is

$$\exp(\eta) = \frac{\begin{array}{c}\{[\mathcal{N}_c + \mathcal{N}_d(\beta^{-1}+1-C) - \mathcal{N}_a(1-C)]^2 - 4\beta^{-1}\mathcal{N}_d \times \\ \times(\mathcal{N}_d - \mathcal{N}_a)(1-C)\}^{1/2} - [\mathcal{N}_c + \mathcal{N}_d(\beta^{-1}-1-C) + \mathcal{N}_a(1+C)]\end{array}}{2[\mathcal{N}_c + C\mathcal{N}_d(\beta^{-1}-1) + C\mathcal{N}_a]} \tag{351.6}$$

At sufficiently *low* temperatures, this of course asymptotically approaches the form required by Eq. (351.3); while (not surprisingly) $\exp(\eta)$ tends towards $(\mathcal{N}_d - \mathcal{N}_a)/\mathcal{N}_c$ at sufficiently *high* temperatures. At intermediate temperatures, when the populations of the impurity band and the conduction band are comparable, Eq. (351.6) is not exactly a simple expression to visualize.

Fig. 35.3 shows how ϕ and η vary with temperature when the impurity metal is derived from a conduction band with $m_c = m_0$ (i.e. $\mathcal{N}_c = 4{\cdot}83 \times 10^{15} T^{3/2}$ cm^{-3}) and a set of 10^{18} cm^{-3} donors for which $\beta^{-1} = 2$. The uppermost curve in each part of the figure relates to a condition of zero compensation, $\mathcal{N}_a = 0$. As has been remarked in earlier sections, compensation can never be completely absent in any real material; but the curves would not be appreciably different from those shown provided that $\mathcal{N}_a$ were smaller than, say, $0{\cdot}01\mathcal{N}_d$. As noted in connection with Eq. (351.3), the reduced Fermi level is zero at 0°K for $\beta^{-1} = 2$ and $\mathcal{N}_a = 0$. The two pairs of curves for $\mathcal{N}_a = 2 \times 10^{17}$ cm^{-3} (20% compensation) and $\mathcal{N}_a = 4 \times 10^{17}$ cm^{-3} (40% compensation) illustrate the marked effect of compensation on η and ϕ, particularly at low temperatures.

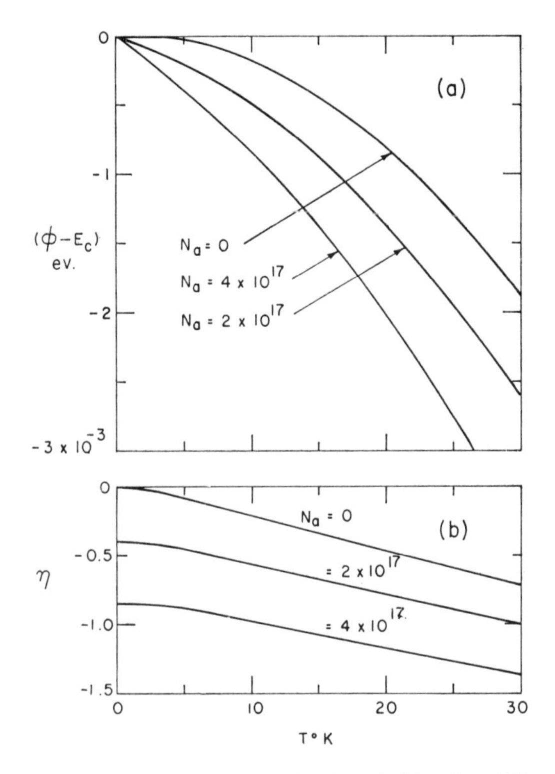

FIG. 35.3. Variation of (a) Fermi level, and (b) reduced Fermi level with temperature for a weak impurity metal. Conduction band supposed with $m_c = m_0$, and 10^{18} cm^{-3} donors for which $\beta^{-1} = 2$. Curves show the effect of 40%, 20%, or zero compensation.

3.5.2 Strong Impurity Metals §

It has been supposed in the last sub-section that the density of impurity atoms was large enough to create an impurity band, but not much more. In such a context it was reasonable to suppose that the impurity band would be very narrow in energy, situated just about at E_c. It was also reasonable to suppose that $g(E)$ for the conduction band would be not appreciably affected by the subtraction of states needed for the impurity band.

Such assumptions cease to be permissible if the impurity density is very large, say 10^{20} cm^{-3} or more. The situation then becomes what we choose to call that of a "strong" impurity metal. Fig. 35.4 indicates qualitatively the features of a weak impurity metal and what might be expected for a strong impurity metal. In the latter case, overlap between impurity wave-functions is so strong that the impurity band must cover an appreciable range of energy. The center of gravity for

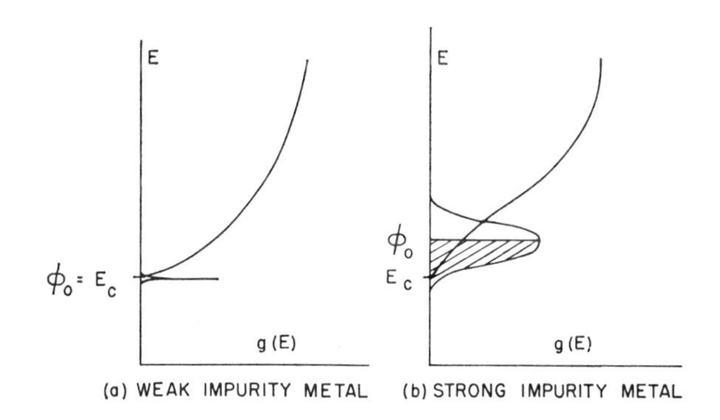

FIG. 35.4. Possible variation of the density of states with energy (a) for a weak impurity metal in which the impurity band is very narrow, situated at about E_c on the energy scale, and not appreciably affecting the density of states function for the conduction band; (b) for a strong impurity metal in which the impurity band is rather broad, possibly centered on an energy higher than E_c, and such that $g(E)$ for the conduction band is seriously perturbed.

this distribution may occur at an energy above E_c. The presence of this large impurity band must necessarily have a considerable effect on $g(E)$ for the original conduction band. This effect should be most pronounced on the lower energy states of the conduction band, making that band non-parabolic as suggested in the figure.

For a strong impurity band compounded from donor states with $\beta^{-1} = 2$, the Fermi level will be a little below the midpoint of the impurity band at low temperatures (the exact position depending on the number of accessible conduction band states and the extent of compensation). This Fermi level will decrease very slowly on warming and will remain above E_c up to fairly high temperatures.

A theoretical understanding of strong impurity bands and their effect on the conduction band parameters is blocked by formidable mathematical problems. Thus we are not in a position to suggest analytic forms for $g(E)$ in either of the bands illustrated by Fig. 35.4(b), and do not propose to enter into any more detailed discussion. At least the preceding remarks do give some qualitative indications of the expected behavior for a strong impurity metal. There is considerable interest in these problems, for such materials occur in important semiconducting devices. Thus the degree of doping is probably enough to move the Fermi level into either the conduction or valence band in the emitter region of many transistors, and in tunnel diodes (1958:**5**).

3.5.3 Occupancy of Weakly Interacting Impurities §

When the spacing of impurity centers is moderately large, the overlap of impurity wave-functions is not strong enough to cause the complete breakdown of localized states in the manner of an impurity metal. Erginsoy (1950:**8**) suggested that while the impurity ground states would be localized, excited states might still form impurity bands, some of which could be separated by small energies from the conduction or valence bands. It is difficult to judge realistically what the effect of excited state bands might be, since such bands would presumably be separated from the Fermi level by many kT at low temperatures; however Koshino (1956:**28**) has suggested that they provide the key to some results of Fritzsche (1955:**29**) with gallium doped germanium.

Certainly when majority impurity densities are of the order of 10^{16} cm^{-3} or less, the overlap between impurity wave-functions will be very small and it is not proper to refer to transition of an electron from one impurity to another as constituting impurity *band* conduction. At one time, theoretical discussions of this subject were entangled in the concept that each impurity atom provides two states (of opposite spin) and that a half full impurity band would be realized by the ground states. This concept is false, since the Bloch collective electron treatment is not applicable to a set of very weakly interacting centers; the Heitler–London approach is more appropriate.†

† As is also the case in materials for which the spacing between the atoms of the ordinary lattice is rather large. We have commented on this previously in connection with NiO and related compounds.

For a system of impurity centers sparsely distributed through a semiconductor, charge transfer between the impurities is possible only if some centers have been ionized through the presence of compensating centers. This has been described by Conwell (1956:**29**), Mott (1956:**3**), and Price (1957:**29**, 1958:**21**). It is interesting to consider the basis of Price's model for a set of partly compensated monovalent donor impurities.

Price points out that if there are $N_a \ll N_d$ compensating acceptors present, every one will be ionized, leaving $(N_d - N_a)$ electrons on the N_d donor levels. The distribution of these electrons will not be entirely random. For donor centers which happen to be reasonably close to an ionized acceptor will be rather *less* likely (as a result of Coulomb repulsion) to contain an electron than donors which are far from any ionized acceptors. Price suggests that each acceptor will be surrounded by a small group of r donors which he calls "trapping sites". An electron must have an extra energy E_t to exist on a trapping site† when it is the first site in the group to be occupied, although subsequent sites in the group can be occupied more cheaply, or even free of any penalty.

For simplicity, we consider here the use of *one* trapping site per compensating acceptor. Then there are simply $N_f = (N_d - N_a)$ "free" donor sites at energy $(E_c - E_d)$, and $N_t = N_a$ "trapping" sites at energy $(E_c - E_d + E_t)$. If we denote the density of unoccupied free sites as p_f and the density of unoccupied trapping sites as p_t, then

$$p_t = \frac{N_a}{1+\beta^{-1}\exp(\eta+\epsilon_d-\epsilon_t)} \tag{353.1}$$

$$p_f = \frac{N_d - N_a}{1+\beta^{-1}\exp(\eta+\epsilon_d)} \tag{353.2}$$

Now $(p_f + p_t)$ must equal the sum of N_a and any free electrons left in the conduction band, n_0. Using this fact, we have from Eq. (353.1) and (353.2) that

$$\begin{aligned}\left[\frac{N_d - N_a - p_f}{p_f}\right] &= \beta^{-1}\exp(\epsilon_d+\eta) \\ &= \exp(\epsilon_t)\left[\frac{N_a - p_t}{p_t}\right] \\ &= \exp(\epsilon_t)\left[\frac{p_f - n_0}{N_a + n_0 - p_f}\right]\end{aligned} \tag{353.3}$$

† In other words, a "hole" is trapped by energy E_t on a trapping site.

This can be rearranged as a quadratic equation for p_f:

$$p_f^2(z-1)+p_f[N_d-n_0(z-1)] = (N_d-N_a)(N_a+n_0) \qquad (353.4)$$

where z denotes $\exp(\epsilon_t)$. The solution for the density of holes among the free sites is

$$p_f = \frac{2(N_d-N_a)(N_a+n_0)}{\{[N_d-n_0(z-1)]^2+4(z-1)(N_d-N_a)(N_a+n_0)\}^{1/2}+[N_d-n_0(z-1)]} \qquad (353.5)$$

At high temperatures (such that $E_t \ll kT$ and $z \approx 1$), this reduces to

$$p_f \approx (N_a+n_0)(1-N_a/N_d), \qquad E_t \ll kT \qquad (353.6)$$

which indicates as expected that at a reasonably high temperature there will be (N_a+n_0) vacant donor sites distributed uniformly between the "free" states and the "trapping" states.

At low temperatures, ($E_t \gg kT$, $z \gg 1$), it is reasonable to expect that n_0 will become extremely small. Then Eq. (353.5) reduces to

$$p_f = [N_a(N_d-N_a)]^{1/2}\exp(-E_t/2kT), \qquad E_t \gg kT \qquad (353.7)$$

Experimental results for the temperature dependence of electrical conductivity in doped semiconductors such as germanium and silicon support the general form of Eq. (353.7). Correlation with electrical conductivity of course requires a model for the mobility of holes on "free" donor sites. The theory of Mott and Twose (1959:**12**) suggests that the mobility for hopping between impurity atoms may not depend on temperature. A similar conclusion is reached by Miller and Abrahams (1960:**23**). Some temperature dependence of mobility is however expected from the alternative theories of Kasuya and Koide (1958:**22**) and Conwell (1956:**29**).

Most experimental papers have been content to report the apparent trapping energy E_t from an essentially exponential dependence of conductivity on reciprocal temperature [e.g. (1955:**29**, 1957:**30**, 1960:**9**)]. This author has, however, found (1959:**6**) that experimental results for indium-doped germanium fit the changing temperature dependence of Eq. (353.5) quite well. More elaborate models could presumably give an even more satisfactory description, and Price (1958:**21**) suggests the form such elaborations might take.

PART II.

SEMICONDUCTORS CONTAINING EXCESS CARRIERS

Chapter 4

FACTORS AFFECTING CARRIER TRANSITION RATES

In Part I we considered how densities n_0 and p_0 of free electrons and holes would exist in a semiconductor which is in thermal equilibrium with its environment. Thus, for an intrinsic material it was shown how a particular value ϕ_i of the Fermi level gave equality of electron and hole densities. When impurity levels were important a Fermi level ϕ could always prescribe the occupancy of conduction, valence and impurity levels in a way which corresponded with overall neutrality. Through all of this it was not necessary to worry about *how* electrons came to be distributed over various sets of levels, it was simply assumed that when a semiconductor is brought to a certain temperature and left there for long enough, conditions become stabilized. In Part II, semiconductors are considered with excess carriers present, and the actual mechanisms of electronic transitions now become important.

4.1 RECIPROCITY OF TRANSITION PROBABILITIES

For a semiconductor in thermal equilibrium, there are several forms of energy which can be utilized to raise an electron from one state to another of higher energy. Such excitation processes may be known as generative processes if they generate free electrons or free holes (or both). We shall discuss a number of these processes later in the chapter, but for the present may note as one example that an electron may advance to a state higher in energy by E by absorption of a photon with frequency $\nu = (E/h)$. For each generative or excitation process there is a *converse* recombinative or de-excitation process, in which electrons undergo transitions to states of lower energy, and liberate the energy difference in some form (e.g. as photons). The maintenance of free and trapped carrier densities in thermal equilibrium is determined by a dynamic balance of generative and recombinative processes.

When some external stimulus is suddenly applied to a semiconductor, the opportunities for generative processes change and there follows a period during which carrier densities are functions of time. Provided that the external stimulus is maintained constant, a new steady state distribution of carriers is established, once again determined by the balance of generative against recombinative processes. The removal of stimulation heralds a new period of time-dependent carrier densities before the balance of thermal equilibrium is restored again. In Part II we shall be specifically concerned with these periods of carrier build-up and decay, and with the dynamics of non-equilibrium steady state situations.

4.1.1 The Principle of Detailed Balance

Since for every energy transformation process there is an inverse, we might expect to find a connection between the rate of a process and the rate of its inverse. Such a connection is provided by the principle of detailed balance. This is a very general principle for which no formal proof can be given, but which accounts in a very satisfactory way for the general laws of thermodynamics and statistical mechanics.

The principle of detailed balance is a statistical concept, which may be stated in the form that, *for a system in thermal equilibrium, the rates of a process and of its inverse are equal and balance in detail.* This is closely related to the principle of microscopic reversibility, which asserts that *the transition probabilities for a process and its inverse are equal.* Note that this second principle refers only to transition *probabilities*, not to transition *rates*; it is quantum-mechanical rather than statistical in nature, and is applicable to many systems whether they be in thermodynamic equilibrium or not. Detailed balance will in general not hold for a system which is in a steady non-equilibrium state, though the existence of a steady-state condition together with microscopic reversibility will in general imply also the existence of detailed balance (1961: **5**).

What is meant by balance in detail can be illustrated most readily by an example. Consider a semiconductor in thermal equilibrium for which some fraction of the hole–electron pairs are optically generated (through absorption of infrared photons from the black body radiation field surrounding the sample). Then the *general* balance requires that the *same* fraction of electron–hole recombination should be radiative, the energy being released as a photon. The *detailed balance* requires furthermore that the recombination radiation should have the same spectral characteristics as the radiation absorbed in creating carrier pairs.† Similar reciprocity holds between other pairs of complementary processes, both *in toto* and in detail.

When a semiconductor departs from thermal equilibrium under an external stimulus, the *rates* of reciprocal processes no longer balance,

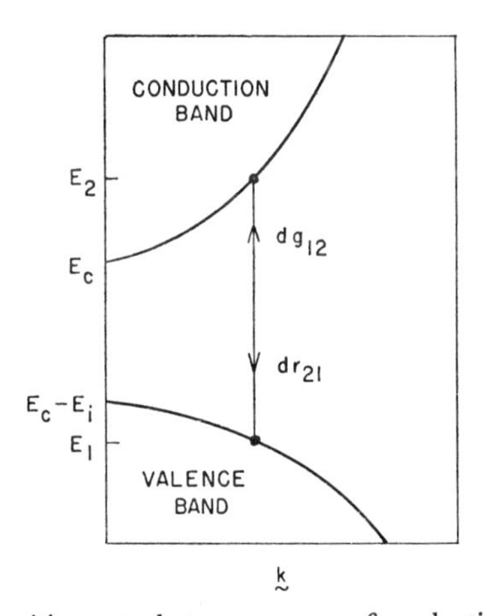

FIG. 41.1. Transition rates between groups of conduction and valence band states.

either in general or in detail,‡ though the *transition probabilities* are the same. To see what goes on, let us return to the example of a semiconductor in which radiative recombination is a process of some importance. Consider the rates of radiative generative transitions and radiative recombinative transitions occurring (as in Fig. 41.1) between

† This is tantamount to a statement of Kirchhoff's law, one of the many manifestations of detailed balance.

‡ Thus under intense illumination the carrier densities n and p are larger than those of equilibrium, n_0 and p_0. The additional free carriers have been excited by an optical process, but this does not imply that they will necessarily decay via an optical transition. The fraction which decays by a radiative process is determined by the relative magnitudes of capture cross-sections for *all* types of recombinative process accessible to the carriers.

a group of levels at energy E_1 in the valence band and another group at energy $E_2 = (E_1 + h\nu_{12})$ in the conduction band. It is not suggested that other types of transition do not occur as well, but the present preoccupation is purely with the relationship of the two complementary radiative processes.

Denote by $Q(h\nu_{12})$ the density of photons per unit energy interval per unit volume for photon energy $(E_2 - E_1) = h\nu_{12}$. The interaction of this photon density with the crystal will excite electrons from E_1 up to E_2 at a rate which can be written in the form

$$\mathrm{d}g_{12} = A_{12}P_e(E_1)P_h(E_2)Q(h\nu_{12})\,\mathrm{d}E \tag{411.1}$$

Here A_{12} is proportional to the square of the matrix element of the initial and final state; it depends on the density of state function in the conduction and valence bands, and on the form of the wave-functions making up each band. $P_e(E) = [1 - P_h(E)]$ is the probability that a state of energy E contains an electron. Under thermal equilibrium conditions, $P_e(E)$ reduces to

$$f(E) = \left[1 + \exp\left(\frac{E-\phi}{kT}\right)\right]^{-1}$$

of Part I, and it is then a simple matter to show that

$$[P_e(E_1)P_h(E_2)]_{\text{eq.}} = \exp\left(\frac{E_2 - E_1}{kT}\right)[P_h(E_1)P_e(E_2)]_{\text{eq.}} \tag{411.2}$$

However, when the conditions are of non-equilibrium, no single Fermi level exists and $P_e(E)$ can not be identified with $f(E)$. (It will be seen in the next sub-section that so-called "quasi Fermi levels" represent attempts to rationalize the description of $P_e(E)$ as a function of energy.)

Corresponding with transitions $1 \to 2$, as given by Eq. (411.1), an expression can be written for the rate of downward transitions, $2 \to 1$, in the form

$$\mathrm{d}r_{21} = P_h(E_1)P_e(E_2)[B_{21} + A_{21}Q(h\nu_{12})]\,\mathrm{d}E \tag{411.3}$$

The term in B_{21} represents the rate of spontaneous recombination between the two sets of states. We shall expect to establish a close relationship between A_{12} and B_{21}, since the latter also depends on the densities of states in the bands, and on a matrix element controlled by the form of the wave functions for each band. Concepts such as capture coefficient and capture cross-section (which will be used frequently in later sections) are contained in the description of B_{21}.

The second term of Eq. (411.3) [that involving $A_{21}Q(h\nu_{12})$] is the rate of downward transitions stimulated by the presence of radiation (1917:**1**). Since the matrix element of a real operator is Hermitian, A_{21} is equal to A_{12}.

Consider Eqs. (411.1) and (411.3) at thermal equilibrium, when $Q(h\nu_{12}) \rightarrow Q(h\nu_{12})_{eq}$. The rates dg_{12} and dr_{21} must then be the same; by equating Eqs. (411.1) and (411.3) and using Eq. (411.2) we have

$$B_{21} = A_{21}Q(h\nu_{12})_{eq.}\left[\exp\left(\frac{h\nu_{12}}{kT}\right) - 1\right] \tag{411.4}$$

This appears at first to indicate a temperature-dependent relationship of B_{21} and A_{21}, which would be a violation of the previous remarks about the purely quantum-mechanical foundation of these transition coefficients. However, from the Planck radiation law,

$$Q(h\nu_{12})_{eq} = (8\pi\nu_{12}^2/c'^3)[\exp(h\nu_{12}/kT) - 1]^{-1} \tag{411.5}$$

where $c' = (c/n)$ is the velocity of light in a medium of refractive index n. Then the ratio of B_{21} to A_{21} is actually

$$(B_{21}/A_{21}) = (8\pi\nu_{12}^2/c'^3) \tag{411.6}$$

depending on nothing except the energy transformed in the two reciprocal processes and the refractive index.

For any other kind of energy transformation process in a semiconductor, a similarly simple relationship exists between the transition coefficients for upward and downward processes involving any two groups of states.

4.1.2 Electrochemical Potentials and Mean Capture Coefficients

It has been possible to characterize the electron and hole densities for a semiconductor in thermal equilibrium by a single parameter, the Fermi level ϕ. Also the product n_0p_0 was very simply related to n_i^2; was in fact *equal* to n_i^2 for any non-degenerate situation.

The action of an external stimulus of some kind will change the carrier densities to values† which will be referred to as n and p, reserving

† Most kinds of stimulation tend to *increase* the densities of both kinds of carrier, so that $np > n_i^2$. It is possible to *decrease* the densities of electrons and holes below their equilibrium values by using samples with rather special kinds of contacts (1954:**12**, 1955:**19**, 1957:**32**), and the following discussion is quite applicable to such cases; the only difference is that of the two electrochemical potentials, ϕ_p will be higher than ϕ_n.

the subscript zero for equilibrium conditions. When $n \neq n_0$ and $p \neq p_0$, no single parameter suffices to describe the total charge densities in the two major bands. However, Shockley (1949:**5**) has suggested that the terminology of carrier statistics should include quantities called "quasi-Fermi levels", each of which is to characterize the total density of carriers in a given band. In this book it is preferred to describe these quantities as thc *electrochemical potentials* for electrons and holes.

In order to explain the use of these terms, it may be noted that if $g_c(E) = 4\pi(2m_c/h^2)^{3/2}(E-E_c)^{1/2}$ is the density-of-states function for the conduction band, the number of electrons per unit volume in all the levels of that band is

$$n = \int_{E_c}^{\infty} P_e(E)g_c(E)\,\mathrm{d}E \tag{412.1}$$

Here $P_e(E)$ is the probability that a state of energy E contains an electron; as has already been remarked, $P_e(E)$ tends towards $f(E)$ of Eq. (122.4) at thermal equilibrium, but may perhaps have a very different form in non-equilibrium (dependent on the method used to create excess carriers).

Nevertheless, the total integrated density n can always be described in terms of an electrochemical potential for electrons, ϕ_n, by writing

$$n = \int_{E_c}^{\infty} P_e(E)g_c(E)\,\mathrm{d}E = N_c\mathscr{F}_{1/2}\left(\frac{\phi_n - E_c}{kT}\right) \tag{412.2}$$

The quantity ϕ_n becomes coincident with the Fermi level itself when thermal equilibrium is restored, but is higher in energy when excess electrons are excited into any conduction band levels.

Corresponding with the relationship of n to ϕ_n, a similar potential ϕ_p for valence band holes can be defined through

$$p = \int_{-\infty}^{E_c-E_i} P_h(E)g_v(E)\,\mathrm{d}E = N_v\mathscr{F}_{1/2}\left[\frac{E_c - E_i - \phi_p}{kT}\right] \tag{412.3}$$

The two quantities ϕ_n and ϕ_p now serve the purpose for which ϕ alone was adequate in thermal equilibrium.

It is obviously desirable to be able to express n or p in terms of the density at thermal equilibrium and the difference between the appropriate electrochemical potential and the ordinary Fermi level. This can be accomplished very readily for a non-degenerate semiconductor which remains non-degenerate even under external stimulus. It will be recalled that with the simplification of non-degeneracy, the densities at thermal equilibrium

$$\left.\begin{aligned} n_0 &= N_c \exp\left[\frac{\phi - E_c}{kT}\right] = N_c \exp(\eta) \\ p_0 &= N_v \exp\left[\frac{E_c - E_i - \phi}{kT}\right] = N_v \exp(-\eta - \epsilon_i) \end{aligned}\right\} \quad (412.4)$$

could be combined with the expression (231.4) for n_i to yield useful relationships between n_0, p_0 and n_i, viz.:

$$\left.\begin{aligned} n_0 &= n_i \exp(\eta - \eta_i) \\ p_0 = (n_i^2/n_0) &= n_i \exp(\eta_i - \eta) \end{aligned}\right\} \quad (412.5)$$

Equations of the same qualitative form can be written for non-equilibrium situations, now based on ϕ_n and ϕ_p; or more compactly in terms of their dimensionless equivalents

$$\eta_n = \left(\frac{\phi_n - E_c}{kT}\right)$$

and

$$\eta_p = \left(\frac{\phi_p - E_c}{kT}\right)$$

Provided that excess carriers are not present in large enough quantities to force ϕ_n into the conduction band or ϕ_p into the valence band, we can write

$$\left.\begin{aligned} n &= N_c \exp(\eta_n) = n_i \exp(\eta_n - \eta_i) \\ p &= N_v \exp(-\eta_p - \epsilon_i) = n_i \exp(\eta_i - \eta_p) \end{aligned}\right\} \quad (412.6)$$

Comparison with Eq. (412.4) or (412.5) shows that the departure of ϕ_n or ϕ_p from ϕ is an indication of how much n or p has changed from the equilibrium values:

$$\left.\begin{aligned} n &= n_0 \exp(\eta_n - \eta) \\ p &= p_0 \exp(\eta - \eta_p) \end{aligned}\right\} \quad (412.7)$$

The product np under non-equilibrium conditions differs from the product $n_0p_0 = n_i^2$ of a non-degenerate semiconductor in equilibrium, yet it can be seen from Eq. (412.7) that

$$(np/n_0p_0) = \exp(\eta_n - \eta_p) \quad (412.8)$$

so that $(\phi_n - \phi_p)$ provides a measure of the carrier density product.

It will be appreciated from Eqs. (412.6)–(412.8) that the use of electrochemical potentials is very helpful in conveying information about the *total* densities of free electrons and holes. Fig. 41.2 sketches how the Fermi level ϕ for an n-type semiconductor in equilibrium

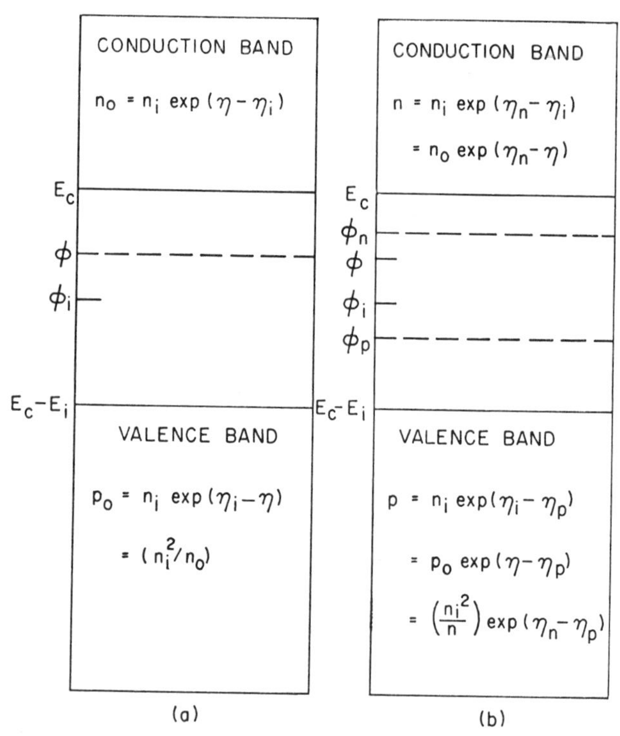

FIG. 41.2. (a) The Fermi level and carrier distributions in thermal equilibrium for an n-type semiconductor. (b) The quasi-Fermi levels corresponding with excess carrier densities when $np > n_0p_0$.

($\phi > \phi_i$) splits into the quantities ϕ_n and ϕ_p when n and p are induced to be larger than n_0 and p_0, respectively. The electrochemical potential for the minority carrier band moves much further from ϕ than that for the majority carrier band, since quite a small number of excess minority carriers can easily be larger than the thermal equilibrium density of this carrier type.

The designation of a ϕ_n indicates how many electrons are in the conduction band, but it does *not* give any information about the detailed distribution of electrons over the band states. Thus curves (a) and (b) in Fig. 41.3 have very different forms. For curve (a) it is supposed that $P_e(E) \propto \exp(-E/kT)$, whereas curve (b) corresponds with a maximum in $P_e(E)$ at the energy E_1. Yet the areas under curves (a) and (b) are the same, and so from Eq. (412.2) the same value of ϕ_n must characterize either electron distribution. That a given ϕ_n can correspond with a host

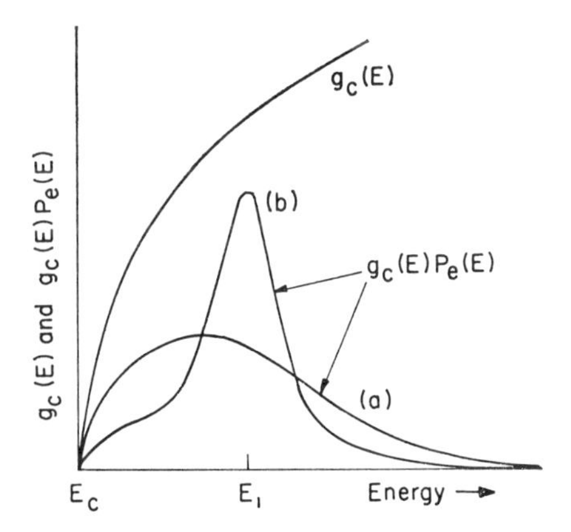

FIG. 41.3. Showing two possible forms which $g_c(E)P_e(E)$ could take as a function of energy above the base of the conduction band which correspond with the same electron quasi-Fermi level ϕ_n. The areas under curves (a) and (b) are the same, thus a single value of ϕ_n characterizes both.

of different distributions of occupancy poses a serious (and usually unmentioned) threat to a number of cherished concepts.

For instance, this volume is not concerned with scattering processes *per se*, but Section 4.2 does consider the continuity equations, which involve terms proportional to the gradients of current densities. It is customary to show that drift and diffusion currents can be added (invoking the Einstein diffusion relationship) to give a current density controlled by the gradient of the electrochemical potential. But such a procedure cannot be justified unless the energy dependence of $P_e(E)$ is very much like $\exp(-E/kT)$, as in thermal equilibrium!

The assumption that the distribution of excess electrons over conduction band states is the same as for thermal equilibrium also lies implicit in the way capture coefficients are defined. Suppose for example that recombinative transitions take place from the conduction band to a set of N_f flaw levels at an energy E_f. Let $c(E)$ be the probability that an electron from an occupied conduction band state at energy E will be captured by an empty flaw state in unit time. Then the rate of downward transitions is

$$r = N_f P_h(E_f) \int_{E_c}^{\infty} c(E) P_e(E) g_c(E) \, dE \tag{412.9}$$

It is customary to define a mean capture coefficient $\langle c_n \rangle$ by expressing this rate as

$$r = n \langle c_n \rangle N_f P_h(E_f) \tag{412.10}$$

Noting that n is given by Eq. (412.1), a comparison of Eqs. (412.9) and (412.10) shows that this mean capture coefficient is

$$\langle c_n \rangle = \frac{\int_{E_c}^{\infty} c(E) P_e(E) g_c(E) \, dE}{\int_{E_c}^{\infty} P_e(E) g_c(E) \, dE} \tag{412.11}$$

It will be appreciated that if $c(E)$ is a reasonably sensitive function of energy, the value obtained for $\langle c_n \rangle$ will depend on just how $P_e(E)$ varies with energy. (Only in the improbable case of an energy-independent capture probability are we relieved of this responsibility.)

Now $\langle c_n \rangle$ will have a well defined value for transitions occurring between the band and the flaw levels *in thermodynamic equilibrium*. Under non-degenerate conditions $P_e(E)$ is then of course just $\exp[(\phi - E)/kT]$. It is almost invariably assumed in discussions of recombination phenomena that the same value for $\langle c_n \rangle$ will hold good when excess electrons are present; which can only be the case if

$$P_e(E) = \exp\left(\frac{\phi_n - E}{kT}\right)$$

rather than some more exotic function.

We hasten to add that this is likely to be a plausible assumption if most carriers are scattered many times between excitation to a band

and de-excitation from that band. The electronic distribution will then resemble that of curve (a) in Fig. 41.3.

Curve (b) of the same figure could be the electron distribution only if most excess electrons were optically excited to states of energy $\sim E_1$ and suffered recombination before undergoing many thermal scattering collisions. The curve shown is probably more exaggerated than could ever occur in practice, but it does serve to remind us that the concept of a unique capture coefficient is a questionable one when lifetimes are very short and comparable with scattering times.

This particular point has been illustrated by discussing transitions to a flaw level. Of course, the same kind of caution must be employed in considering interband transitions. Nevertheless, the following sections and chapters will discuss models of band-to-band and multi-stage recombination based on the usual premise that excess carriers in a band have time to distribute themselves as though they were in internal equilibrium. The preceding remarks indicate that these models may reflect the truth rather imperfectly for materials of short lifetime.

In the discussions of the later chapters, reference will be made again to capture coefficients, and also to the related capture cross-sections. The capture coefficient $\langle c_n \rangle$ of a flaw for a free electron is the product of the capture cross-section σ_n and the mean thermal velocity $\overline{v_n}$ for electrons in the conduction band. The popularity of discussing capture in terms of a cross-section is probably carried over from atomic physics, and is perhaps inspired by a hope that a cross-section might be related to the size of an atom ($\sim 10^{-16}$ cm^{-2}). This turns out to be a gross simplification. Capture cross-sections may lie anywhere in the range of 10^{-25}–10^{-12} cm^2.

4.2 THE CONTINUITY EQUATIONS

When the densities of free electrons and holes are functions of space and time, the rate of change of each can be expressed through a continuity equation. Consider for instance the density $n(x, y, z, t)$ of conduction band electrons. This will tend to change as a net result of: (a) generative processes; (b) recombinative processes; (c) carrier diffusion and drift. The term "generative processes" includes all the mechanisms by which electrons may be thermally excited to the conduction band from the valence band and from impurity states. This includes the re-excitation of electrons which had previously been trapped. The total rate of generation may be denoted as $(g+g_{ph})$, where g_{ph} is the rate at which free electrons are generated by absorption of *excess* illumination,† while g lumps together all the "natural" generative processes.

Similarly, the total rate of recombination can be expressed as $(r+r_{ph})$, where r accounts for all the natural processes whereby an electron can drop to a lower level (either in the valence band or in an intermediate trapping state), while r_{ph} is the rate of downward transitions *induced* by the presence of *excess* electromagnetic radiation.

It will be noted that the word *excess* has been emphasized in connection with radiation causing the transition rates g_{ph} and r_{ph}. The rate of radiative generation produced by the normal black-body background is included in g, and the rate of recombination induced by this background is similarly included in r. Only radiation coming from outside the semiconductor, or created inside by radiative recombination of excess carriers, contributes to the rate g_{ph}. In some of the earlier treatments of this subject, the induced downward rate r_{ph} has not been explicitly included in the continuity equation. As noted in the next chapter, induced recombination can proceed at a considerable rate for a small gap material under strong modulation; however, it is true that for *most* semiconductors under *most* conditions the magnitude of r_{ph} will be small compared with that of other terms in the continuity equation.

Having noted that g_{ph} and r_{ph} are two distinct quantities (which to some extent depend on each other) we shall in the continuity equation use the symbol g_E to denote the *net rate* $(g_{ph}-r_{ph})$ of transitions up to the conduction band caused by *externally applied* ionizing radiation.

In addition to generation and recombination, the passage of current can tend to change the local electron density. An electron current density $\mathbf{I}_n$ signifies the flow of $(-I_n/q)$ electrons per sec across unit area of a surface normal to the direction of the current vector.‡ In order to establish the relationship of $\mathbf{I}_n$ to the time-dependence of n, consider a small volume element bounded by the planes x and $(x+\mathrm{d}x)$, y and $(y+\mathrm{d}y)$, z and $(z+\mathrm{d}z)$.

† Or other stimulation of external origin (atomic particles, etc.).

‡ q is a positive quantity numerically equal to the electronic charge. We could equally well say that q is the charge carried by a hole.

The rate at which electrons flow *into* the element through the plane x is

$$-q^{-1}I_{nx} \, . \, \mathrm{d}y \, . \, \mathrm{d}z \tag{420.1}$$

while they flow *out* through the plane at $(x+\mathrm{d}x)$ at the rate

$$-q^{-1}[I_{nx}+(\partial I_{nx}/\partial x)/\mathrm{d}x] \, \mathrm{d}y \, . \, \mathrm{d}z \tag{420.2}$$

Thus the net rate of electron accretion via these two planes is

$$q^{-1}[\partial I_{nx}/\partial x] \, \mathrm{d}x \, . \, \mathrm{d}y \, . \, \mathrm{d}z \tag{420.3}$$

Using the same argument for the other two pairs of faces, we find that the element $\mathrm{d}x \, . \, \mathrm{d}y \, . \, \mathrm{d}z$ acquires electrons by current flow at a rate

$$q^{-1}\left[\frac{\partial I_{nx}}{\partial x}+\frac{\partial I_{ny}}{\partial y}+\frac{\partial I_{nz}}{\partial z}\right] \mathrm{d}x \, . \, \mathrm{d}y \, . \, \mathrm{d}z = q^{-1}\nabla \, . \, \mathbf{I}_n \, \mathrm{d}x \, . \, \mathrm{d}y \, . \, \mathrm{d}z \tag{420.4}$$

As a result of generation, recombination and current flow, the rate of change of local free electron density can be summarized in the continuity equation

$$\frac{\partial n}{\partial t} = (g-r)+g_E+q^{-1}\nabla \, . \, \mathbf{I}_n \tag{420.5}$$

A continuity equation of the same character summarizes the rate of change of free hole density:

$$\frac{\partial p}{\partial t} = (g'-r')+g'_E-q^{-1}\nabla \, . \, \mathbf{I}_p \tag{420.6}$$

The primes on the generative and recombinative symbols serve as a reminder that each of these quantities can be different from the rate appropriate in the electron equation. The rates g_E and g'_E will be equal if there is no interaction between externally applied light and impurity states, and this assumption is often a justifiable one. But there is hope of finding g equal to g' and r equal to r' only in carefully purified semiconductors of small intrinsic gap width at high temperatures, when band-to-band processes dominate the behavior. Such situations are reviewed in Chapters 5 and 6.

4.2.1 Some Definitions of Carrier Lifetime

It is the general tendency of a non-equilibrium electron density n to try and restore itself towards the equilibrium value n_0. The strength of this tendency may not be precisely proportional to the excess density

$n_e = (n-n_0)$, but the tendency will not usually be very far from linear in n_e. This encourages us to replace $(g-r)$ in Eq. (420.5) by $-n_e/\tau_n$ or $-n_e\nu_n$, where the quantities τ_n and ν_n will either be completely independent of n_e or will depend on this variable in a rather gradual fashion. Thus the continuity equation is written

$$\frac{\partial n_e}{\partial t} = g_E + q^{-1}\nabla \cdot \mathbf{I}_n - \frac{n_e}{\tau_n}$$
$$= g_E + q^{-1}\nabla \cdot \mathbf{I}_n - n_e\nu_n \tag{421.1}$$

The left-hand side is written as $(\partial n_e/\partial t)$ since this is manifestly the same thing as $(\partial n/\partial t)$.

The quantity τ_n, with dimensions of time, is usually called the *electron bulk lifetime*. Its reciprocal, ν_n, should properly be described by a name such as "bulk recombination coefficient", but in fact it is usually referred to in the literature as the *recombination rate*. Such a description is a little confusing since the same name is applied to the quantity r, yet the two quantities are not synonymous and even have different dimensions. When the name "recombination rate" is used, it will usually be clear from the context whether r or ν is meant.

The simplest hypothetical model for a semiconductor assumes that $\tau_n = \nu_n^{-1}$ does not depend on n_e at all. It is then possible (1960:**4**) to solve Eq. (421.1) no matter how g_E and $\mathbf{I}_n$ depend on position and time. Chapter 10 comments on solutions of this type, which assist in an appreciation of the phenomena occurring in a semiconductor sample of finite size.

When τ_n depends on the excess electron density n_e (as it usually does) it becomes extraordinarily difficult to solve Eq. (421.1) unless $\nabla \cdot \mathbf{I}_n$ vanishes and g_E does not depend on the positional variables. This would be true of a semiconducting sample whose surfaces were completely inactive in recombination if it were possible by some magical trick to create excess carriers perfectly uniformly in space. It is customary to make these idealistic assumptions in establishing the dynamics of creation and recombination, then an attempt is made afterwards to assess the perturbing effects of spatial non-uniformity in n_e.

At any rate, when $\nabla \cdot \mathbf{I}_n$ and ∇g_E vanish, Eq. (421.1) becomes an ordinary differential equation.

$$\frac{dn_e}{dt} = g_E - n_e/\tau_n$$
$$= g_E - n_e\nu_n \tag{421.2}$$

The equation gives us a good idea of the connotations associated with the terms "bulk lifetime" and "bulk recombination rate". Thus when excess generation is maintained at a constant rate for a long time, the "steady state bulk lifetime" is simply the excess electron density divided by the excess generation rate required to maintain it; $\tau_n = n_e/g_E$. When excess generation ceases, $\nu_n = -n_e^{-1}(dn_e/dt)$ is the logarithmic decrement of the excess population, setting the rate at which conditions may return towards equilibrium.

Analogous with the phenomena of the conduction band, a bulk lifetime $\tau_p = \nu_p^{-1}$ can be defined to characterize the dynamics of situations involving a uniform excess hole density $p_e = (p-p_0)$. In terms of τ_p, the continuity equation is

$$\frac{\partial p}{\partial t} = g'_E - q^{-1}\nabla \cdot \mathbf{I}_p - \frac{p_e}{\tau_p} \tag{421.3}$$

which can be handled in exactly the same fashion as Eq. (421.1).

When recombination occurs through band-to-band transitions, τ_n and τ_p are the same. Only under special circumstances do the two lifetimes coincide if recombination is controlled by flaw states within the intrinsic gap.

4.3 BAND-TO-BAND AND BAND-TO-FLAW TRANSITIONS §

4.3.1 Transitions Across the Intrinsic Gap

When an electron drops from the conduction band into an empty state of the valence band, the potential energy of the hole–electron pair is transformed into some other kind of energy. In order to develop a theory for the dynamics of band-to-band recombination, it is necessary to know which physical process is dominant, i.e. into what form the energy of recombination is transformed.

The term *radiative* recombination is applied when a photon is released as a carrier pair annihilates itself. For a *direct* or *vertical* radiative transition (see the beginning of Section 1.5), all the energy is given to the photon. For an *indirect* or *non-vertical* transition, a phonon is either emitted or absorbed at the same time.

Recombination is usually rather loosely termed *radiationless* when all the potential energy of the hole–electron pair is dissipated as a shower of phonons. This is usually considered to be a highly unlikely event.

The energy of the pair can alternatively be given as kinetic energy to a third carrier (either an electron or a hole). Such a process is variously described as one of Auger, impact, or three-body recombination.

We shall consider these band-to-band processes in rather more detail in the following chapters. Chapter 5 establishes the continuity equation for a semiconductor dominated by radiative and radiationless intrinsic transitions; and shows how the lifetime varies with temperature, impurity concentrations, strength of external stimulation, etc. Chapter 6 provides the corresponding information for a semiconductor dominated by direct Auger recombination.

4.3.2 Transitions to a Localized State (Flaw)

When an electron goes from the conduction band to a localized state whose energy is indicated by a position within the intrinsic gap, the difference in energy is released in some other form. As in the previous sub-section, this recombination energy may be in the form of electromagnetic radiation, lattice vibrations or kinetic energy of another free particle. Thus again there are possibilities of radiative, radiationless, and Auger transitions. The same principles hold good for the transition of an electron from a localized state to an empty state in the valence band. This of course is the process of hole capture by the localized level.

As noted in Section 1.6, the term "flaw" is a useful one for any permanent perturbation of the lattice which produces localized levels within the intrinsic gap of a semiconductor. When a flaw is monovalent (only two possible charge conditions, separated by the amount q), a single level is presented which is either occupied or not. Other kinds of flaw are multivalent, and a series of levels are presented as electrons added or subtracted one by one.

Chapters 7, 8 and 9 are concerned with capture at flaw levels. The first of these examines the dynamics of one kind of flaw and a single band, but goes on to comment generally about flaw capture from both bands. Chapter 8 discusses in detail the case of a semiconductor for which electron–hole recombination is dominated by a single species of monovalent flaw.

The more complicated models (several sets of flaws, multivalent flaws, etc.) do not lend themselves to a complete analytic study. Chapter 9 indicates the general features of several such models.

4.3.3 Relative Importance of Recombination Processes

The order in which the various models for electron–hole recombination are discussed in the following chapters is that of increasing difficulty, and should not be confused with any order of decreasing or increasing importance.

The relative importance of the various processes depends to a large extent on the ratio of the intrinsic gap width E_i to the thermal energy kT. For the purification techniques which are employed with semiconducting materials at the time of writing, it is impossible to avoid domination by flaw recombinative processes when $E_i \gtrsim 20kT$ ($\approx 0{\cdot}5$ eV at room temperature). With materials for which purification techniques are less surely established, or in samples containing deliberately added recombination centers, band-to-band processes will be unimportant even when (E_i/kT) is considerably less than 20.

Thus the direct recombination models of Chapters 5 and 6 are expected to play a significant role for semiconductors of rather small energy gap at reasonably high temperatures. These chapters discuss the implication of the models for lower temperatures in the expectation that purification techniques will be improved over the years, so that flaw recombination might sometimes be subordinated even for large values of (E_i/kT).

Chapters 5 and 6 discuss radiative and Auger recombination in turn as though each was the *only* process going on, which is a simplification of reality. In practice, when radiative recombination is important there will always be an Auger component as well, and this must predominate at some sufficiently high temperature. Thus for highly pure tellurium (1960:**11**) there are enough residual flaws to control the lifetime below ~200°K. Radiative recombination is the limiting process between 200°K and 350°K, but Auger processes assume control above ~350°K. For a different semiconductor the temperature range of radiative domination could be much wider or much narrower.

Then in reading the following chapters, which present models one by one, it is well to remember that in any real semiconductor there will be differences—slight or serious—due to the perturbing effects of competing recombination mechanisms.

Chapter 5

RADIATIVE AND RADIATIONLESS RECOMBINATION

THE two processes of concern in this chapter are both forms of band-to-band recombination. It is convenient to consider them together since they both lead to the same form of continuity equation.

5.1 THE PHYSICS OF THE TWO PROCESSES

5.1.1 RADIATIVE RECOMBINATION §

It is possible to found a theory of radiative recombination on a quantum-mechanical treatment, considering the matrix elements for transitions from one state to another. Dumke (1957:**15**) has in fact made such calculations for the vertical and non-vertical transitions in germanium.

This fundamental kind of recombination theory is simplest if the conduction and valence bands each have a single non-degenerate extremum at the same position in **k**-space, and can each be described by a spherically symmetrical energy-independent effective mass. Such simplicity cannot usually be expected. It is known that a band often has multiple extrema, with anisotropic and energy-dependent effective mass components, and that the most probable transitions are often the non-vertical ones. When enough complexities are added to the problem, the probability of reaching a correct solution to the quantum-mechanical problem becomes rather small.

Fortunately, this does not prohibit calculation of the radiative recombination rate if it is possible to measure the macroscopic properties of the semiconductor, principally the optical absorption coefficient K_i

(in cm^{-1}) corresponding with the production of intrinsic carrier pairs. As normally measured, the total optical absorption coefficient (which is a function of photon energy $h\nu$) contains some small components in addition to K_i (corresponding to free carrier absorption, etc.). When these are subtracted, the value of K_i for any $h\nu$ is a measure of the strength of the interaction between pairs of valence and conduction states separated in energy by $h\nu$ (for vertical transitions) or by $(h\nu - k\theta)$ or $(h\nu + k\theta)$ (for non-vertical transitions). When the value of $h\nu$ is appropriate for either vertical or non-vertical transitions, K_i will reflect the contributions of both. K_i starts from zero at photon energy $h\nu = (E_i - k\theta)$ or $h\nu = E_i$ as the case may be, and is usually as large as 10^4 or 10^5 cm^{-1} for photon energies only a few-tenths of an electron volt higher.

van Roosbroeck and Shockley (1954:**15**) described the basis for using data on the observable quantity K_i to deduce the radiative recombination rate. Their presentation was based on the principle of detailed balance, which has already been discussed in Sub-section 4.1.1 for the relationship of radiative generation to radiative recombination. That principle provided a simple result for the ratio (A_{21}/B_{21}), though in Sub-section 4.1.1 the value of A_{21} itself was left as a quantum-mechanical problem. It must now be recognized that K_i for a given $h\nu$ depends on the sum of A_{21} for *all* pairs of states separated by that photon energy. It is not necessary to know the wave-functions of initial and final states. It does not matter whether transitions are predominantly vertical or non-vertical; the experimental K_1 provides all the necessary information about the *total* probability of upward transitions.

The theory of van Roosbroeck and Shockley allows for dispersion of the refractive index n. This is not an important elaboration of the theory, and it is assumed here that the refractive index n and electromagnetic wave group velocity $c' = (c/n)$ do not depend on photon energy $h\nu$.

Inside a solid of refractive index n which is in thermal equilibrium at temperature T, the number of photons per unit volume having frequencies within a range $d\nu$ is given by the Planck expression

$$Q_{\text{eq.}} \,.\, d\nu = \frac{8\pi(\nu^2/c'^3) \,.\, d\nu}{\exp(h\nu/kT)-1}$$

$$= \frac{8\pi(n^3\nu^2/c^3) \,.\, d\nu}{\exp(h\nu/kT)-1} \tag{511.1}$$

This radiation is moving through the solid at a speed $c' = (c/n)$ and interacts with the solid in several ways. That interaction which produces hole–electron pairs is described through K_i.

The rate (per unit volume) at which pairs are generated radiatively can be expressed as $(g_e + g_r)$, where g_e refers to the influence of *externally applied* ionizing radiation. We shall use the capitalized symbol G_r to denote the value assumed by g_r under conditions of thermal equilibrium. Then G_r must be given by

$$G_r = \int_0^\infty c' K_i \,.\, Q_{eq.}\, d\nu \qquad (511.2)$$

When the value of $Q_{eq.}$ is inserted from Eq. (511.1) and the integral expressed in terms of photon energy $h\nu$,

$$G_r = 8\pi h^{-3}(n/c)^2 \int_0^\infty \frac{K_i \,.\, (h\nu)^2 \,.\, d(h\nu)}{[\exp(h\nu/kT) - 1]} \qquad (511.3)$$

The lower limit is given as zero, but of course K_i does not become finite until $h\nu$ approaches E_i. Most of the contribution to the integral (511.3) comes from the spectral region starting at $h\nu \approx E_i$ up to a photon energy some 10 kT higher. The absorption coefficient is customarily expressed as a curve rather than as an analytic function of $h\nu$, and so the integral (511.3) must be evaluated numerically or graphically.

This is illustrated in Fig. 51.1, which shows how $Q_{eq.}$, K_i and their product vary with $h\nu$ for germanium at 300°K. The curve for the product shows a first peak for indirect (non-vertical) transitions; and a second, rather sharper, peak corresponding with the most important region for direct (vertical) transitions. Fig. 51.1 corresponds with one for germanium at room temperature given in the original paper of van Roosbroeck and Shockley. The figure shown here represents an improvement only in that it is based on more recent and complete optical absorption data of Dash and Newman (1955:**10**).

Calculation of G_r is only a means to the desired end of knowing the radiative recombination rate. We signify this latter quantity as r_r, and capitalize as R_r for the rate in thermal equilibrium. Thermodynamic balance requires that the generative and recombinative rates be the same in thermal equilibrium,

$$G_r = R_r \qquad (511.4)$$

thus the integration (511.3) actually provides the value of R_r.

When the intrinsic gap E_i is very large compared with kT (as is true for germanium at room temperature), it makes little difference whether $Q_{eq.}$ is given by the correct Planck expression or by Wien's asymptotic form. By this we mean that the denominator of Eq. (511.1) [and of

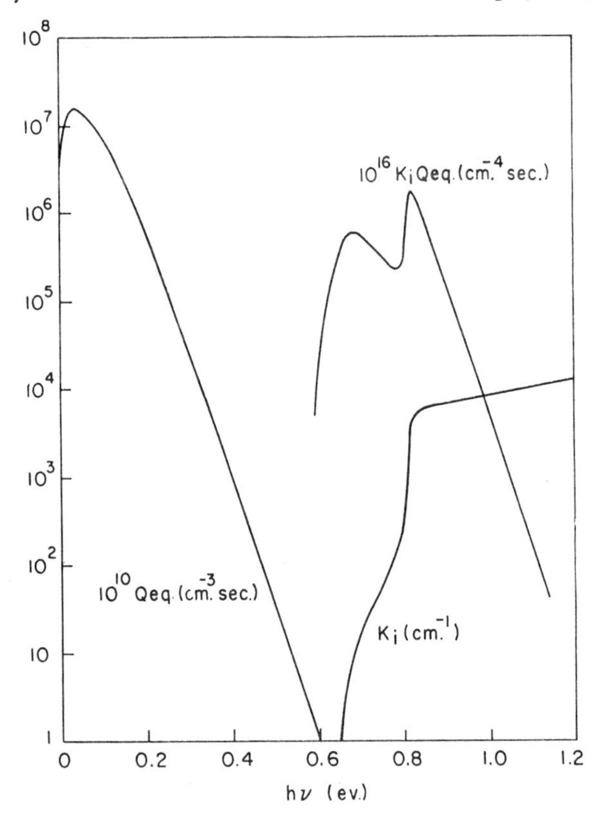

FIG. 51.1. Variation of $Q_{eq.}$, K_i and their product with photon energy for 300°K black body radiation and germanium. The area under the curve of $K_iQ_{eq.}$ corresponds with $G_r = 2{\cdot}8 \times 10^{13}$ cm^{-3} sec^{-1}.

Eq. (511.3)] could be simplified to $\exp(h\nu/kT)$ without appreciable error. This can be verified from Fig. 51.1; in the important spectral range the energy dependence of $Q_{eq.}$ is dominated by the exponential in the denominator.

For a material of very small intrinsic gap, however, it would not be warrantable to calculate G_r by numerically integrating

$$8\pi h^{-3}(n/c)^2 \int_0^\infty \frac{K_i \,.\, (h\nu)^2 \,.\, \mathrm{d}(h\nu)}{\exp(h\nu/kT)} \tag{511.5}$$

In any case there is a real physical significance to the quantity (511.5)—it is the rate of *spontaneous* radiative *recombination* for thermal equilibrium.

For, as emphasized in the last chapter, radiative recombination is the sum of spontaneous and stimulated components

$$\left.\begin{aligned} r_r &= r_{sp} + r_{st} && \text{in general} \\ R_r &= R_{sp} + R_{st} && \text{in thermal equilibrium} \end{aligned}\right\} \tag{511.6}$$

In Chapter 4 it was shown [see Eq. (411.4)] that transition probabilities for states separated by an optical energy $h\nu$ must be in a ratio such that

$$\frac{\mathrm{d}R_{sp}}{\mathrm{d}R_{st}} = [\exp(h\nu/kT) - 1] \tag{511.7}$$

From Eqs. (511.3), (511.4), (511.6) and (511.7) it can easily be shown that the respective rates of the two varieties of downward transition will be

$$R_{sp} = 8\pi h^{-3}(n/c)^2 \int_0^\infty \frac{K_i \,.\, (h\nu)^2 \,.\, \mathrm{d}(h\nu)}{\exp(h\nu/kT)} \tag{511.8}$$

and

$$R_{st} = 8\pi h^{-3}(n/c)^2 \int_0^\infty \frac{K_i \,.\, (h\nu)^2 \,.\, \mathrm{d}(h\nu)}{\exp(h\nu/kT)[\exp(h\nu/kT) - 1]} \tag{511.9}$$

in thermal equilibrium. The spontaneous rate R_{sp} is the previously mentioned quantity (511.5).

Suppose that band-to-band radiative transitions form the only recombination mechanism in a semiconductor. Then electrical neutrality requires that when thermal equilibrium is disturbed, the same excess carrier density will be found in the conduction and valence bands; $n_e = (n - n_0) = (p - p_0)$. The presence of excess carrier pairs makes recombination speed up, and we should like to establish a continuity equation and define a "radiative lifetime". This turns out to be rather difficult, for a most curious reason.

As remarked in Sub-section 4.2.1, the details of a recombination process are conventionally discussed by supposing a very large sample (so that the continuity equation does not need to contain any spatially dependent terms, and the boundary conditions of surface recombination are eliminated). Now Dumke (1957:**15**) points out that recombination radiation will tend to be re-absorbed within a large sample, producing another hole–electron pair. Since there is no degradation of the photon energy, this cycle could be repeated many times. Dumke suggests that an experimentally observed lifetime must be limited by the take-over of *other* bulk recombinative processes and by the escape of some recombination radiation through sample surfaces.†

Dumke's picture is incomplete in two respects. He did not account for free carrier absorption, which will assist in the dissipation of recombination radiation. Also he did not distinguish between spontaneous and stimulated recombination. When this distinction is taken into account we may note the following:

(a) The generation rate g_r will be larger than G_r to the extent that the semiconductor is inundated with excess recombination radiation.

(b) In a non-degenerate semiconductor, the spontaneous recombination rate r_{sp} will be proportional to the product np of the free electron density and the free hole density. Since this rate is R_{sp} in thermal equilibrium, evidently

$$r_{sp} = R_{sp}\left(\frac{np}{n_0 p_0}\right) = R_{sp}\left(\frac{np}{n_i^2}\right) \qquad (511.10)$$

van Roosbroeck and Shockley pointed out that proportionality to the product np must break down if the Fermi level enters either the conduction or the valence band, since the velocity distribution of carriers then depends on the concentration. This complication of a degenerate semiconductor has been examined by Landsberg (1957:**22**) but will not be considered further here. A further assumption implicit in Eq. (511.10) is that the occupancy probabilities $P_e(E)$ in the conduction band and $P_n(E)$ in the valence band are smooth exponential functions of $(E-\phi_n)/kT$ and $(\phi_p-E)/kT$, respectively. As noted in Sub-section 4.1.2, this assumption is reasonable if the lifetime is long compared with scattering times.

(c) The stimulated downwards rate r_{st} will be larger than its equilibrium value R_{st} *both* by virtue of the increased carrier densities *and* by the presence of excess recombination radiation. In fact if the excess densities are large enough to make the difference of electrochemical

† Remember that this chapter was written in 1960, prior to the advent of semiconductor lasers. See Preface.

potentials, $(\phi_n - \phi_p)$, comparable with the intrinsic gap, excess radiation provokes almost as many *downward* as *upward* transitions. (This is true also for externally applied radiation when carrier modulation is very large; for this reason we took care in Section 4.2 to define g_E as the *net* rate of upwards transitions provoked by external radiation.)

It is not particularly fruitful to attempt setting up a continuity equation for this system, since photon disposal does depend on the sample dimensions and on the efficacy of free carrier absorption in dissipating photons. Instead, we retreat to the conventional position, and overlook any effects which might be caused by the repeated trapping of photons. For this simplified model

$$\left.\begin{aligned} g_r &= G_r \\ r_{sp} &= R_{sp}\left(\frac{np}{n_i^2}\right) \\ r_{st} &= R_{st}\left(\frac{np}{n_i^2}\right) \end{aligned}\right\} \tag{511.11}$$

when the semiconductor is non-degenerate, i.e.

$$r_r = (r_{sp}+r_{st}) = G_r\left(\frac{np}{n_i^2}\right) \tag{511.12}$$

by virtue of Eqs. (511.4) and (511.6).

When spatial dependence is excluded from Eq. (420.5), the resulting simple continuity equation is

$$\begin{aligned} g_E - \frac{\mathrm{d}n}{\mathrm{d}t} &= (r_r - g_r) \\ &= G_r\left(\frac{np - n_i^2}{n_i^2}\right) \end{aligned} \tag{511.13}$$

It will be recalled from Sub-section 4.2.1 that the lifetime is defined as $n_e/(r-g)$; then this quantity is given by

$$\tau = \frac{n_i^2}{G_r(n_0 + p_0 + n_e)} \tag{511.14}$$

since $n_e = (n - n_0) = (p - p_0)$.

5.1.2 Radiationless (Multiphonon) Recombination §

At one time it was generally assumed that recombination in a semiconductor would predominantly occur from one band to the other. Since recombination radiation was not detected from solids in which rapid recombination was evidently occurring, it seemed plausible to assume that band-to-band radiationless recombination (in which the electron–hole energy is released as a group of phonons) must be an important process.

This viewpoint is no longer widely held. It is now realized that much of the non-radiative recombination in wide gap materials occurs through flaws—a realization which took over a decade to spread from the phosphor field to the semiconductor field. It does in fact seem rather likely that band-to-band radiationless recombination will be an extremely rare process, unlikely to dominate the dynamics of any semiconductor. For the recombination energy must usually be assumed by several phonons (perhaps as many as twenty); while theoretical estimates of the corresponding transition probability vary rather widely, none of them suggest that this probability could be very large. The crux of this argument is that at least one of the carriers should be strongly coupled to the lattice for efficient dissipation of the energy, and this can not be when the electron and hole undergoing recombination are both free. Much better opportunities can exist for multi-phonon capture of a free carrier by a localized level, as discussed later.

For any direct radiationless recombination which *does* occur, the generation rate should be independent of excess carrier densities, while the recombination rate should (in non-degenerate semiconductors) be proportional to the product np. Thus the continuity equation has exactly the same form as Eq. (511.13) for radiative recombination. In any discussion of excess carrier dynamics, we can regard radiationless direct recombination as providing a small correction to the effective value of G_r in Eqs. (511.13) and (511.14). The generation rate for any band-to-band radiationless transitions should even have approximately the same temperature dependence as for radiative recombination, more or less as $\exp(-E_i/kT)$.

5.2 BEHAVIOR OF THE RADIATIVE LIFETIME

We now wish to consider the dependence on modulation, doping and temperature of the lifetime for a semiconductor which is dominated by radiative band-to-band transitions (with perhaps a minor contribution from radiationless processes). It was shown in the previous section that if spatial dependencies are ignored, the excess electron density n_e for such situations satisfies a continuity equation

$$g_E - \frac{\mathrm{d}n_e}{\mathrm{d}t} = (r-g)$$

$$= \frac{G_r n_e(n_0+p_0+n_e)}{n_i^2} \qquad (520.1)$$

This forms the basis for discussing how n_e varies with strength of excitation, time, etc.

5.2.1 Equivalence of All Definitions of Lifetime

In Sub-section 4.2.1 the lifetime of an electron was defined as $n_e/(r-g)$; then in the present context

$$\frac{n_e}{(r-g)} = \tau_R = \frac{n_i^2}{G_r(n_0+p_0+n_e)} \qquad (521.1)$$

A simplifying characteristic of direct recombination is that the quantity described by Eq. (521.1) fulfils all the requirements of the term "lifetime" under various circumstances. This is not the case when recombination occurs via a large concentration of flaws; then the term "lifetime" must be qualified by an explanation of the meaning being given to the word. For instance, Bube (1960:**10**) defines five types of lifetime which *can* differ from each other, though with direct recombination they are are all numerically the same.

Thus under conditions of steady state illumination, n_e attains a constant value $[(\mathrm{d}n_e/\mathrm{d}t) = 0]$. From Eq. (520.1), the lifetime τ_R of Eq. (521.1) is obviously the ratio of the excess pair density n_e to the generation rate g_E responsible for it. This can be regarded as the average interval between creation and recombination of a pair.

The τ_R of Eq. (521.1) can equally properly be described as the time constant of excess carrier decay when illumination is interrupted or modified in intensity. When g_E stops, τ_R is the reciprocal of the logarithmic decrement of n_e, i.e. at any moment the temporal dependence of n_e could be described as $\exp(-t/\tau_R)$. Of course, n_e does not decay as a *simple exponential* from a large initial value, since τ_R is itself a function of n_e; but at any instant τ_R *does* characterize the decay.

5.2.2 Variation of Lifetime with Doping and Modulation

At any given temperature (which fixes the values of G_r and n_i) the lifetime τ_R of Eq. (521.1) depends on the doping of the semiconductor and on the excess pair density n_e. The lifetime is largest for small modulation,

$$\tau_0 = \frac{n_i^2}{G_r(n_0+p_0)} \qquad \text{when} \qquad n_e \ll (n_0+p_0) \qquad (522.1)$$

and this is smaller for extrinsic material than the low-modulation lifetime in an intrinsic semiconductor

$$\tau_{\max} = \frac{n_i}{2G_r}, \qquad \text{when} \quad \begin{cases} n_0 = p_0 = n_i \\ n_e \ll n_i \end{cases} \qquad (522.2)$$

The value of this maximum lifetime depends on the intrinsic gap of the semiconductor and the temperature. For germanium at room temperature, the evidence of Fig. 51.1 is that $G_r = 2{\cdot}8 \times 10^{13}$ cm^{-3} sec^{-1}. Since intrinsic carriers have a density $n_i = 1{\cdot}7 \times 10^{13}$ cm^{-3} in Ge at 300°K, the maximum radiative lifetime is $\tau_{\max} \approx 0{\cdot}30$ sec. With the wider intrinsic gap of silicon, $\tau_{\max} \sim 3$ hr at room temperature, while it is less than a microsecond in the narrow gap compound InSb.

Fig. 52.1 shows how radiative lifetime depends on the equilibrium Fermi level in the semiconductor—both for infinitesimal modulation and for several finite values of the ratio (n_e/n_i). The abscissa in this figure is marked as a logarithmic scale of (n_0/n_i), but this can of course be regarded as a linear scale of the Fermi level ϕ, centered on the intrinsic position ϕ_i.

With this double logarithmic presentation of Fig. 52.1, note that the shoulders of the curve for τ_0 have slopes of $+1$ and -1, because τ_0 is inversely proportional to the majority carrier density in markedly extrinsic material [see Eq. (522.1)]. The figure is symmetrical about the intrinsic point, a feature which may be contrasted with the consequences of Auger recombination (to be discussed in Chapter 6).

Another feature of Fig. 52.1 is that the lifetime for a *large* excess pair density is essentially independent of doping for a range of Fermi level symmetrical about ϕ_i. This insensitivity of τ_R to n_0 (or p_0) occurs

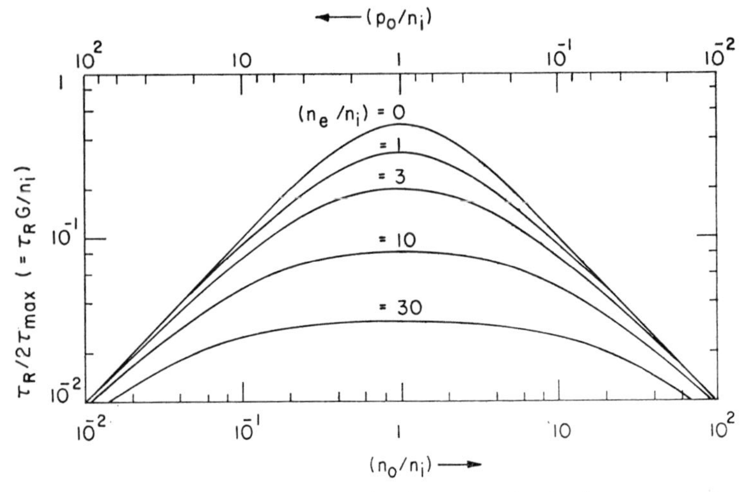

FIG. 52.1. Radiative lifetime as a function of carrier density at constant temperature, for small modulation and for three progressively larger values of n_e. The abscissa is essentially a linear one for the Fermi level ϕ.

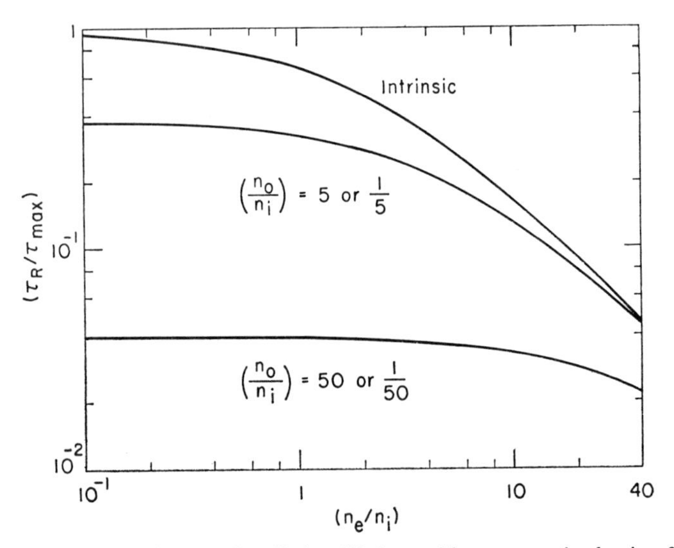

FIG. 52.2. Variation of radiative lifetime with excess pair density for intrinsic material and for two stages of doping.

because when n_e is large compared with (n_0+p_0), an "excess" carrier of one type is more likely to encounter an "excess" carrier of the other type than a member of the "permanent" population. Such a form of recombination is often described as "bimolecular". In the bimolecular range, τ_R may be insensitive to doping, but it is very sensitive to n_e; indeed

$$\tau_R \approx \frac{n_i^2}{n_e G_r} \quad \text{when} \quad n_e \gg (n_0+p_0) \tag{522.3}$$

Fig. 52.2 illustrates the progression of the lifetime between the limiting forms of (522.1) and (522.3) as the excess pair density increases. For the intrinsic case and the less strongly doped of the two extrinsic examples, τ_R has essentially reached the form of (522.3) at the right of the figure.

5.2.3 The Dependence on Excess Generation Rate

When excess generation is externally provoked at a rate g_E for a long time, the excess pair density n_e assumes a steady value. The second term on the left side of Eq. (520.1) vanishes under these conditions, and n_e and g_E are related by a quadratic equation:

$$G_r n_e^2 + G_r n_e(n_0+p_0) = g_E n_i^2 \tag{523.1}$$

This has the solution

$$n_e = 2\left(\frac{g_E}{G_r}\right)\left(\frac{n_i^2}{n_0+p_0}\right)\left\{1+\left[1+4\left(\frac{g_E}{G_r}\right)\left(\frac{n_i}{n_0+p_0}\right)^2\right]^{1/2}\right\}^{-1} \tag{523.2}$$

which incorporating the terminology of Eq. (522.1) can be written

$$n_e = 2\tau_0 g_E\left\{1+\left[1+\frac{4\tau_0 g_E}{n_0+p_0}\right]^{1/2}\right\}^{-1} \tag{523.3}$$

When the excitation rate g_E is small, n_e is directly proportional to g_E, but this linearity ceases to hold when the generation is sufficiently vigorous to make n_e comparable with (n_0+p_0). Indeed, n_e varies as $g_E^{1/2}$ when the modulation is very large (the bimolecular recombination region in which $\tau_R \propto n_e^{-1}$). Part (a) of Fig. 52.3 sketches the general appearance of a log–log plot of n_e and g_E.

The corresponding lifetime $\tau_R = (n_e/g_E)$ has of course the value τ_0 of Eq. (522.1) when the excitation and modulation are small. As indicated by part (*b*) of Fig. 52.3, τ_R declines as $g_E^{-1/2}$ (i.e. as n_e^{-1}) when g_E is very large.

In recapitulation of the asymptotic forms:

$$n_e = \tau_0 g_E \approx \left(\frac{g_E}{G_r}\right)\left(\frac{n_i^2}{n_0+p_0}\right) \quad \text{when} \quad \begin{Bmatrix} n_e \ll (n_0+p_0) \\ g_E \ll G_r\left(\dfrac{n_0+p_0}{n_i}\right)^2 \end{Bmatrix} \tag{523.4}$$

and

$$n_e = \tau_R g_E \approx n_i\left(\frac{g_E}{G_r}\right)^{1/2} \quad \text{when} \quad \begin{Bmatrix} n_e \gg (n_0+p_0) \\ g_E \gg G_r\left(\dfrac{n_0+p_0}{n_i}\right)^2 \end{Bmatrix} \tag{523.5}$$

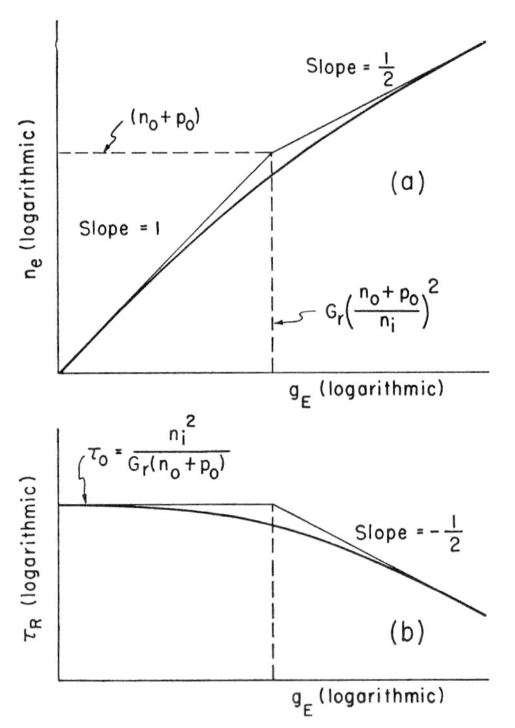

FIG. 52.3. Variation of (a) excess pair density n_e, and (b) effective lifetime τ_R, with steady state generation rate g_E, when radiative recombination is dominant.

5.2.4 Transient Decay

The transformation of the recombination characteristic between the limits $n_e \ll (n_0+p_0)$ and $n_e \gg (n_0+p_0)$ necessarily has an influence on the form of excess pair build-up and decay when excess generation begins or ends. For simplicity the case of transient decay will be considered, supposing that an excess pair density $\mathcal{N}$ has been built up by

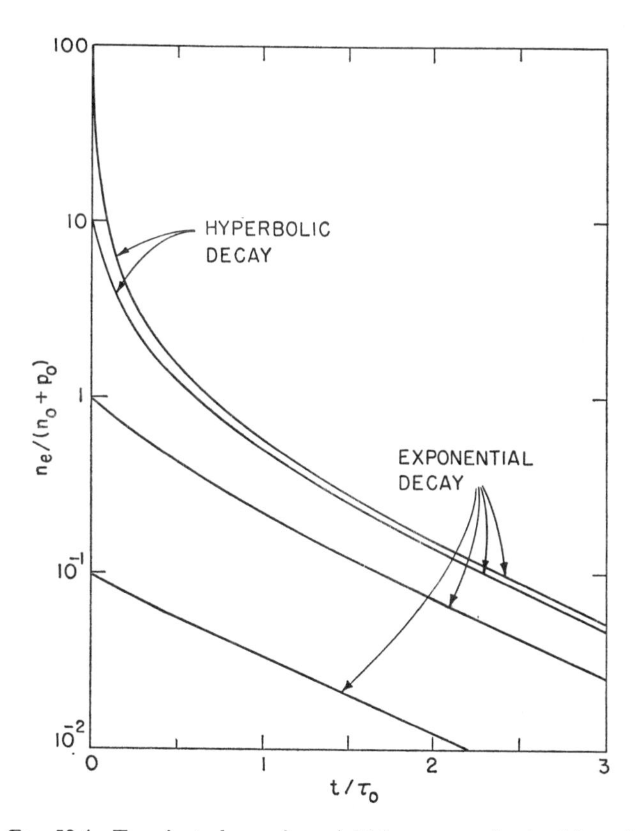

Fig. 52.4. Transient decay from initial excess pair densities of $\mathcal{N} =$ 100 (n_0+p_0), 10 (n_0+p_0), (n_0+p_0) and 0·1 (n_0+p_0). When $\mathcal{N} \gg (n_0+p_0)$ the initial portion of the decay is hyperbolic; but in every case the decay is exponential with time constant $\tau_0 = n_i^2/G_r(n_0+p_0)$ for the range of time in which $n_e \ll (n_0+p_0)$.

illumination which stopped abruptly at time $t = 0$. Then during the ensuing decay, Eq. (520.1) requires that

$$-\frac{dn_e}{dt} = \frac{G_r n_e(n_0+p_0+n_e)}{n_i^2}, \qquad t \geqslant 0 \tag{524.1}$$

The variables n_e and t can be separated, and integration of Eq. (524.1) is quite straightforward. When the initial condition $n_e = \mathcal{N}$ at $t = 0$ is imposed, the solution is

$$n_e = \frac{\mathcal{N}(n_0+p_0)}{(n_0+p_0+\mathcal{N})\exp(t/\tau_0)-\mathcal{N}}, \qquad t \geqslant 0 \tag{524.2}$$

where τ_0 is the usual low-modulation lifetime of Eq. (522.1).

Fig. 52.4 illustrates the form of the decay (524.2) for four values of $\mathcal{N}$. No matter what value is supposed for $\mathcal{N}$, the decay eventually becomes exponential [varying as $\exp(-t/\tau_0)$]. Indeed if $\mathcal{N} < (n_0+p_0)$, the decay is virtually exponential throughout its course. But if a very large initial excess pair density is supposed, the decay is extremely rapid during the interval $0 > t > 0{\cdot}25\tau_0$.

When the short time simplification of Eq. (524.2) is considered,

$$n_e \approx \frac{\mathcal{N}}{1+t[\mathcal{N}/\tau_0(p_0+n_0)]}, \qquad t \ll \tau \tag{524.3}$$

it can be seen that the initial decay of n_e is hyperbolic if $\mathcal{N} \gg (n_0+p_0)$. It is impressive to note that, *no matter how large $\mathcal{N}$ may be*, this vigorous hyperbolic decay brings n_e down to a fraction of (n_0+p_0) within the time interval τ_0. The upper curve in Fig. 52.4 is actually for

$$\mathcal{N} = 100(n_0+p_0)$$

but at times later than $0{\cdot}1\ \tau_0$ it is indistinguishable from the limiting curve† of infinite $\mathcal{N}$.

† It will be seen in the next chapter that the large-modulation recombination is also extremely vigorous for band-to-band Auger processes. This stands in contrast to the behavior to be found in Chapters 8 and 9 for recombination through flaws. With flaw recombinative processes, the lifetime may decline to some extent as the excess carrier density increases, but it is still possible to have a disturbance larger than (n_0+p_0) at a time long after the beginning of a decay provided that the initial disturbance is made *sufficiently* large.

5.2.5 Variation with Temperature

When the temperature in a semiconductor is raised, the supply of photons in equilibrium with the environment increases for all frequencies, though the increase is particularly marked for the high frequency end of the spectrum, $\nu \gg kT/h$. This means that the equilibrium generation rate G_r of Eq. (511.3) should be a strong positive function of temperature. Since G_r depends on the availability of photons with energies from E_i upwards, we may anticipate that G_r should vary crudely as $\exp[-(E_i+\delta)/kT]$, where δ would be rather small compared with the intrinsic gap E_i.

As a graphical example, the steepest curve in Fig. 52.5 shows the variation of G_r with reciprocal temperature for the elemental semi-

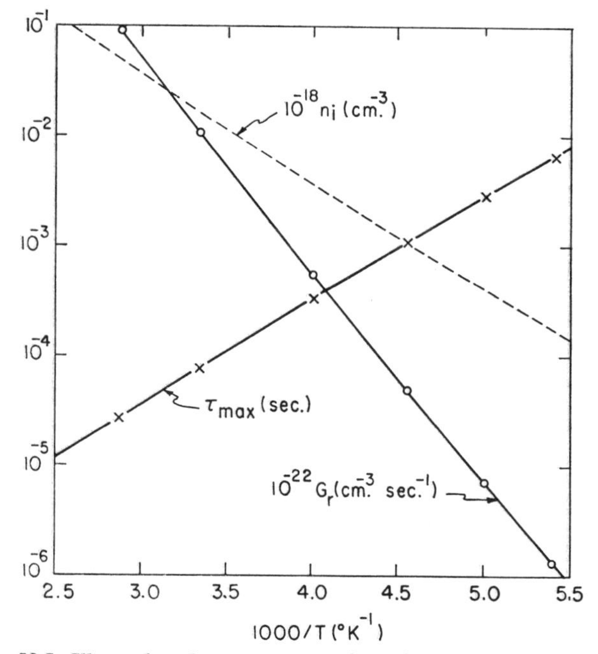

Fig. 52.5. Illustrating the temperature dependence of the factors which control the radiative lifetime. The curves show how for tellurium, the radiative generation rate in thermal equilibrium G_r, the intrinsic pair density n_i, and the corresponding maximum lifetime $\tau_{max} = n_i/2G_r$ vary with $1000/T$. G_r has been calculated by integration of Eq. (511.3) at six temperatures. After Blakemore (1960:**11**).

conductor tellurium. This illustrates some calculations once made by the present author (1960:**11**); G_r was calculated at six temperatures by graphical evaluation of the integral (511.3), and a smooth line drawn to connect the six points. Fig. 52.5 shows also the increase of the intrinsic pair density n_i with temperature, and the resultant maximum radiative lifetime $\tau_{max} = n_i/2G_r$ (for small modulation when the semiconductor

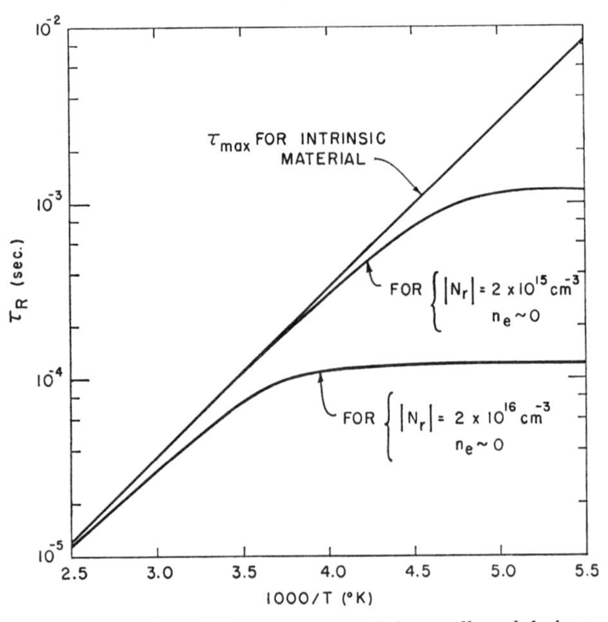

FIG. 52.6. Variation with temperature of the small-modulation radiative lifetime in tellurium, showing the transition from intrinsic to extrinsic behavior. The intrinsic curve of τ_{max} is identical with that of Fig. 52.5.

is in the intrinsic condition). Since G_r is about twice as sensitive as n_i to temperature change, the intrinsic radiative lifetime declines on warming.

Fig. 52.6 reproduces the curve of τ_{max} from Fig. 52.5, and also shows how the small-modulation radiative lifetime varies with temperature for a semiconductor containing a finite density of impurities.

A semiconductor normally contains both donors and acceptors, and Section 2.4 used the symbol N_r to denote the excess of ionized donors over ionized acceptors. This must also be the excess of free electrons over free holes:

$$n_0 - p_0 = N_r \tag{525.1}$$

in an electrically neutral semiconductor. Since $n_0 p_0 = n_i^2$ in a non-degenerate semiconductor (a restriction adopted throughout this discussion), it is elementary to demonstrate that

$$(n_0 + p_0) = [4n_i^2 + N_r^2]^{1/2} \tag{525.2}$$

When Eq. (525.2) is incorporated into Eq. (521.1), the expression for radiative lifetime becomes

$$\tau_R = \frac{n_i^2}{G_r\{[4n_i^2 + N_r^2]^{1/2} + n_e\}} \tag{525.3}$$

This simplifies appropriately to τ_{max} for small modulation at temperatures so high that the semiconductor is completely intrinsic. On considering progressively lower temperatures, the radiative lifetime tends to the form

$$\tau_R \approx \frac{n_i^2}{G_r\{|N_r| + n_e\}}, \qquad |N_r| \gg n_i \tag{525.4}$$

when the semiconductor becomes completely extrinsic. Note that only the modulus of N_r is required, since p-type and n-type cases of the same majority density enjoy the same radiative lifetime.

The curves of Fig. 52.6 for finite values of N_r demonstrate that the small-modulation lifetime is essentially temperature-independent† in the temperature range governed by Eq. (525.4). This insensitivity to temperature occurs since G_r has about the same temperature dependence as n_i^2 (for the physical reason mentioned at the beginning of this sub-section).

† The lifetime will, of course, increase again when the temperature is lowered sufficiently to de-ionize an appreciable fraction of the impurities.

Chapter 6

BAND-TO-BAND AUGER RECOMBINATION

Just as radiative recombination is a process complementary to optical absorption, so Auger recombination is complementary to impact ionization.

Impact ionization has two important forms. The *extrinsic* version consists of the ionization of neutral impurities by fast moving free carriers. This phenomenon is prominent when a moderate electric field is applied to doped germanium at low temperatures (1954:**17**). The converse process of *extrinsic* Auger recombination (in which the transition of an electron to a bound state is accompanied by the transfer of energy to a free carrier) has been the subject of several theories (1955:**30**, 1955:**31**, 1957:**17**, 1950:**9**). However it is proposed to defer detailed consideration of transitions to bound states until Chapters 7–9.

The present chapter concentrates on *band-to-band* processes. The generative process then consists of a fast electron or hole losing most of its kinetic energy in the act of creating a hole–electron pair. This is very prominent in the behavior of a semiconductor in a very large electric field—as occurs in a strongly biased *p–n* junction. At one time it was thought likely that Zener transitions (1934:**2**) controlled the breakdown of a *p–n* junction (1951:**16**), but it is now fairly well established (e.g. 1955:**32**, 1955:**33**) that the abrupt breakdown of a *p–n* junction is an avalanche phenomenon triggered by impact ionization, except in exceedingly narrow junctions (1957:**12**).

Even for a semiconductor in thermal equilibrium, there will be some free carriers whose kinetic energies are large enough to make band-to-band impact generation possible. Detailed balance requires that Auger recombination must occur at an equal rate, re-creating the identical spectrum of fast carriers. A quantum-mechanical model described by Beattie and Landsberg (1959:**15**, 1959:**16**) suggests expressions for the two important contributions to the Auger generative rate in thermal equilibrium. The results of this model are embodied in the following discussion of non-equilibrium recombination rates.

6.1 ELECTRON–ELECTRON AND HOLE–HOLE COLLISIONS §

Auger recombination actually comprises two processes which occur in parallel. One involves electron–electron collisions and the other hole–hole collisions. These two processes and their inverses are symbolized in the four parts of Fig. 61.1, which has the following meaning.

(a) There is a finite probability that two electrons, 1 and 2, may

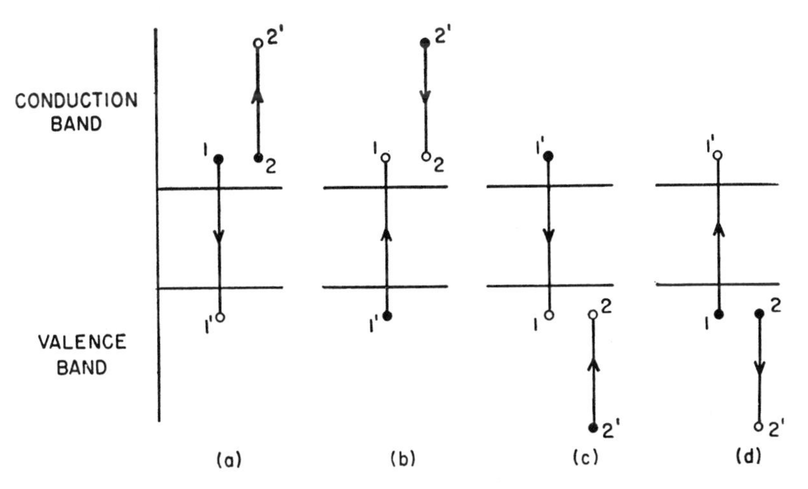

FIG. 61.1. Auger processes which lead to creation or destruction of a hole–electron pair. (a) Destruction of a pair by *e–e* collision. (b) Creation of a pair by the reverse phenomenon (fast electron impact ionization). (c) Destruction of a pair by *h–h* collision. (d) Pair creation by the inverse process (fast hole impact ionization). After Beattie and Landsberg (1959:**16**).

collide in such a fashion that 1 drops to the empty state 1′ in the valence band while 2 assumes all this recombination energy in advancing to the empty state 2′ high in the conduction band. The rate at which pairs recombine because of electron–electron (*e–e*) collisions is denoted as r_{ee}. In conformity with the nomenclature adopted in Chapter 5, this is capitalized as R_{ee} for the rate occurring in thermal equilibrium.

(b) The rate of pair creation resulting from impact ionization by fast electrons (the inverse of the previous process) is denoted as g_{ee}. In thermal equilibrium this becomes G_{ee} (which from detailed balance considerations must equal R_{ee}).

(c) Hole–hole (h–h) collisions can occur in a manner which excites one of them to a very low state in the valence band, while the other recombines with an electron from the conduction band. The rate of this annihilation is r_{hh} (R_{hh} in equilibrium).

(d) Pair creation from h–h processes occurs at a rate g_{hh} (whose equilibrium value G_{hh} equals R_{hh}).

In a semiconductor with rather heavy holes, so that $\mu = (m_c/m_v) < 1$, the difference of r_{ee} and g_{ee} will dominate the recombinative behavior of n-type, intrinsic, and even mildly p-type situations. Only when the semiconductor is *strongly* p-type can h–h processes involving $(r_{hh}-g_{hh})$ become the dominant factor. [The converse of these statements is of course true for any semiconductor in which $\mu = (m_c/m_v) > 1$.]

6.1.1 The Model of Beattie and Landsberg

In order to establish a quantum-mechanical basis for the probability of Auger transitions, it is necessary to make some assumptions about the conduction and valence bands, and the occupancy of states within them. Beattie and Landsberg (1959:**16**) assume that the conduction band minimum and the valence band maximum occur at the same point in the reduced zone. For each band the density-of-states function is taken to be that for a scalar, energy-independent, effective mass—m_c or m_v. It is further assumed that the lifetime is large compared with the scattering time, so that the electron occupancy probability can be

$$P_e(E) = \frac{1}{1+\exp\left(\dfrac{E-\phi_n}{kT}\right)} \tag{611.1}$$

for the conduction band, and the hole probability

$$P_h(E) = \frac{1}{1+\exp\left(\dfrac{\phi_p-E}{kT}\right)} \tag{611.2}$$

for the valence band.

The usual band theory, in which states are described by Bloch one-electron functions, is based on a Hartree–Fock approximation, whereby the Coulomb interaction between electrons is replaced by a self-consistent field. Beattie and Landsberg remark that a description of Auger transitions requires an explicit consideration of Coulomb interaction terms in the Hamiltonian relating to outer shell electrons. The Auger transition probability is then determined by the change this makes in the Hamiltonian; and on this Beattie and Landsberg build their perturbation theory. The states of the crystal are described by normalized determinants of orthonormal one-electron functions.

When the electrons involved in a transition are marked 1 and 2 (separated by distance r_{12}), and all other electrons are supposed unaffected by the transition, only the term involving† $(q^2/\kappa r_{12})$ of the perturbation operator can have a non-zero matrix element. In the original model this was modified to take account of screening, and the effective potential was written as

$$(q^2/\kappa r)\exp(-\lambda r) \tag{611.3}$$

However, it is not necessary to introduce the refinement of screening except for degenerate semiconductors, and we shall give only the simple unscreened non-degenerate result.

The matrix element linking initial and final states can be written as a multiple sum over reciprocal lattice vectors. Many of the terms correspond to Umklapp-type processes (1955:**35**), but these have a negligible effect on the result. For the recombination rate is obtained by integrating the matrix element over all permissible initial and final states, these states being weighted by the probabilities (611.1) and (611.2). Since with Umklapp-processes the initial and final states are far from the band edges, they receive very little weight. Considering the dominant term, Beattie and Landsberg find that the thermal equilibrium generation rate due to *e–e* processes is

$$G_{ee} = \frac{8(2\pi)^{5/2}q^4 m_c |F_1F_2|^2 n_0 (kT/E_i)^{3/2}}{h^3\kappa^2(1+\mu)^{1/2}(1+2\mu)} \exp\left[-\left(\frac{1+2\mu}{1+\mu}\right)\frac{E_i}{kT}\right] \tag{611.4}$$

in a non-degenerate semiconductor. The expression is rather more involved for a degenerate semiconductor but that complication will not be pursued in this chapter.

† Here κ is the dielectric constant.

The quantities F_1, F_2 are overlap integrals of the periodic parts of Bloch functions,

$$F_1 = \int u_c^*(\mathbf{k}_1, \mathbf{r}) u_v(\mathbf{k}_1', \mathbf{r})\, d\mathbf{r} \tag{611.5}$$

$$F_2 = \int u_c^*(\mathbf{k}_2, \mathbf{r}) u_c(\mathbf{k}_2', \mathbf{r})\, d\mathbf{r} \tag{611.6}$$

The magnitude of these integrals depends on the interatomic spacing and potential in the semiconductor, and must be evaluated for each material. Using a Kronig–Penney model, Beattie and Landsberg first estimated (1959:**16**) that $|F_1F_2|$ should be $\sim 0{\cdot}1$ for Insb, but have since concluded from some more detailed calculations (1960:**12**) that a value of $\sim 0{\cdot}25$ is more appropriate.

When the numerical values for h, q and m_0 are placed in Eq. (611.4), this reads

$$\begin{aligned} G_{ee} &= \left[\frac{8(2\pi)^{5/2}q^4 m_0}{h^3}\right]\left[\frac{(m_c/m_0)|F_1F_2|^2}{\kappa^2(1+\mu)^{1/2}(1+2\mu)}\right] \times \\ &\qquad \times n_0(kT/E_i)^{3/2} \exp\left[-\left(\frac{1+2\mu}{1+\mu}\right)\frac{E_i}{kT}\right] \\ &= 1{\cdot}32\times 10^{17}\left[\frac{(m_c/m_0)|F_1F_2|^2}{\kappa^2(1+\mu)^{1/2}(1+2\mu)}\right]\times \\ &\qquad \times n_0(kT/E_i)^{3/2} \exp\left[-\left(\frac{1+2\mu}{1+\mu}\right)\frac{E_i}{kT}\right] \text{cm}^{-3}\,\text{sec}^{-1} \end{aligned} \tag{611.7}$$

In similar fashion, for h–h processes

$$\begin{aligned} G_{hh} &= 1{\cdot}32\times 10^{17}\left[\frac{(m_v/m_0)|F_1F_2|^2}{\kappa^2(1+1/\mu)^{1/2}(1+2/\mu)}\right]\times \\ &\qquad \times p_0(kT/E_i)^{3/2} \exp\left[-\left(\frac{2+\mu}{1+\mu}\right)\frac{E_i}{kT}\right] \text{cm}^{-3}\,\text{sec}^{-1} \end{aligned} \tag{611.8}$$

There are several things to be noted about these two equations.

Since an Auger transition is a three-body process involving two electrons and a hole, or two holes and an electron, it might perhaps have been expected to find that $G_{ee} \propto n_0 n_i^2$ while $G_{hh} \propto p_0 n_i^2$. In fact G_{ee} and G_{hh} turn out to be more rapidly temperature-dependent than this. G_{ee} is proportional to $n_i^2 T^{-3/2} \exp[-\mu E_i/(1+\mu)kT]$, and G_{hh} to $n_i^2 T^{-3/2} \exp[-E_i/(1+\mu)kT]$. This happens because the two recombining particles in an Auger transition are *not* at their respective band extrema. Requirements of *momentum conservation* as well as *energy conservation* make the transitions occur primarily over energy intervals rather larger than the minimum gap width.

Considering the recombination process in part (a) of Fig. 61.1, analysis of the momentum and energy conditions shows that a transition is most probable when the electrons 1 and 2 initially have about the same energy—but this must be higher than the conduction band minimum by an amount depending on the intrinsic gap and the effective mass ratio $\mu = (m_c/m_v)$:

$$E_1 = E_2 = E_c + \mu^2 E_i/(1+3\mu+2\mu^2) \tag{611.9}$$

The final state of the first electron is also displaced from the valence band maximum,

$$(E_v - E_{1'}) = \mu^{-1}(E_1 - E_c) \tag{611.10}$$

Only when $\mu = (m_c/m_v) \ll 1$ can an Auger transition take place from the bottom of the conduction band to the top of the valence band.

The expressions (611.7) and (611.8) for G_{ee} and G_{hh} should be satisfactory both when $\mu = (m_c/m_v)$ is smaller than unity and when it becomes larger than unity. The formulation of the model was originally expected to break down for the case of equal electron and hole masses $\mu = 1$), but Beattie and Landsberg have since confirmed (1960: **12**) that the expressions (611.7) and (611.8) are still valid for that case.

6.1.2 Net Recombination Rate in Non-equilibrium

At the point of thermal equilibrium, Auger *e–e* processes account for electron–hole pair generation and annihilation at the rate G_{ee}. For *h–h* processes, G_{hh} denotes the equal rates of upward and downward transitions. Now when the semiconductor contains excess carrier pairs, of density $n_e = (n - n_0) = (p - p_0)$, the recombination rate for each kind of process exceeds its companion generation rate.

Since *e–e* recombination involves two electrons and one hole, the rate in a non-degenerate semiconductor should be proportional to n^2p [provided, as usual, that $P_e(E)$ and $P_h(E)$ are exponential functions of (E/kT)]. Thus this rate should be

$$r_{ee} = G_{ee}\left(\frac{n^2p}{n_0^2p_0}\right) \tag{612.1}$$

The generative process of electron impact ionization should, under the same conditions, satisfy

$$g_{ee} = G_{ee}\left(\frac{n}{n_0}\right) \tag{612.2}$$

since it depends on the supply of fast electrons in internal equilibrium with the remaining free electrons. The *net* rate of *e–e* recombination is then

$$(r_{ee}-g_{ee}) = G_{ee}\left(\frac{np-n_i^2}{n_i^2}\right)\left(\frac{n}{n_0}\right) \tag{612.3}$$

Similarly for *h–h* processes, the *net* recombination rate is

$$(r_{hh}-g_{hh}) = G_{hh}\left(\frac{np-n_i^2}{n_i^2}\right)\left(\frac{p}{p_0}\right) \tag{612.4}$$

When a semiconductor has recombinative behavior dominated by these two processes, the continuity equation (420.5) must then be

$$g_E - \frac{\mathrm{d}n}{\mathrm{d}t} = (r_{ee}+r_{hh})-(g_{ee}+g_{hh}) = \frac{(np-n_i^2)(G_{ee}np_0+G_{hh}pn_0)}{n_i^4} \tag{612.5}$$

if spatial effects are excluded. The right side of Eq. (612.5) can of course be written as n_e/τ_A, so that the expression for the Auger lifetime is

$$\tau_A = \frac{n_i^4}{(n_0+p_0+n_e)(G_{ee}np_0+G_{hh}pn_0)} \tag{612.6}$$

The foundation has now been laid for studying the dependence of this lifetime on temperature, excess pair density, etc.

6.2 BEHAVIOR OF THE AUGER LIFETIME WHEN $m_c < m_v$

As with radiative and radiationless recombination (Chapter 5), there is only one lifetime when band-to-band Auger recombination dominates a semiconductor. The time constant which characterizes the transient changes of excess pair density is also the value of (n_e/g_E) under continuous external stimulation.

We need to know the characteristic form of this lifetime for *n*-type, *p*-type, and intrinsic material—whether n_e be large or small. In the following discussion the expressions used for G_{ee} and G_{hh} are those resulting from the model of Landsberg and Beattie—as a matter of convenience. For any semiconductor which does not meet the conditions of their model, τ_A should still have essentially the same functional dependences.

It is equally convenient to describe the behavior for a semiconductor with $\mu > 1$ as for $\mu < 1$. In the former case, *h–h* processes tend to dominate; while *e–e* processes are usually more important in the latter. As an arbitrary choice, this section is written in terms of a semiconductor for which $\mu < 1$ $(m_c < m_v)$. It will be evident throughout that the discussion can be applied to a semiconductor (such as CdAs or CdS) in which m_c is larger than m_v by reversing the role of pairs of terms such as "electron"–"hole", or "*n*-type"–"*p*-type", etc.

At any rate, for a semiconductor in which μ *is* smaller than unity, it is convenient to write the Auger lifetime (612.6) in the form

$$\tau_A = \frac{2n_i^2\tau_i}{(n_0+p_0+n_e)[(n_0+n_e)+\beta(p_0+n_e)]} \tag{620.1}$$

Adopting Eqs. (611.7) and (611.8) for the equilibrium generation rates of the two Auger processes, the quantity τ_i in Eq. (620.1) is

$$\tau_i = \frac{3{\cdot}8\times 10^{-18}\kappa^2(1+\mu)^{1/2}(1+2\mu)\exp\left[\left(\dfrac{1+2\mu}{1+\mu}\right)\dfrac{E_i}{kT}\right]}{(m_c/m_0)|F_1F_2|^2(kT/E_i)^{3/2}} \text{ sec} \tag{620.2}$$

while

$$\beta = \frac{\mu^{1/2}(1+2\mu)}{(2+\mu)}\exp\left[-\left(\frac{1-\mu}{1+\mu}\right)\frac{E_i}{kT}\right] \tag{620.3}$$

The quantity τ_i is the lifetime for intrinsic material with very small modulation provided that $\beta(p_0+n_e) \ll (n_0+n_e)$. This is the condition that *h–h* processes should be insignificant, since the quantity $\beta(p_0+n_e)$ in the denominator of Eq. (620.1) represents the influence of *h–h* processes. As β will be much smaller than unity for the chosen type of material (in which $\mu < 1$), this term will not affect τ_A to any significant degree except in strongly *p*-type material with very few excess carriers. Thus Eq. (620.1) is written in the form which brings out most clearly the dependence of the *e–e* lifetime on temperature and carrier densities. Note that the activation energy of τ_i is larger than the intrinsic gap width.

The sub-sections which follow examine in some detail how lifetime does depend on the various factors, and how changes in doping and excess pair density can swing the balance from *e–e* to *h–h* domination and back again. In three figures used to illustrate the temperature dependence of the lifetime, a semiconductor is supposed for which

$$\left.\begin{aligned} E_i &= 0{\cdot}32 - 0{\cdot}00003T \text{ eV} \\ \kappa &= 28 \\ |F_1F_2| &= 0{\cdot}1 \\ m_v &= 0{\cdot}75m_0 \\ m_c &= 0{\cdot}24m_0 \\ \mu &= (m_c/m_v) = 0{\cdot}32 \end{aligned}\right\} \tag{620.4}$$

These happen to be the numerical values appropriate for the elemental semiconductor tellurium. Behavior suggesting the dominance of Auger recombination has been observed in tellurium above room temperature (1960:**11**), and this material will certainly serve as well as any other for the basis of some illustrations. Using the numerical values of Eq. (620.4), the important parameters in (620.1) are

$$\left.\begin{aligned} n_i &= 1{\cdot}55 \times 10^{15}T^{3/2} \exp(-1850/T) \text{ cm}^{-3} \\ \tau_i &= 3{\cdot}5 \times 10^{-7}T^{-3/2} \exp(4600/T) \text{ sec} \\ \beta &= 0{\cdot}48 \exp(-1900/T) \end{aligned}\right\} \tag{620.5}$$

for tellurium. Parameters corresponding with a semiconductor of smaller energy gap are used in another graphical example.

6.2.1 Dependence on Doping and Modulation

As with any other process, the Auger lifetime at a given temperature is influenced by the doping of the semiconductor and by the density of excess hole–electron pairs. The small-modulation lifetime

$$\tau_0 = \frac{2n_i^2\tau_i}{(n_0+p_0)(n_0+\beta p_0)} \qquad n_e \ll n_0,\, p_0 \tag{621.1}$$

for any values of n_0 and p_0 is necessarily larger than that for finite modulation. When $\beta \ll 1$ (as it will be supposed to be throughout this section), τ_i is indeed the small-modulation lifetime for *intrinsic* material, controlled by *e–e* recombination.

Fig. 62.1 is used to show how the Auger lifetime varies with doping, for small modulation and several finite values of n_e. The figure also indicates the regions in which *e–e* and *h–h* processes dominate each other. For it can be seen from Eq. (620.1) that *h–h* processes are dominant when $\beta(p_0+n_e) > (n_0+n_e)$; this condition is satisfied only within the shaded region of Fig. 62.1. In all other regions of the figure

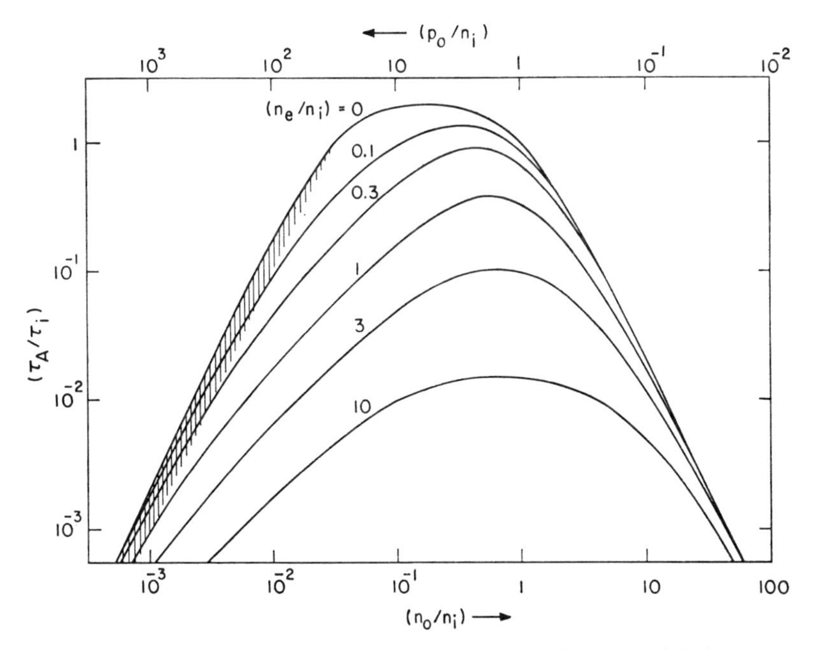

FIG. 62.1. Variation of Auger lifetime with doping status for zero modulation and several finite excess pair densities, in a semiconductor for which $\beta = 10^{-3}$. The *h–h* processes are dominant only within the shaded area.

either n_0 or n_e is large enough to make *e–e* processes more important—and usually to an overwhelming degree.

It was remarked in the previous chapter that the curves of Fig. 52.1 were symmetrical about the intrinsic point; this certainly can not be said for the Auger model of Fig. 62.1. The maximum lifetime of $2\tau_i$ is reached for material which is sufficiently *p*-type to make $n_0 \ll n_i$, yet not so p-type that βp_0 becomes comparable with n_0. It is just about possible to satisfy such a condition with the value 0·001 chosen† for β in Fig. 62.1.

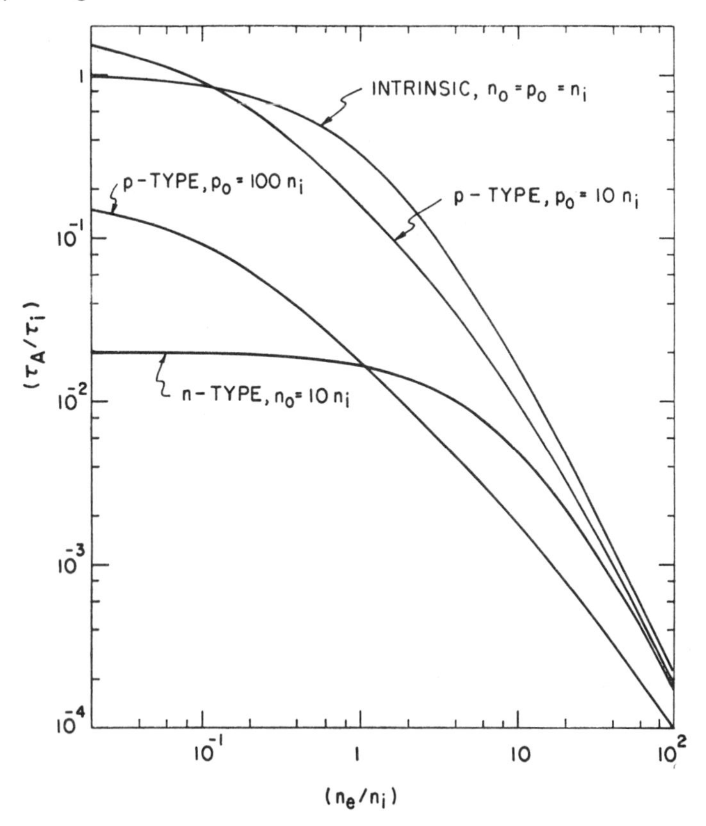

Fig. 62.2. Variation of Auger lifetime with excess pair density when $\beta = 10^{-3}$. For intrinsic material, one n-type and two p-type cases. The stronger p-type case of $p_0 = 100\ n_i$ is dominated by h–h transitions for weak modulation, $n_e < 0{\cdot}1\ n_i$.

A number of features of Fig. 62.1 should be apparent by inspection of Eq. (620.1). Thus for n-type material, lifetime varies inversely as the

† For a semiconductor with parameters as given by Eqs. (620.4) and (620.5), $\beta \approx 0{\cdot}001$ at room temperature.

square of the electron density $[\tau_A \approx 2\tau_i n_i^2/(n_0+n_e)^2]$ to provide a limiting slope of -2 in the log–log plot. Similarly, there is a slope of $+2$ at the left of the figure, since for h–h dominated material (strongly p-type, very small modulation), lifetime *does* vary as p_0^{-2}. When this material is stimulated more strongly, e–e recombination takes over and $\tau_A \propto 1/n_e p_0$.

Fig. 62.2 attempts to show the course of τ_A vs. n_e for several positions of the equilibrium Fermi level. (The value of β is taken to be the same as for the previous figure.) For each case, lifetime becomes independent of n_e when this modulation is *sufficiently small*; while for *sufficiently large* modulation all the curves must eventually approach the limiting behavior of

$$\tau_\infty = 2\tau_i(n_i/n_e)^2 \tag{621.2}$$

The range of possible modes of behavior for intermediate modulation is too broad to permit complete categorization, depending as it does on the relative magnitudes of n_0, p_0, n_e and β. In passing it can be noted that for n-type material, the transition from a constant lifetime to one varying as n_e^{-2} occurs moderately abruptly (within two decades); whereas a region in which τ_A varies as n_e^{-1} can persist for several decades in p-type material.

6.2.2 The Variation with Generation Rate

When steady state external stimulation produces the generation rate g_E, the relationship between n_e and g_E is at first linear, but becomes a cube root one for the strongest excitation. In between, a variety of courses is offered by the cubic equation

$$n_e^3+n_e^2[n_0+(1+\beta)(n_0+p_0)]+n_e(n_0+p_0)(n_0+\beta p_0) = 2n_i^2\tau_i g_E \tag{622.1}$$

which describes the equilibrium. However, the general trend for n-type and p-type cases will be as sketched in Fig. 62.3 (supposing conditions of doping which give the same low level lifetime for the two cases). In the p-type case the linear relationship breaks down for rather small modulation [as soon as $n_e > n_0$, as may be seen from Eq. (622.1)], and as g_E increases there may be several decades in which $n_e \propto g_E^{1/2}$ before the limiting behavior of

$$n_e = (2n_i^2\tau_i g_E)^{1/3}, \qquad n_e \gg (p_0+n_0) \tag{622.2}$$

is reached. For n-type material there is no such intermediate range.

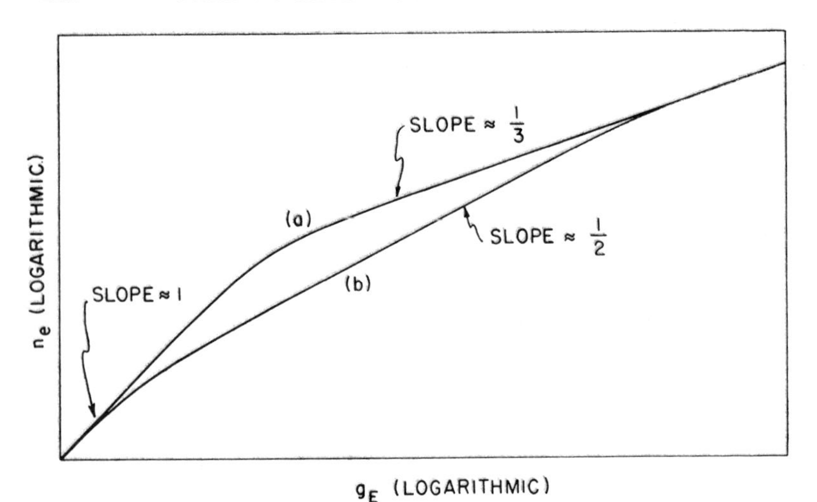

FIG. 62.3. Schematic variation of excess pair density n_e with externally induced generation rate, under steady state conditions. For an Auger-dominated semiconductor when $\beta \ll 1$. (a) Typical characteristic for n-type material. (b) Typical characteristic for p-type material.

6.2.3 Transient Decay

It was pointed out in the last chapter that transient decay involving radiative recombination is very rapid in the early stages, but that it eventually becomes an exponential function of time. Behavior of the same general character can be expected for Auger recombination, though not necessarily with a hyperbolic shape for the early decay.

When some excitation process has been effective in the past but has now ceased, the decay of n_e is governed by

$$\frac{dn_e}{dt} = -\frac{n_e}{\tau_A} = -\frac{n_e(n_e+n_0+p_0)[(n_0+n_e)+\beta(p_0+n_e)]}{2n_i^2\tau_i} \quad (623.1)$$

The solution subject to the condition that $n_e = \mathcal{N}$ at time $t = 0$ is:

$$\ln\left[\frac{n_e}{\mathcal{N}}\right] + \frac{(n_0+\beta p_0)}{(p_0+\beta n_0)}\ln\left[\frac{n_e+n_0+p_0}{\mathcal{N}+n_0+p_0}\right] -$$

$$-\frac{(1+\beta)(p_0+n_0)}{(p_0+\beta n_0)}\ln\left[\frac{n_e(1+\beta)+(n_0+\beta p_0)}{\mathcal{N}(1+\beta)+(n_0+\beta p_0)}\right] = -(t/\tau_0) \quad (623.2)$$

where τ_0 is given by Eq. (621.1). The form of the decay described by Eq. (623.2) is not intuitively obvious, but when expressed in a semi-logarithmic plot of n_e vs. t/τ_0, it is *qualitatively* similar to the appearance of the curves in Fig. 52.4 (for radiative recombination). The only important difference with Auger decay is that the initial decay from a very large $\mathcal{N}$ is even more rapid (especially for n-type material) since the high level lifetime is inversely proportional to the *square* of the excess density.

6.2.4 Lifetime–Temperature Relationship

At the risk of laboring the point, the reader is again reminded that the model of Auger recombination being discussed presupposes that $m_c < m_v$ to make $\beta \ll 1$. For such a model, the ranges of interest can be divided as follows:

(i) *Intrinsic Range*

Throughout the range of temperature for which $n_0 = p_0 = n_i$, the quantity τ_i of Eq. (620.2) describes the lifetime for rather small modulation. This is usually the quantity of most interest for the intrinsic range, since at high temperatures when n_i is large it is not often that external stimulation will be sufficiently vigorous to maintain a very massive excess density. When such conditions do arise,

$$\tau_A = \frac{2n_i^2\tau_i}{(2n_i+n_e)(n_i+n_e)}, \quad \text{when } n_0 = p_0 = n_i \qquad (624.1)$$

$$\approx \tau_i(1-3n_e/2n_i) \quad \text{for } n_e \ll n_i \qquad (624.2)$$

The typical temperature dependence of τ_i is shown in curve (a) of Fig. 62.4. This uses the numerical values prescribed by Eq. (620.5). The predominant temperature dependence is that of the exponential factor in Eq. (620.5) [or Eq. (620.2)], as evidenced by the fact that ln τ_i is almost completely a linear function of reciprocal temperature. (The very slight curvature of the line shows the influence of the $T^{-3/2}$ term.) As noted earlier in the chapter, the exponential term in τ_i has an activation energy $E_i[(2\mu+1)/(\mu+1)]$, which for our supposed numerical model is almost 25% larger than the width of the intrinsic gap.

As an intrinsic semiconductor is cooled, control of the Fermi level is eventually taken by the impurities present. The influence of this on the Auger lifetime depends very much on whether the extrinsic transition occurs to an n-type or p-type status.

(ii) *Extrinsic n-Type Behavior*

When donors are more numerous than acceptors, the semiconductor becomes n-type on cooling. Since the majority carriers are electrons (the carriers most efficient in promoting recombination when $\mu < 1$), it can be expected that a considerable recombination rate will be maintained over a wide range of temperature.

As before, $N_r = (n_0 - p_0)$ is used to denote the excess of ionized donors over ionized acceptors; then

$$\left.\begin{aligned} n_0 &= \tfrac{1}{2}N_r + \sqrt{(\tfrac{1}{4}N_r^2 + n_i^2)} \\ (n_0 + p_0) &= \sqrt{(N_r^2 + 4n_i^2)} \end{aligned}\right\} \tag{624.3}$$

Assuming that h–h collisions are of negligible importance,

$$(n_0 + n_e) \gg \beta(p_0 + n_e)$$

Eq. (620.1) may be rewritten in the form

$$\tau_A = \frac{4n_i^2\tau_i}{[n_e + \sqrt{(N_r^2 + 4n_i^2)}][2n_e + N_r + \sqrt{(N_r^2 + 4n_i^2)}]} \tag{624.4}$$

The lifetime of (624.4) begins to diverge from (624.1) when the semiconductor is cooled to a point at which n_i is no longer much larger than N_r. On continuing to cool into the extrinsic region, the lifetime eventually approaches the limiting form of

$$\tau_A \approx \frac{2n_i^2\tau_i}{(N_r + n_e)^2}, \qquad n_0 \approx N_r \gg n_i \tag{624.5}$$

Curves (b) and (c) of Fig. 62.4 illustrate the behavior of (624.4) between the limiting forms of (624.1) and (624.5) for *small* modulation. The term small modulation is applied here in the sense that $n_e \ll N_r$. This is not a severe restriction when it is noted that curves (b) and (c) correspond with $N_r = 10^{15}$ cm^{-3} and $N_r = 2 \times 10^{16}$ cm^{-3}, respectively. It will not happen too often in practice that excess carrier pairs will be present in densities as large as these.

Since the case under discussion is dominated by *e–e* collisions, the recombination rate is *linear* in total *hole* density and *quadratic* only in total *electron* density.† Then n_e may be large or small compared with p_0

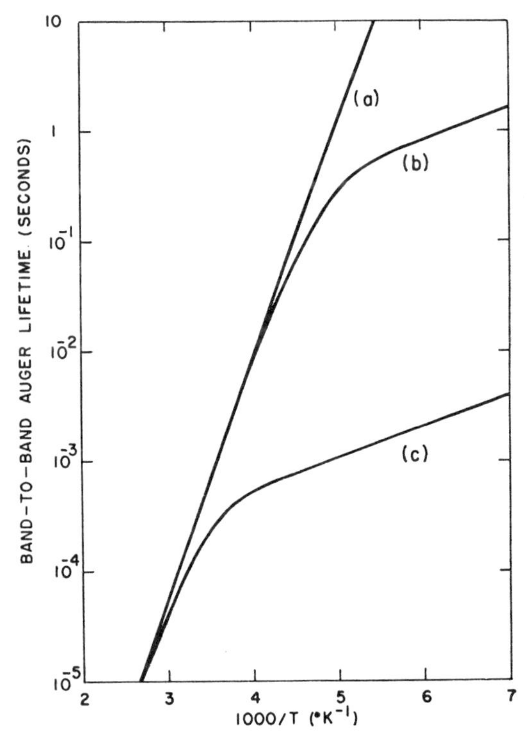

FIG. 62.4. Temperature dependence of small-modulation Auger lifetime for a semiconductor described by the parameters of Eqs. (620.4) and (620.5). (a) For intrinsic material, $n_0 = p_0 = n_i$. (b) For *n*-type material, $(n_0 - p_0) = 10^{15}$ cm^{-3}. (c) For $(n_0 - p_0) = 2 \times 10^{16}$ cm^{-3}.

without affecting the lifetime at all. Only when n_e becomes appreciable compared with n_0 (i.e. with N_r) does the lifetime start to droop below the value characteristic of zero modulation.

† Note that the two extrinsic curves of Fig. 62.4 differ in ordinate by a factor of 400, while the corresponding values of N_r differ by a factor of 20. This happens because recombination is *quadratic* in *electron* density for *e–e* processes.

When radiative recombination was reviewed in Chapter 5, a temperature-independent lifetime was found in the extrinsic range. This does not happen for Auger processes, since the energy of a recombining pair is larger than the intrinsic gap. For extrinsic n-type material, the temperature dependence of $n_i^2\tau_i$ in Eq. (624.5) is

$$T^{3/2}\exp\left[\left(\frac{\mu}{1+\mu}\right)\frac{E_i}{kT}\right]$$

The exponential factor provides most of the extrinsic temperature dependence for curves (b) and (c) of Fig. 62.4, which is based on the parameters of Eqs. (620.4) and (620.5).

(iii) *Zero-Modulation p-Type Behavior*

In starting to discuss the lifetime in p-type material for which $\mu < 1$, it is useful to suppose first that any departure from thermal equilibrium is *very small*, $n_e \ll$ both p_0 and n_0. The lifetime appropriate to this condition is τ_0 of Eq. (621.1). This can be rearranged to read

$$\tau_0 = \frac{2\tau_i}{(1+n_0/p_0)(1+\beta p_0/n_0)} \tag{624.6}$$

Throughout the intrinsic range, the first factor in the denominator equals 2, while the second factor is imperceptibly different from unity (provided that $\beta \ll 1$, which is supposed to be the case).

On cooling into the p-type extrinsic range, $(1+\beta p_0/n_0)$ will remain essentially unity for a considerable range of temperature. On the other hand, $(1+n_0/p_0)$ approaches unity when the temperature is lower than that of the extrinsic–intrinsic transition. Thus the first effect of cooling to a p-type status is that of reducing the denominator of Eq. (624.6) from 2 to 1. This makes the lifetime twice as large as τ_i.

The physical reason for this is that the source of electrons for e–e collision recombination is being depleted more rapidly on cooling than would have been the case in undoped material, and this is only partially offset by the greater availability of holes to complete the process. At any rate, the *low-modulation* lifetime τ_0 behaves like $2\tau_i$ for a considerable part of the extrinsic temperature range. This is illustrated by the curves of Fig. 62.5. Curve (a) is that of completely undoped intrinsic material, just as in Fig. 62.4. Curve (c) also corresponds exactly with curve (c) of Fig. 62.4; that for a material with $(n_0-p_0) = 2\times10^{16}$ cm^{-3}.

These curves are used to throw into sharper contrast the low-modulation lifetime behavior of a p-type sample. Curve (b) is calculated assuming $(p_0 - n_0) = 2 \times 10^{16}\ \text{cm}^{-3}$ and it will be seen that $\tau_0 \approx 2\tau_i$ from 300°K down to about 180°K.

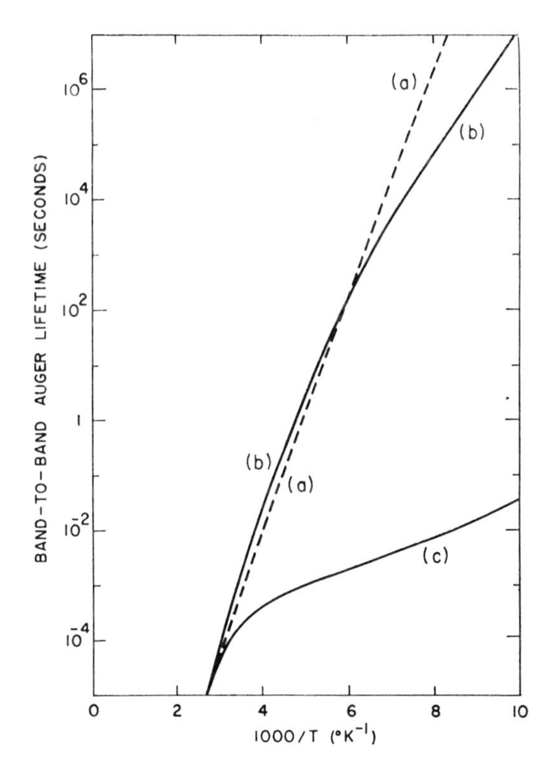

FIG. 62.5. Temperature dependence of τ_0 for a semiconductor described by the parameters of Eqs. (620.4) and (620.5). (a) For intrinsic material. (b) For p-type material, $(p_0 - n_0) = 2 \times 10^{16}\ \text{cm}^{-3}$. (c) For n-type material, in which $(n_0 - p_0) = 2 \times 10^{16}\ \text{cm}^{-3}$.

On further cooling, the lifetime rises less rapidly, crossing the intrinsic line at a temperature T_a and becoming appreciably smaller than τ_i at lower temperatures. This happens when the electron supply is so limited compared with that of free holes that h–h recombination processes finally are able to dominate over *e–e* collisions. The two mechanisms are of equal strength at temperature T_a, when the second factor in the denominator of (624.6) reaches a value of 2; thus the position of this cross-over is determined by the majority hole density in the semiconductor.

$$\left.\begin{aligned} p_0 &= n_i\beta^{-1/2} = n_0\beta^{-1} \\ &= (N_cN_v)^{1/2}\left(\frac{2+\mu}{1+2\mu}\right)^{1/2}\mu^{-1/4}\exp\left[-\left(\frac{\mu}{1+\mu}\right)\frac{E_i}{kT}\right] \end{aligned}\right\} \text{at } T = T_a \quad (624.7)$$

At temperatures rather lower than T_a, the less favored *h–h* processes take over completely and the lifetime assumes the form

$$\tau_0 \approx \frac{2n_i^2\tau_i}{\beta p_0^2} \propto T^{3/2}\exp\left[\left(\frac{1}{1+\mu}\right)\frac{E_i}{kT}\right], \qquad T < T_a \qquad (624.8)$$

This is substantially the case below about 130°K for curve (b) in Fig. 62.5.

There is a similarity between the expressions describing the zero-modulation lifetime for *n*-type and *p*-type cases. [Compare Eqs. (624.5) and (624.8).] However, the activation energy in the *n*-type case is $\mu E_i/(1+\mu)$, whereas it is larger by a factor of μ^{-1} in the *p*-type case. The low-temperature activation energy of curve (b) in Fig. 62.5 is smaller than the intrinsic gap—but not by a very large amount.

The low-temperature slopes of curves (b) and (c) in Fig. 62.5 do in fact indicate the temperature dependence of the effective interaction cross-sections for *h–h* and *e–e* processes. It has already been remarked that momentum as well as energy must be preserved in an Auger transition, and this makes the cross-sections decrease on cooling. For a semiconductor in which $\mu < 1$, the *h–h* cross-section decreases more rapidly than the *e–e* cross-section; hence the steep slope of curve (*b*) compared with that of curve (c).

(iv) *p-Type Behavior with Finite Modulation*

This rapid drop-off of *h–h* efficiency on cooling means that when any finite excess pair density n_e is maintained, *h–h* processes *must* be overshadowed by *e–e* processes at *sufficiently* low temperatures. Consider a semiconductor which is quite *p*-type ($p_0 \gg n_0$), and suppose that excess pairs are present in a density which is still small compared with the majority density p_0—though large enough to be reckoned with n_0 at low temperatures. Under these conditions the first term in the denominator of Eq. (624.6) can be left as unity, and the second must be modified to account for the additional possibilities of *e–e* recombination by using an *excess* electron as the recoil particle. Thus for these conditions

$$\tau_A \approx \frac{2\tau_i}{1+\beta(p_0/n_0)+(n_e/n_0)} \qquad \left.\begin{array}{l} p_0 \gg n_0 \\ p_0 \gg n_e \end{array}\right\} \tag{624.9}$$

From the preceding discussion it is known that unity is the most important term in the denominator for a considerable temperature range (in which the lifetime is $2\tau_i$, controlled by *e–e* collisions). Moreover, $\beta(p_0/n_0)$ becomes larger than unity when $T < T_a$, representing the influence of *h–h* collisions. But now the additional possibilities for *e–e* collisions are represented by the third term in the denominator.

When n_e is smaller than $n_0 = n_i^2/p_0$ for the temperature T_a, *h–h* collision recombination will take over as previously described, but it will remain predominant only down to a second temperature $T_b < T_a$, characterized by

$$\left.\begin{aligned} (n_e/p_0) &= \beta \\ &= \mu^{1/2}\left(\frac{1+2\mu}{2+\mu}\right)\exp\left[-\left(\frac{1-\mu}{1+\mu}\right)\frac{E_i}{kT}\right] \end{aligned}\right\} \text{ at } T = T_b \tag{624.10}$$

For all temperatures lower than T_b, the *e–e* recombinative term (n_e/n_0) is the largest in the denominator, and the lifetime increases much less rapidly with decreasing temperature. In this range the lifetime can be expressed as

$$\tau_A \approx \frac{2n_i^2\tau_i}{p_0 n_e} \quad T < T_b \tag{624.11}$$

which has the same *temperature* dependence† as Eq. (624.5) for an *n*-type sample.

When n_e is sufficiently large, τ_a changes over from $2\tau_i$ to the form of Eq. (624.11) before the temperature T_a is reached. Recombination is then *e–e* dominated over the entire temperature scale. Fig. 62.6 shows curves of τ_A vs. $1/T$ for the *p*-type sample previously discussed and with

† Lifetime varies as $T^{3/2}\exp\left[\left(\frac{\mu}{1+\mu}\right)\frac{E_i}{kT}\right]$.

various added pair densities. The transition temperature T_a for this example is 165°K ($p_0 = 2 \times 10^{16}$ cm^{-3}, $n_0 = 10^{11}$ cm^{-3}), and a temperature range of h–h domination can only occur when $n_e < 10^{11}$ cm^{-3}. This

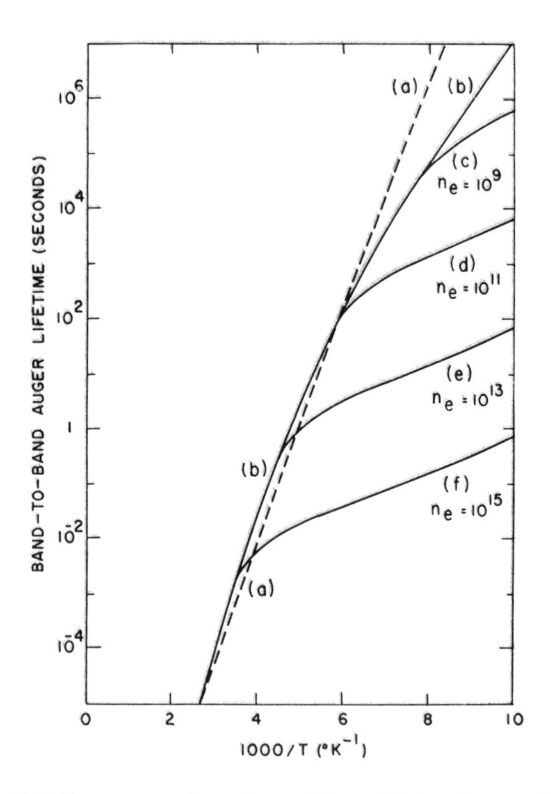

FIG. 62.6. Temperature dependence of Auger lifetime for a semiconductor with parameters as given by Eqs. (620.4) and (620.5). (a) For intrinsic material, $n_e \approx 0$. (b) For material doped with 2×10^{16} cm^{-3} excess acceptors when $n_e \approx 0$. (c) (d) (e) (f) Similarly doped material with progressively larger excess pair densities (in cm^{-3} as marked).

criterion is satisfied in curve (c) of Fig. 62.6, but never quite happens with curve (d). For the excess pair densities supposed in curves (e) and (f), e–e domination is complete at all temperatures.

(v) *Effect of a Smaller Intrinsic Gap*

It will be appreciated that much of the preceding discussion is of a purely academic character, in that we have scrutinized the temperature dependence of lifetime for various conditions without regard for other

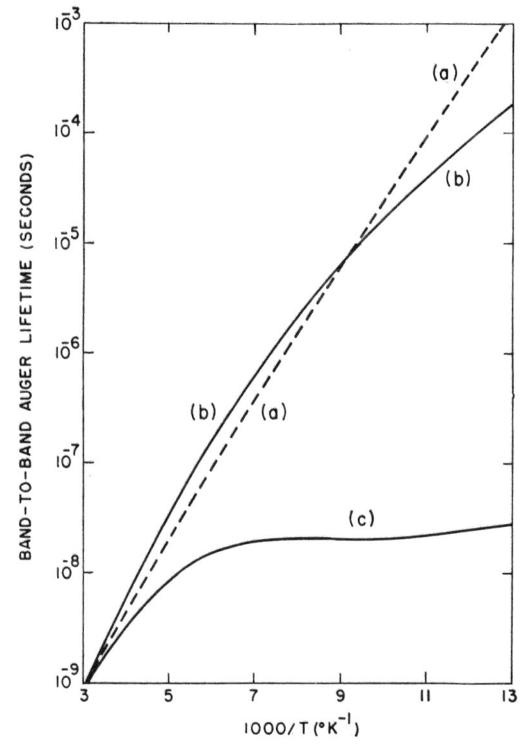

FIG. 62.7. Zero-modulation Auger lifetime for a semiconductor if $E_i \approx 0{\cdot}09$ eV and $\mu = 0{\cdot}25$. (a) In intrinsic material. (b) With 5×10^{16} cm^{-3} excess acceptors. (c) With 5×10^{16} cm^{-3} excess donors.

recombination mechanisms which would supervene in any real solid. Thus the extremely long lifetimes depicted for *p*-type material with small modulation could never be expected to be realized in practice; other, more vigorous, recombination mechanisms would inevitably dominate the behavior.

This is not so likely to happen for a material with a small energy gap (such as gray tin or mercury selenide for example). This statement can be made since Auger lifetimes and their temperature dependences are greatly reduced when the energy gap is smaller, and the factor differentiating between the probabilities of *e–e* and *h–h* processes is also smaller. As an illustration of this, Fig. 62.7 shows how the zero-modulation Auger lifetime should depend on temperature for intrinsic, *n*-type and *p*-type examples of a hypothetical semiconductor in which $E_i \sim 0{\cdot}09$ eV and $\mu = (m_c/m_v) = 0{\cdot}25$. This calculation is not exact in that degeneracy has been ignored, which is not a safe assumption with such a small energy gap and rather large doping concentrations. Nevertheless, the figure does indicate the general features to be expected of Auger recombination in a small gap semiconductor.

It will be noted that when the electrons form the majority population, τ_A is quite insensitive to temperature, since $T^{3/2}$ and

$$\exp\{[\mu/(1+\mu)](E_i/kT)\}$$

have almost canceling effects over a broad range. Also, the life-time for *p*-type material is much smaller than in the example previously discussed (for a much larger intrinsic gap). It is not, then, so implausible that Auger transitions could actually be the controlling factor in the lifetime of a small gap semiconductor in both *n*-type and *p*-type configurations.

Chapter 7

FREE CARRIER CAPTURE BY FLAWS

In this chapter, the important considerations are the excitation of free carriers from flaws, and the ways in which they can be recaptured. For the first two sections of the chapter, attention is focused on the interactions between a single species of donor flaw and the conduction band —when transitions to and from the valence band are negligible.† Section 7.1 describes the basic mechanisms which can contribute to such transitions, and Section 7.2 the dynamics of the models.‡ These problems differ from those of Chapters 5 and 6 in that a set of donor flaws represents a limited source of electrons for excitation.

Flaws must offer capture possibilities for both electrons and holes. This is discussed in Section 7.3 as a preparation for Chapters 8 and 9.

7.1 FLAW CAPTURE MECHANISMS §

As noted in Sub-section 4.3.2, a free electron can undergo a transition to a localized flaw state only if some suitable means is found of liberating the recombination energy. This energy can appear as a photon (radiative recombination), as lattice vibrations (phonon recombination), or as added kinetic energy for a free carrier (Auger recombination).

The model to be used for this section is illustrated by Fig. 71.1. As an arbitrary choice, the material is supposed to be *n*-type with donors

† Entirely similar considerations should apply for a model of transitions between a set of acceptor flaws and the valence band, if the conduction band can be ignored.

‡ Rittner (1956:**13**) has discussed the behavior of the extrinsic lifetime, but did so for a supposedly uncompensated semiconductor. This will not usually be a satisfactory assumption.

at the energy $(E_c - E_d)$ more numerous than all the various kinds of low-lying compensating acceptors. The reactions which are of interest for the present involve only the donors and the conduction band. Indeed, we shall go a stage beyond Fig. 71.1 in supposing temperatures

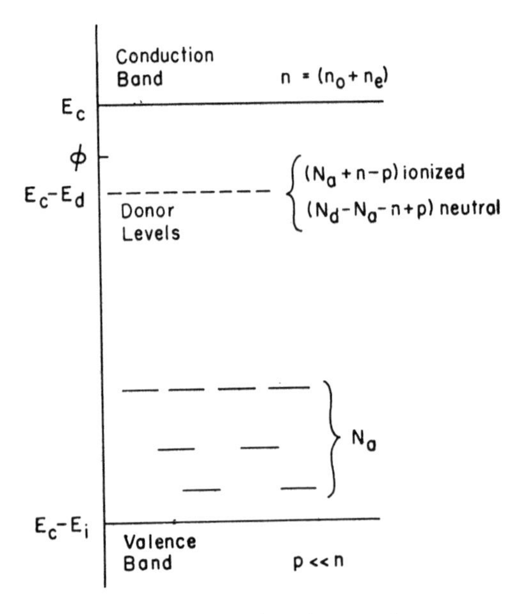

FIG. 71.1. Model of an *n*-type semiconductor at low temperatures used for the discussion of Sections 7.1 and 7.2.

so low that p is *completely negligible* in the expressions for neutral and ionized donor densities.†

As in the two previous chapters, spatial effects will be ignored in considering the continuity equation. The symbol g_E now denotes the rate at which electrons are excited from the donors to the conduction

† This does not imply that flaw ⟷ band transitions are not important at higher temperatures; in later sections the electron–hole recombination is studied which results from the interaction of flaws with *both* bands. But excitation and recombination between flaws and a single band can most readily be separated from other phenomena at low temperatures.

band by external stimulation. Then the continuity equation can be expressed in the form

$$g_E - \frac{dn_e}{dt} = n_e\left[\frac{1}{\tau_R} + \frac{1}{\tau_P} + \frac{1}{\tau_A}\right] \tag{710.1}$$

where the three lifetimes are characteristic of the radiative, phonon, and Auger processes. Each term on the right side of Eq. (710.1) is the *net* difference of recombination and generation rates for a process:

$$\left.\begin{aligned} \frac{n_e}{\tau_R} &= (r_R - g_R) \quad \text{radiative process} \\ \frac{n_e}{\tau_P} &= (r_P - g_P) \quad \text{phonon process} \\ \frac{n_e}{\tau_A} &= (r_A - g_A) \quad \text{Auger process} \end{aligned}\right\} \tag{710.2}$$

The following sub-sections consider the functional form of $(r-g)$ for each of these three processes, and comment on assessments which have been made about their importance.

7.1.1 Radiative Recombination

When the conduction band is non-degenerate and the probability function (even with excess electrons present) is of the Boltzmann type, the radiative capture rate r_R should be proportional to the total electron density n. It should also be proportional to the number of ionized donors with which recombination is possible. Thus when the rate is G_R in thermal equilibrium, the capture rate in general is

$$r_R = G_R\left[\frac{n(n+N_a)}{n_0(n_0+N_a)}\right] \tag{711.1}$$

Similarly, the generation rate must depend on the density of neutral donors. From the requirements of detailed balance in thermal equilibrium,

$$g_R = G_R\left[\frac{n_d - N_a - n}{N_d - N_a - n_0}\right] \tag{711.2}$$

The *net* radiative recombination is the difference of Eqs. (711.1) and

(711.2), and so

$$\frac{r_R - g_R}{n_e} = \frac{1}{\tau_R} = \left(\frac{G_R}{n_0}\right)\left[\frac{(N_d - N_a)}{(N_d - N_a - n_0)} + \frac{(n_0 + n_e)}{(n_0 + N_a)}\right] \qquad (711.3)$$

Some idea of the order of magnitude of G_R can be obtained from the model of Sclar and Burstein (1955:**30**), in which the cross-section for capture is calculated by assuming that donor centers are hydrogen-like. When the standard quantum-mechanical result (e.g. 1933:**3**) is renormalized to allow for a dielectric constant κ and effective mass m_c, the capture cross-section for electrons of energy E is

$$\sigma_R(E) \approx 1{\cdot}7 \times 10^{-22} \kappa^{1/2} \left(\frac{m_0}{m_c}\right)^2 \left(\frac{E_d}{E - E_c}\right) \text{cm}^2 \qquad (711.4)$$

The mean capture coefficient $\langle c_R \rangle$ can be determined as described in Sub-section 4.1.2; the result then is

$$\langle c_R \rangle = \frac{G_R}{n_0(n_0 + N_a)} \approx \frac{1{\cdot}2 \times 10^{-12} \kappa^{1/2} E_d}{T^{1/2}} \left(\frac{m_0}{m_c}\right)^{5/2} \text{cm}^3 \text{ sec}^{-1} \qquad (711.5)$$

with the donor ionization energy E_d expressed in electron-volts.

When impurity states are non-hydrogenic, the capture coefficient is not likely to differ from the result (711.5) by more than an order of magnitude. Yet the capture coefficients determined experimentally for various impurities in germanium and silicon are several orders of magnitude larger than provided for by Eq. (711.5). This is taken (1955:**30**) to indicate that radiative capture is much less efficient than the other possible processes.

It may be noted in passing that the radiative generation rate at thermal equilibrium can always be calculated by the method of van Roosbroeck and Shockley (1954:**15**). This requires knowledge of the optical absorption coefficient for impurity ionization over the spectrum. Such information is available for some types of chemical donors and acceptors in silicon (e.g. 1956:**17**, 1956:**18**, 1955:**38**). None of these impurities show the very strong optical absorption which would be a required sign for vigorous extrinsic radiative recombination.

The most direct proof of optical recombination is of course the detection of recombination radiation. Such radiation has been definitely associated with free carrier capture by impurities (e.g. 1956:**31**, 1960:**7**), but the small amounts of radiation detected demonstrate only that *some* radiative transitions take place, not that this is the dominant process.

7.1.2 Phonon Recombination

When the recombination energy of a captured electron is released as one or more phonons, the continuity equation has the same functional form as for radiative capture. For the capture rate r_p depends on both n and $(n+N_a)$; while the excitation rate depends on (N_d-N_a-n). As a companion to Eq. (711.3), the equation for phonon recombination can be expressed immediately as

$$\frac{r_P-g_P}{n_e} = \frac{1}{\tau_P} = \left(\frac{G_P}{n_0}\right)\left[\frac{(N_d-N_a)}{(N_d-N_a-n_0)} + \frac{(n_0+n_e)}{(n_0+N_a)}\right] \qquad (712.1)$$

A number of theoretical models have been advanced for electron excitation and capture involving absorption and emission of phonon(s). A crucial feature of such theories must be the way they allow for multi-phonon processes, since in many cases the energy to be accounted for is larger than possible for a single phonon.

One of the earlier models was that of Goodman *et al.* (1947:**2**), who described the interaction of the electron with the lattice by an interaction potential which depended only on the motion of the donor atom. They allowed for multi-phonon processes through higher order terms in the expansion of this interaction potential, but found that the resultant transition probability was diminished by a factor of 10^6 for each additional required phonon. Thus the model suggested a noticeable transition rate only for single-phonon processes.

Gummel and Lax (1955:**34**) have calculated the ionization rate due to single-phonon absorption, when a Coulomb wave-function is used for the final state. This increased the probability by two orders of magnitude compared with the Goodman–Lawson–Schiff result for a final state composed of plane Bloch waves. An increase by a further order of magnitude resulted from use of the Bardeen–Shockley deformation potential (1950:**7**), and Gummel and Lax then found that for typically expected semiconductor parameters the capture coefficient would be

$$\langle c_P \rangle = \frac{G_P}{n_0(n_0+N_a)} \approx 6\times 10^{-8} T^{-1/2} \text{ cm}^3 \text{ sec}^{-1} \qquad (712.2)$$

Kubo (1952:**11**) has questioned the Goodman–Lawson–Schiff treatment of multi-phonon processes. He argues that the lattice vibrational modes are dependent on the occupancy of electronic states, and shows that such an argument could lead to a greatly enhanced probability for transitions involving several phonons. Haken (1954:**19**) has given rather different arguments for expecting reasonable probabilities for multi-phonon transitions.

A comprehensive account of multi-phonon capture is given by Lax (1960:**15**), based on the reasonable premise that capture takes place first into an excited state of large orbit. This is followed by a cascade of one-phonon transitions, the electron finally reaching the ground state. Both optical and acoustical branch phonons can assist in these processes, which are dependent on the charge carried by the impurity center. It appears that Lax's model can account for the varied forms of capture cross-section temperature dependence, and is capable of explaining the extremely large cross-sections (as large as 10^{-12} cm^2) exhibited by some types of impurity.

7.1.3 Auger Recombination

For the extrinsic n-type model currently under discussion, the only Auger capture process which can occur involves electron capture by a donor when a second free electron is excited to a high energy state. Then the recombination rate should be proportional to n^2 and to the density of ionized donors which can receive an electron:

$$r_A = G_A\left[\frac{n^2(n+N_a)}{n_0{}^2(n_0+N_a)}\right] \tag{713.1}$$

The excitation rate must be proportional† to n and to the number of neutral donors. Detailed balance in thermal equilibrium then demands that

$$g_A = G_A\left[\frac{n(N_d-N_a-n)}{n_0(N_d-N_a-n_0)}\right] \tag{713.2}$$

From the difference of Eqs. (713.1) and (713.2) in non-equilibrium,

† This proportionality is required since the supply of fast electrons which can ionize donors is a constant fraction of the total free electron density, provided that $P_e(E) = \exp[(\phi_n-E)/kT]$.

the Auger lifetime of Eq. (710.2) will satisfy

$$\frac{r_A - g_A}{n_e} = \frac{1}{\tau_A} = \frac{G_A(n_0 + n_e)}{n_0^2}\left[\frac{(N_d - N_a)}{(N_d - N_a - n_0)} + \frac{(n_0 + n_e)}{(n_0 + N_a)}\right] \tag{713.3}$$

Sclar and Burstein (1955:**30**) have calculated G_A for a situation involving impurities with hydrogen-like levels, using the Born approximation (1926:**2**). This procedure overestimates the cross-section (1949:**9**), but probably not to an alarming extent, and it does enable use of the well-known result (1949:**8**) for the cross-section of hydrogen atoms with electrons incident. Sclar and Burstein renormalize this result to allow for effective mass and dielectric constant, and integrate over conduction states to obtain the total transition rate. The result is

$$\frac{\langle c_A \rangle}{n_0} = \frac{G_A}{n_0^2(n_0 + N_a)} \approx \frac{2 \times 10^{-20}(m_0/m_c)^2}{T^2 E_d} \text{ cm}^6 \text{ sec}^{-1} \tag{713.4}$$

if E_d is expressed in electron-volts.

This result will be modified for impurities with non-hydrogenic states, and will be considerably different if the impurity is not electrically neutral after capturing an electron by an Auger process (as is often the case for multivalent flaws).

Bess (1957:**17**) has also calculated Auger transition rates for hydrogen-like impurities in the Born approximation. The most important difference from Sclar and Burstein's model is the consideration of other kinds of Auger process which become important when there is a considerable free hole density. This will be referred to in Section 7.3.

7.1.4 Relative Probability of the Various Processes

Enough has been said already to indicate that radiative capture—while always present to some extent—is unlikely to dominate the recombination of electrons with impurities. The choice for a dominant process must lie between phonon and Auger recombination.

Lax (1960:**15**) suggests that phonon-aided recombination of the cascade type will usually prevail unless the center bears a strong charge which is repulsive for the carrier to be captured. For monovalent donors, each ionized center carries a charge q which assists in Coulomb attraction of a free electron. It is only for multivalent flaws that electron capture may be required by centers which already have a negative charge of one or more units.

Certainly, measurements of the recapture time for simple donors do not usually show a functional dependence which would indicate the activity of Auger processes. For the sake of completeness, however, Section 7.2 does consider the functional behavior of the lifetime both for phonon-dominated recombination [Eq. (712.1)] and for Auger-dominated capture [Eq. (713.3)].

7.2 BEHAVIOR OF THE EXTRINSIC LIFETIME

7.2.1 For Phonon-aided Recombination

Eq. (712.1) describes the relationship of excess carrier density to lifetime when Auger and radiative capture processes are of very minor significance. The zero-modulation lifetime τ_0 can be written as

$$\tau_0 = \frac{n_0(N_a+n_0)}{G_P}\left[n_0 + \frac{(N_a+n_0)(N_d-N_a)}{(N_d-N_a-n_0)}\right]^{-1} \qquad (721.1)$$

It should be noted that the quantity $n_0(N_a+n_0)/G_P$ in Eq. (721.1) is likely to be but feebly dependent on the temperature, since this corresponds to $1/\langle c_P \rangle$ of Eq. (712.2).

In terms of τ_0, the lifetime for any finite modulation is

$$\tau = \tau_0\left[\frac{n_0(N_d-N_a-n_0)+(N_a+n_0)(N_d-N_a)}{(n_0+n_e)(N_d-N_a-n_0)+(N_a+n_0)(N_d-N_a)}\right] \qquad (721.2)$$

which falls below τ_0 when n_e exceeds whichever is the larger of n_0 or N_a.

In practice, deliberate extrinsic modulation of a semiconductor is usually carried out at very low temperatures—such that $n_0 \ll N_a < N_d$. The temperature range for which this condition is satisfied has been discussed in Sub-section 3.2.2. Equations (721.1) and (721.2) simplify at low temperatures to

$$\tau_0 = \frac{n_0}{G_P} = \frac{1}{N_a\langle c_P \rangle}, \qquad n_0 \ll N_a < N_d \qquad (721.3)$$

and

$$\tau = \frac{\tau_0}{1+n_e/N_a}, \qquad n_0 \ll N_a < N_d \qquad (721.4)$$

This form of behavior† is closely parallel to that of Chapter 5 for band-to-band recombination in a semiconductor with a temperature independent majority carrier density (corresponding here with the density of ionized donors).

When a semiconductor is maintained at a very low temperature, so-called "background radiation" leaked from neighboring warmer surfaces often makes n considerably larger than n_0 even before any deliberate "signal" illumination is turned on. For a small signal, the lifetime of importance is then the *incremental lifetime* $\tau_{\text{inc}} = (\mathrm{d}n_e/\mathrm{d}g_E)$ rather than (n_e/g_E) itself. In the temperature range for which Eqs. (721.3) and (721.4) are valid,

$$\tau_{\text{inc}} = \frac{\mathrm{d}n_e}{\mathrm{d}g_E} = \frac{\tau_0}{(1+2n_e/\mathcal{N}_a)} \tag{721.5}$$

It is possible for τ_{inc} to be only a minute fraction of the lifetime τ_0 enjoyed when "background radiation" is eliminated.

Excess generation produced by photons from outside the semiconductor hinges on how many donors are already ionized. It is not possible for n_e to exceed $(\mathcal{N}_d - \mathcal{N}_a - n_0)$, and when this limiting value is reached, photons are not absorbed usefully at all.‡ Thus if the cross-section for absorption of a photon by a neutral donor is σ_d, the absorption coefficient is σ_d multiplied by $(\mathcal{N}_d - \mathcal{N}_a - n)$, the density of such donors. For an incident photon flux I, the ionization rate becomes

$$g_E = I\sigma_d(\mathcal{N}_d - \mathcal{N}_a - n) \tag{721.6}$$

Under steady state conditions, g_E is also equal to (n_e/τ), with a lifetime given by Eq. (721.2) in the general case, or by Eq. (721.4) at sufficiently low temperatures. Then n_e is related to I by a quadratic equation. For the very low temperature range when $\tau_0 = 1/\mathcal{N}_a\langle c_P\rangle$, this quadratic relationship is

$$n_e^2 + n_e[\mathcal{N}_a + I\sigma_d/\langle c_P\rangle] = (\mathcal{N}_d - \mathcal{N}_a)I\sigma_d/\langle c_P\rangle \tag{721.7}$$

When the incident photon flux is small, n_e is directly proportional to I, but with increasing flux a range of proportionality to $I^{1/2}$ is reached.

† As one experimental example, Ascarelli and Brown (1960:**13**) find that the recombination time for electrons with As and Sb donors in Ge at 4°K is in accordance with Eq. (721.4). They study transient decay, which is bimolecular for large modulation and becomes exponential as expected when $n_e < \mathcal{N}_a$.

‡ In order to keep the problem reasonably simple it is assumed that stimulated radiative recombination is too slow a process to have any influence.

This gives way in turn to a saturation condition when I is large enough to make n_e approach $(N_d - N_a)$. These properties of the relationship (721.7) can be seen in the calculated curves of Fig. 72.1. The two curves shown are for a set of donors which is either 1% or 10% compensated.

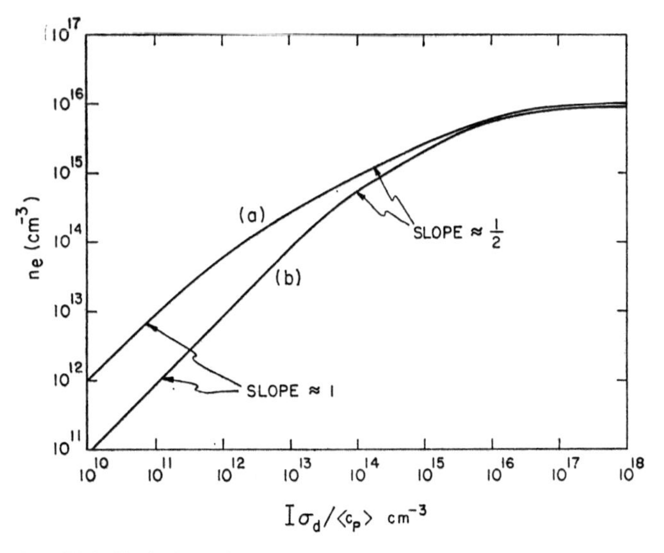

FIG. 72.1. Variation of excess electron density with incident photon flux I, for a semiconductor with $N_d = 10^{16}$ cm^{-3} donor centers and (a) 10^{14} cm^{-3}, (b) 10^{15} cm^{-3} compensating acceptor levels. Temperature is supposed sufficiently low to make $n_0 \ll N_a < N_d$.

7.2.2 FOR AUGER RECOMBINATION

The essential features of excess carrier dynamics with Auger recombination dominant can be seen by considering the behavior for very low temperatures, when $n_0 \ll N_a < N_d$. In this temperature range, the lifetime of Eq. (713.3) reduces for *very small modulation* to

$$\tau_0 = \frac{n_0}{G_A}, \qquad n_0 \ll N_a < N_d \tag{722.1}$$

Both n_0 and G_A are functions of temperature, the dependence of n_0

being given by Eq. (322.8). If the Sclar and Burstein model leading to Eq. (713.4) is at all realistic, G_A has essentially the temperature dependence of n_0^2 at low temperatures.† Thus τ_0 should vary approximately as $\exp(E_d/kT)$.

An interesting aspect of Auger recombination is that the zero-modulation lifetime τ_0 should not depend on the density of compensating centers until this becomes comparable with N_d itself. This can be verified by substitution from Eqs. (322.8) and (713.4) into Eq. (722.1).

With the model of phonon recombination (Sub-section 7.2.1) the lifetime was degraded below τ_0 only when n_e became comparable with the density N_a of normally vacant donors. However, for Auger recombination the lifetime τ_0 holds good only when $n_e \ll n_0$. A second change in the behavior occurs for excess electron densities comparable with N_a. From Eqs. (713.3) and (722.1),

$$\tau = \frac{\tau_0}{(1+n_e/n_0)(1+n_e/N_a)}, \qquad \text{low temperatures} \qquad (722.2)$$

This form of concentration dependence occurs because Auger capture involves two electrons and one ionized donor.

The incremental lifetime when Auger recombination dominates (just as for the previously considered model of phonon recombination) can be drastically reduced when background radiation maintains a steady non-equilibrium population of electrons. The relation between n_e and incident photon flux is cubic, and there are possibilities for n_e to vary directly as I, as $I^{1/2}$, and as $I^{1/3}$ before saturation is reached. The procedure to be followed is obvious and will not be discussed further.

For many kinds of impurity, the Auger low-modulation lifetime is likely to be much larger than that for phonon–cascade capture. But since the Auger lifetime decreases rapidly when excess carriers are added, the electron capture can become dominated by Auger transitions for sufficiently strong modulation. Conditions for which the two kinds of process go on at the same rate depend on the type of impurity, degree of compensation, temperature *and* incident photon flux. The preponderance of phonon or Auger recombination may be controlled by the extent to which "background radiation" can be suppressed.

† The exponential factor involved should be more powerful than the factor T^{-2} in promoting temperature dependence.

7.3 INTERACTION WITH BOTH BANDS

The preceding discussion has been concerned exclusively with transitions between a set of localized levels and *one* band (specifically, between donors and the conduction band). As an introduction to the subject matter of the next two chapters, it must now be acknowledged that a localized flaw of any kind will have *some* interaction with both the valence and conduction bands. Not only can a neutral donor give the conduction band an electron, and an ionized donor capture such an electron; there must be a chance that a neutral donor can capture a free hole, and that an ionized donor can expel a hole to the valence band.

The previously discussed radiative, phonon and Auger capture processes must be kept in mind for the interactions of a flaw with both bands. Radiative capture from the conduction band to flaw levels has been demonstrated by observation of emitted photons both for flaws very close to E_c and for flaws almost as low as the valence band. Thus Koenig and Brown (1960:**7**) have detected 0·01 eV photons emitted in electron capture to shallow antimony donor states in germanium. At the opposite end of the energy scale, Haynes and Westphal (1956:**31**) report that photons are liberated when electrons drop from the silicon conduction band into boron, gallium and indium acceptor states; $h\nu$ is then almost as large as E_i. The observation of emitted photons shows only that *some* capture is radiative, not that radiative capture is the dominant process, and indeed Koenig and Brown estimate that only 1 in 10^9 of the transitions they induced were radiative. On the other hand, Pokrovsky and Svistunova (1961 : **6**) demonstrate that *most* of the capture acts of free electrons by neutral indium acceptors in silicon are radiative. We may expect that a flaw which captures carriers from one band predominantly by one process can be controled by quite different processes in its relationship with the other band.

Bess (1957:**17**) considered a hydrogenic model for a flaw level a nd calculated the Auger capture coefficients for both bands. Four processes must be considered; electron capture using an electron or a hole as the recoil particle, and hole capture with the same two choices of recoil particle. Bess notes that excitons as well as free carrier pairs can be annihilated by Auger processes involving flaws; however, he finds that the rate of this should be very small, a conclusion in agreement with that of Toyazawa (1954:**18**).

The phonon-cascade model of Lax (1960:**15**), previously referred to in Sub-section 7.1.2, allows for capture of both kinds of free carrier.

It is likely that this kind of process is the dominant one for most kinds of flaws encountered in semiconductors, since it can account in a plausible fashion for the wide range of observed capture cross-sections and of cross-section temperature dependences.

Phonon-aided recombination requires the capture cross-section to be concentration independent, which experiment indicates to be usually the case. Cross-sections proportional to the majority carrier density, as reported for *some* kinds of flaw in silicon (1955:**36**, 1955:**37**) and in lead sulfide (1953:**13**), are an indication of Auger activity. Lax suggests that in these cases the flaws have a double or treble repulsive charge for the majority carrier to be captured, and that this repulsion inhibits phonon recombination to such an extent that Auger recombination is enabled to take over. As can be seen from several published tables (1958:**15**, 1960:**15**, 1960:**16**) for various kinds of center in silicon and germanium, the capture cross-sections show a marked progression with flaw charge.

The asymmetry of capture cross-sections has a profound influence on the principal function of a flaw—whether it should be regarded as a recombination center for holes and electrons or as a trap for one kind of free carrier. Thus when a flaw captures a free electron, it can return to its original charge state in two ways:

(a) The electron can be re-excited to the conduction band. In this case, the flaw has behaved as a *temporary electron trap.*

(b) The flaw instead can capture a free hole. In this case the flaw has behaved as a *recombination center.*

In practice, flaws will perform both of these functions to a greater or lesser degree. The relative importance of trapping and recombination depends on the relationship of the flaw level to the Fermi energy and on the asymmetry of the capture cross-sections.

The distinction between the trapping and recombinative functions made above is in agreement with that drawn by Rose (e.g. 1955:**16**, 1957:**20**) and Bube (1960:**10**) among other writers. It should be pointed out that when the energy, cross-sections, etc., of flaws places them definitely in the recombination center class, they may still have a considerable *trapping effect* in the sense that the flaws produce a marked disparity between the densities of excess electrons and excess holes. This is demonstrated in the next chapter.

Chapter 8

RECOMBINATION THROUGH A SET OF MONOVALENT FLAWS

THE band-to-band models of electron–hole recombination described in Chapters 5 and 6 are particularly important for small energy gap semiconductors. It is more likely that the dominant mechanism for electron–hole annihilation in a material with a large energy gap will involve the successive capture of an electron and a hole by a flaw. The importance of this kind of process has been recognized for a long time by those working in the field of phosphors (e.g. 1939:**2**), but it was not applied to semiconductors until a number of years later (1952:**7**, 1952:**8**).

The concept of carrier capture by a flaw was explored in the previous chapter, and it was noted at that time that flaws tend to interact with free carriers of both types. As the title of the present chapter indicates, it is now proposed to consider the dynamics of a semiconductor when a single species of monovalent flaw controls the electron–hole recombination rate. More complicated models are deferred to Chapter 9.

8.1 THE TWO CONTINUITY EQUATIONS

8.1.1 Capture Cross-sections and Capture Coefficients

The model forming the basis for this chapter is shown in Fig. 81.1. Monovalent flaws of density N_f per unit volume each present a level at energy E_f within the intrinsic gap. The two possible states of this flaw are called "empty" and "full". When empty, a flaw has a cross-section σ_n for capturing a free electron. When the charge on the center has been changed by $-q$ through addition of such an electron, a flaw is full, and has a cross section σ_p for hole capture.

It will be noted that we have not specified whether the flaw is donor-like or acceptor-like in character. If a flaw is donor-like, then it will be electrically neutral when "full" and will be ionized (carrying a net charge q) when empty. The capture cross-sections for this kind of flaw must have a relationship such that $\sigma_n > \sigma_p$; since electron capture is aided by Coulomb attraction, but hole capture is not. Conversely,

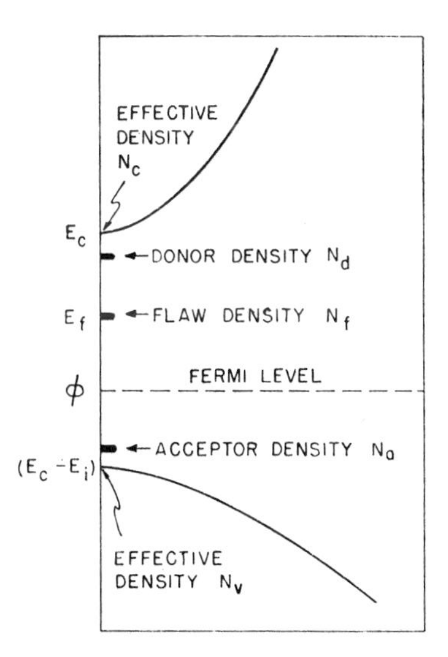

FIG. 81.1. Semiconductor model used in considering recombination through the set of $\mathcal{N}_f$ flaws.

$\sigma_p > \sigma_n$ for an acceptor-like flaw which is neutral when "empty" and charged when "full". The continuity equations, and their solutions for flaw recombination, can be studied without need for distinguishing between donor-like or acceptor-like behavior of a flaw.

Fig. 81.1 indicates donor and acceptor impurities in addition to the flaws of interest. It is assumed that these are far above and below the Fermi level ϕ, so that they remain permanently ionized and do not have any direct influence on electronic transitions. Whether $(n-p)$ is larger than or smaller than $(\mathcal{N}_d - \mathcal{N}_a)$ depends on whether the flaws are donor-like or acceptor-like in character; however, we do not concern ourselves with the values of $\mathcal{N}_d$ and $\mathcal{N}_a$ but use instead the Fermi level as the sole criterion of the equilibrium free carrier densities:

$$\left.\begin{aligned} n_0 &= N_c \mathscr{F}_{1/2}\left(\frac{\phi - E_c}{kT}\right) \\ p_0 &= N_v \mathscr{F}_{1/2}\left(\frac{E_c - E_i - \phi}{kT}\right) \end{aligned}\right\} \tag{811.1}$$

In practice, it will be assumed throughout this chapter that the free carrier densities are non-degenerate,† so that

$$\left.\begin{aligned} n_0 &= N_c \exp\left(\frac{\phi - E_c}{kT}\right) \\ p_0 &= N_v \exp\left(\frac{E_c - E_i - \phi}{kT}\right) \end{aligned}\right\} \tag{811.2}$$

in thermal equilibrium, and

$$\left.\begin{aligned} (n_0 + n_e) &= n = N_c \exp\left(\frac{\phi_n - E_c}{kT}\right) \\ (p_0 + p_e) &= p = N_v \exp\left(\frac{E_c - E_i - \phi_p}{kT}\right) \end{aligned}\right\} \tag{811.3}$$

even when excess carriers are present.

The possibilities for capture of electrons and holes depend on the fraction $P_e(E_f)$ of the flaws which are "filled". In thermal equilibrium this can be expressed in terms of the Fermi level:

$$f(E_f) = \frac{1}{1 + \exp\left(\frac{E_f - \phi}{kT}\right)} \tag{811.4}$$

Note that no spin degeneracy factor is used here. The "empty" and "full" conditions of a flaw will normally have different spin and orbital degeneracy choices, but this is absorbed in the definition of E_f.

† This assumption has been made in the well known treatment of Shockley and Read (1952:**7**) and in most subsequent discsssions of the subject. Landsberg (1957:**22**) attempted to treat the more complicated problem of a degenerate semiconductor, but was forced to treat the result in terms of integrals which can only be evaluated by making special assumptions.

It is useful at this point to define a quantity n_1 as the thermal free electron density when ϕ is coincident with E_f; and the corresponding hole density p_1. Thus

$$\left.\begin{aligned} n_1 &= N_c \exp\left(\frac{E_f - E_c}{kT}\right) = n_0 \exp\left(\frac{E_f - \phi}{kT}\right) \\ p_1 &= N_v \exp\left(\frac{E_c - E_i - E_f}{kT}\right) = p_0 \exp\left(\frac{\phi - E_f}{kT}\right) \end{aligned}\right\} \quad (811.5)$$

in terms of which

$$f(E_f) = \frac{n_0}{n_0 + n_1} = \frac{p_1}{p_0 + p_1} \quad (811.6)$$

When the free carrier densities are different from those of thermal equilibrium, any discrepancy between n_e and p_e must be accounted for by a change in the number of "full" flaws and by an electrostatic charge on the semiconductor. Then if the semiconductor is required to remain electrically neutral,

$$[1 - P_h(E_f)] = P_e(E_f) = \left[\frac{p_1}{p_0 + p_1} + \frac{p_e - n_e}{N_f}\right] \quad (811.7)$$

At all times, the flaws are capturing and re-exciting electrons and holes to various energy states in the conduction and valence bands. As an example, the rate of electron capture r must depend on the density of empty flaws, $N_f P_h(E_f)$. It also depends on an integral over all occupied conduction band states and the capture coefficient therefrom:

$$r = N_f P_h(E_f) \int_{E_c}^{\infty} c_n(E) \, . \, P_e(E) \, . \, g_c(E) \, . \, \mathrm{d}E \quad (811.8)$$

According to the procedures of Sub-section 4.1.2, this can be written

$$r = n \langle c_n \rangle N_f P_h(E_f) \quad (811.9)$$

It must of course be remembered that $\langle c_n \rangle$ has an unambiguous meaning only if the electron distribution is non-degenerate and well-behaved, so that

$$P_e(E) \approx \exp\left(\frac{\phi_n - E}{kT}\right)$$

For the discussion of electron–hole recombination through flaws, it is useful to compound two more symbols from N_f and $\langle c_n \rangle$,

$$C_n = \frac{1}{\tau_{n0}} = N_f \langle c_n \rangle \tag{811.10}$$

Now $C_n\,dt$ is the probability that an electron will be captured by any of a set of N_f empty flaws within the interval dt. τ_{n0} is the shortest possible time constant for electron capture.

As a companion to electron capture, the hole capture rate in a non-degenerate semiconductor can be expressed as

$$r' = p \langle c_p \rangle N_f P_e(E_f) \tag{811.11}$$

where $\langle c_p \rangle$ is the appropriate average over valence band states. Corresponding with Eq. (811.10), the probability that a hole will be captured in unit time by any of a set of "full flaws" is written

$$C_p = \frac{1}{\tau_{p0}} = N_f \langle c_p \rangle \tag{811.12}$$

The quantities C_n and C_p are of course usually appreciably different. For a donor-like flaw, the ratio $\gamma = (C_p/C_n) = (\tau_{n0}/\tau_{p0})$ is smaller than unity, while $\gamma > 1$ with acceptor centers.

8.1.2 Balance Between Generation and Recombination

Equations (811.9) and (811.10) indicate that the electron capture rate should be written in the form

$$r = \frac{n P_h(E_f)}{\tau_{n0}} \tag{812.1}$$

where the flaw occupancy is governed by Eq. (811.7). In this equation, n and $P_h(E_f)$ are sensitive to the presence of excess carriers (and τ_{n0} may be as well if Auger processes are important in the band-flaw transitions). In thermal equilibrium, flaws capture and emit electrons at the same rate, which from Eqs. (812.1) and (811.7) is

$$G = \frac{n_0 n_1}{\tau_{n0}(n_0 + n_1)} \tag{812.2}$$

Since in general the electron emission rate is expected to depend on

$P_e(E_f)$, this must be given by

$$g = \frac{n_1 P_e(E_f)}{\tau_{n0}} \tag{812.3}$$

Thus the *net* rate of electron capture is

$$(r-g) = \frac{nP_h(E_f) - n_1 P_e(E_f)}{\tau_{n0}}$$

$$= \frac{1}{\tau_{n0}}\left[\frac{(n_0+n_1+n_e)(n_e-p_e)}{N_f} + \frac{n_e n_1}{(n_1+n_0)}\right] \tag{812.4}$$

Similarly, the net rate of hole capture by the flaws is

$$(r'-g') = \frac{pP_e(E_f) - p_1 P_h(E_f)}{\tau_{p0}}$$

$$= \frac{1}{\tau_{p0}}\left[\frac{(p_0+p_1+p_e)(p_e-n_e)}{N_f} + \frac{p_e p_1}{(p_0+p_1)}\right] \tag{812.5}$$

When a model for a semiconductor is supposed for which the transitions to the flaw levels represent the only important chances for recombination, the electron lifetime τ_n (of Sub-section 4.2.1) is equal to $n_e/(r-g)$, and the hole lifetime $\tau_p = p_e/(r'-g')$. In contrast to the models considered in Chapters 5 and 6, τ_n is not usually equal to τ_p.

If we suppose a large semiconductor sample with no drift or diffusion currents, and let g_E be the rate at which hole–electron pairs are created by external stimulation, the continuity equations (420.5) and (420.6) become

$$g_E - \frac{\mathrm{d}n_e}{\mathrm{d}t} = \frac{n_e}{\tau_n} = \frac{1}{\tau_{n0}}\left[\frac{(n_0+n_1+n_e)(n_e-p_e)}{N_f} + \frac{n_e n_1}{(n_0+n_1)}\right] \tag{812.6}$$

and

$$g_E - \frac{\mathrm{d}p_e}{\mathrm{d}t} = \frac{p_e}{\tau_p} = \frac{1}{\tau_{p0}}\left[\frac{(p_0+p_1+p_e)(p_e-n_e)}{N_f} + \frac{p_e p_1}{(p_0+p_1)}\right] \tag{812.7}$$

Under steady state illumination, $\tau_n = (n_e/g_E)$ and $\tau_p = (p_e/g_E)$, and so the electron and hole lifetimes are in the ratio of their respective excess densities. We shall see subsequently that $n_e \neq p_e$ unless N_f is small or unless the Fermi level and flaw level have a special relationship, $p_1\tau_{n0} = p_0\tau_{p0}$.

When excess generation ceases, the lifetime for each kind of carrier is the inverse of the logarithmic decrement, $\tau_n = -n_e(dt/dn_e)$ and $\tau_p = -p_e(dt/dp_e)$. The principal difficulty, as may be seen from Eqs. (812.6) and (812.7), is that these expressions involve *both* n_e and p_e.

What makes the problem so complicated is that the flaws indulge in both recombination and trapping. It was noted in Section 7.3 that a flaw is behaving primarily as a *recombination center* if, after capturing an electron, it is most likely to return to the empty condition by capturing a free hole. On the other hand, the flaw is acting primarily as an *electron trap* if it is more likely to return the electron to the conduction band.

The relative strengths of the recombinative and trapping tendencies vary with the conditions of excitation. Steady state excitation is at least a little simpler to understand in that the *net* trapping rate is zero. But during transient decay, (dn_e/dt) and (dp_e/dt) vary continuously during the course of the decay, and their difference is the net rate at which flaws are trapping electrons.

This chapter explores so far as practicable the steady state relationship of illumination rate to the excess densities n_e, p_e; and the dynamics of excess carrier decay. However, a complete analytic solution is not possible for the transient problem with N_f, n_e and p_e of arbitrary magnitude. In a transient case, Eqs. (812.6) and (812.7) can be solved simultaneously to yield an equation for n_e and its time derivatives, and another for p_e and its derivatives. But these highly non-linear second-order differential equations can at best be reduced only to a general form of Abel's differential equation of the first kind (1956:**30**). Solutions are known only for certain restrictive values of the parameters, since this equation defines new transcendental functions. Perturbation methods necessarily fail since all terms in the equations assume comparable importance in some part of the decay.

8.1.3 Adoption of a Dimensionless Notation

In some previous work on transient decay through flaws it has been found convenient (1958:**13**, 1961:**1**) to resort at times to a dimensionless notation. Since much of the discussion concerns p-type semiconductors, the equilibrium hole density p_0 is used as a normalizing parameter. In the notation to be used, $x = (n_e/p_0)$ and $y = (p_e/p_0)$ are the important variables; and $N = (N_f/p_0)$, $a = (n_1/p_0)$ and $b = (p_1/p_0)$ are the parameters associated with them in (812.6) and (812.7). Thus

$ab = (n_0/p_0)$, which is less than unity for a p-type semiconductor, but becomes larger than unity in n-type material.

The symbol $\gamma = (\tau_{n0}/\tau_{p0})$ has previously been defined. The time scale is made dimensionless by setting $\mathscr{T} = (t/\tau_{n0})$. In this notation, $x' = (dx/d\mathscr{T})$, etc. The externally provoked generation rate is expressed as the dimensionless quantity $G_E = (g_E\tau_{n0}/p_0)$.

In terms of these symbols, the continuity equations (812.6) and (812.7) become

$$G_E - x' = \frac{(x-y)[x+a(1+b)]}{N} + \frac{x}{1+b} \tag{813.1}$$

and

$$G_E - y' = \frac{\gamma(y-x)[y+1+b]}{N} + \frac{\gamma b y}{1+b} \tag{813.2}$$

8.1.4 Steady State and Transient Decay Equations

When the generation rate G_E is continued for a long time, the terms x' and y' in (813.1) and (813.2) disappear. These two equations can then be solved simultaneously, giving separate cubic equations in x and y:

$$\begin{aligned} x^3 + x^2\{(1+a+2ab) + N/(1+b) - G_E(1+1/\gamma)\} + \\ + x\{a(1+b)(1+ab) + Nab/(1+b) - \\ - G_E(1+b)(1+a+2a/\gamma) - NG_E(2+b)/(1+b)\} - \\ - G_E\{a(1+b)^2(1+a/\gamma) - N(G_E - ab)\} = 0 \end{aligned} \tag{814.1}$$

and

$$\begin{aligned} y^3 + y^2\{(2+b+ab) + Nb/(1+b) - G_E(1+1/\gamma)\} + \\ + y\{(1+b)(1+ab) + Nb/(1+b) - \\ - (G_E/\gamma)(1+b)(1+a+2\gamma) - NG_E(1+2b)/\gamma(1+b)\} - \\ - G_E\{(1+b)^2(1+a/\gamma) - N(G_E-\gamma)/\gamma^2\} = 0 \end{aligned} \tag{814.2}$$

The usual Shockley–Read (1952:**7**) treatment discusses the solutions only for small flaw density or for small excess carrier densities. The former is the case for which τ_n and τ_p coincide; this model is reviewed in Section 8.3. Section 8.4 is concerned with steady state conditions for arbitrary flaw density and carrier densities, and includes the Shockley–Read result as the small-modulation limiting case.

It is also possible to solve Eqs. (813.1) and (813.2) simultaneously for the conditions of transient decay, when $G_E = 0$. Thus Eq. (813.1) leads to

$$y = \frac{\mathcal{N}x' + x[x + a(1+b) + \mathcal{N}/(1+b)]}{x + a(1+b)} \qquad (814.3)$$

This substitution can be made at three places in Eq. (813.2), and the result of differentiating y placed on the left side of that equation. The result is a second-order equation for x:

$$\begin{aligned} &\mathcal{N}\{x''[x + a(1+b)] - x'^2(1-\gamma)\} + \\ &\quad + x'\{x^2(1+\gamma) + x[(1+b)(\gamma + \gamma a + 2a) + \\ &\qquad + \gamma\mathcal{N}(2+b)/(1+b)] + a[(1+b)^2(a+\gamma) + \mathcal{N}(1+\gamma b)]\} + \\ &\qquad\quad + \gamma x\{x^2 + x[(1+a+2ab) + \mathcal{N}/(1+b)] + \\ &\qquad\qquad + a[(1+b)(1+ab) + \mathcal{N}b/(1+b)]\} = 0 \qquad (814.4) \end{aligned}$$

The corresponding equation describing the decay of y is

$$\begin{aligned} &\mathcal{N}\{y''(y+1+b) - y'^2(1-1/\gamma)\} + \\ &\quad + y'\{y^2(1+\gamma) + y[(1+b)(1+a+2\gamma) + \\ &\qquad + \mathcal{N}(1+2b)/(1+b)] + [(1+b)^2(a+\gamma) + \mathcal{N}(1+\gamma b)]\} + \\ &\qquad\quad + \gamma y\{y^2 + y[(2+b+ab) + \mathcal{N}b/(1+b)] + \\ &\qquad\qquad + [(1+b)(1+ab) + \mathcal{N}b/(1+b)]\} = 0 \qquad (814.5) \end{aligned}$$

Section 8.5 is devoted to a review of the modes of decay for arbitrary densities of flaws. The problem is divided into cases of Class I and Class II decay, this sub-division being made as described below.

8.2 THE CRITERIA OF TRAPPING

8.2.1 Class I and Class II Situations

It might seem that the equations describing the behavior of excess electrons and holes could be simplified in four ways, by noting which terms are most important for n-type and p-type semiconductors ($\phi > \phi_i$ and $\phi < \phi_i$), and for flaws in the upper and lower halves of the intrinsic gap ($E_f > \phi_i$ and $E_f < \phi_i$). This approach leads, however, to needless duplication, since only two of the four types of situation mentioned above are actually different.

Thus merely an interchange of the roles of electrons and holes separates the description of an n-type semiconductor with $E_f > \phi_i$ and of a p-type material with $E_f < \phi_i$. Similarly, results deduced for a model when $E_f > \phi_i > \phi$ can be applied to the case of $\phi > \phi_i > E_f$ by interchanging the symbols.

This chapter will use the term Class I for situations in which the flaw level and Fermi energy are in the same half of the intrinsic gap, and Class II for situations in which they are in opposite halves of the gap. This follows the terminology of Nomura and Blakemore (1958:**13**, 1961:**1**).

As mentioned at the beginning of Sub-section 8.1.3, many of the solutions given in this chapter are for a p-type semiconductor. This choice is a purely arbitrary one and does not prevent us from regarding the same processes as going on in n-type Class I and Class II situations. However, the expressions given in Section 8.5 are *usually* given in the nomenclature for *p-type* Class I decay ($E_f < \phi_i$) and *p-type* Class II decay ($E_f > \phi_i$).

8.2.2 Electron and Hole Trapping

As will be demonstrated in Sub-section 8.2.3, trapping is negligible when the flaw density is sufficiently small, and p_e is then equal to n_e whether these excess densities are large or small. Even when flaws are numerous, trapping is completely absent for one special relationship of the flaw energy and Fermi level. This relationship is that E_f must coincide with the energy

$$\xi = \phi + kT\ln(\gamma) \tag{822.1}$$

[as will later become apparent from the form of Eq. (823.3)].

When flaws are at all numerous, either one type of carrier or the other must tend to be trapped when $E_f \neq \xi$. The ratio (n_e/p_e) may be comparatively close to unity when the semiconductor is strongly modulated, but moves monotonically further from unity as progressively smaller excess densities are considered. Electron trapping results when $E_f > \xi$ and hole trapping whenever $E_f < \xi$.

Fig. 82.1 attempts to illustrate the relative positions of Fermi level and flaw level for various kinds of trapping. This figure is based on a p-type semiconductor and donor-like flaws [for which $\gamma < 1$ and $kT\ln(\gamma)$ is a negative quantity]. An analogous figure could of course equally well have been drawn for an *n*-type semiconductor and/or for donor-like flaws. Majority hole trapping will occur under the conditions of part (a) in the figure. Trapping must be absent for the conditions of part (b), while parts (c), (d) and (e) all correspond with minority electron trapping. The distinction between the situations of parts (c), (d) and (e) will become apparent in Section 8.5.

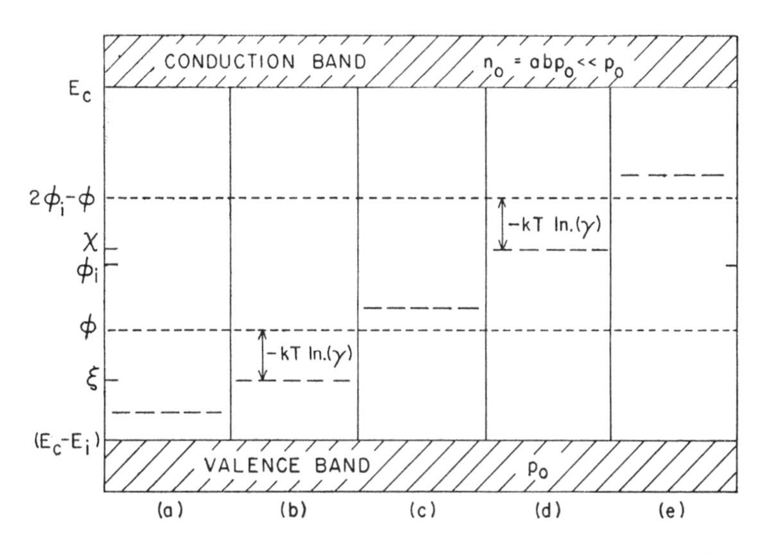

FIG. 82.1. The varieties of trapping for various flaw energy positions when the Fermi energy ϕ is in the lower half of the gap and the flaws are donor-like ($\gamma < 1$). $kT \ln(\gamma)$ is a negative quantity, thus $\xi = \phi + kT \ln(\gamma)$ appears lower than ϕ, while $\chi = (2\phi_i - \phi) + kT \ln(\gamma)$ is lower than $(2\phi_i - \phi)$.
(a) Majority hole trapping when $\gamma b > 1$, $E_f < \xi$.
(b) No trapping when $\gamma b = 1$, $E_f = \xi$.
(c) Electron trapping whenever $\gamma b < 1$, $E_f > \xi$.
This is essentially "permanent" when $a < \gamma$, E_f lower than the "level of equality" χ.
(d) "Semi-permanent" trapping when $E_f = \chi$.
(e) "Temporary" trapping when $a > \gamma$, $E_f > \chi$.

8.2.3 The Excess Carrier Ratio

A useful quantity in the analysis of trapping phenomena is the limit of the ratio of excess electron density to excess hole density for vanishingly small disturbance of equilibrium:

$$S = \lim_{n_e \to 0,\ p_e \to 0} (n_e/p_e) = \lim_{x \to 0,\ y \to 0} (x/y) \tag{823.1}$$

When the characteristics of the semiconductor are such that $S < 1$, electron trapping must occur to some extent for *any* values of the excess densities; the same holds for hole trapping if $S > 1$.

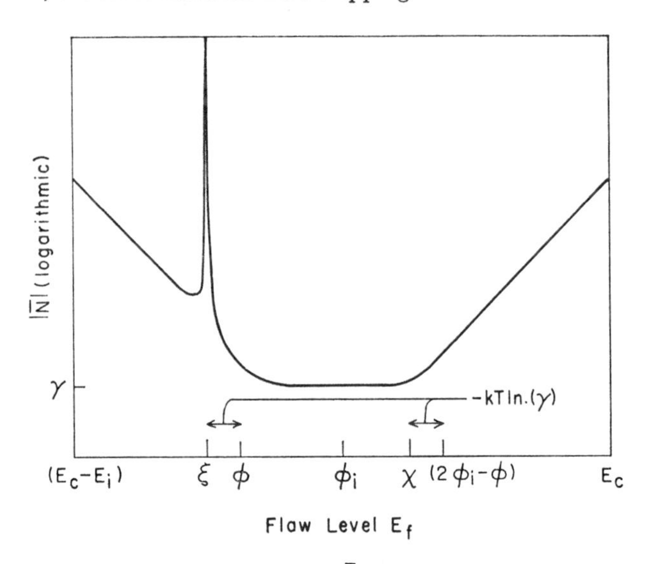

FIG. 82.2. Variation of the quantity $\bar{\mathcal{N}}$ defined by Eq. (823.3) with flaw energy, for donor-like flaws in a p-type semiconductor.

Under steady state conditions, the right sides of Eqs. (813.1) and (813.2) are equal; if each is divided by y and the zero-modulation limit taken, then S can be expressed as

$$S = \frac{\gamma b \mathcal{N} + (a+\gamma)(1+b)^2}{\mathcal{N} + (a+\gamma)(1+b)^2} \tag{823.2}$$

It follows from Eq. (823.2) that trapping will be negligible whenever $\mathcal{N} \ll |\bar{\mathcal{N}}|$, where the quantity $\bar{\mathcal{N}}$ is defined by

$$\bar{\mathcal{N}} = \frac{(a+\gamma)(1+b)^2}{(1-\gamma b)} \tag{823.3}$$

Fig. 82.2 sketches the way the quantity $|\bar{N}|$ will vary with flaw energy—this figure is again based on donor-like flaws in a p-type semiconductor. A large number of flaws can be tolerated if their energy is very close to one band or the other, but for flaws having energies within a broad range in the middle of the gap, trapping is important unless $N \ll N \approx \gamma$. The spike in the figure for one position of E_f corresponds to $\gamma b = 1$ and $E_f = \xi$, when no trapping occurs for *any* density of flaws. $\bar{N}$ is of course a negative quantity when the conditions are those of hole trapping, $E_f < \xi$.

When $G_E = 0$, and transient decay occurs, the ratio (x/y) can be obtained by dividing Eq. (813.1) by (813.2), then dividing numerator and denominator by y. When the limit of infinitesimal modulation is taken, the resulting equation for S is

$$\gamma S^2 + S\left[(a-\gamma) + \frac{N(1-\gamma b)}{(1+b)^2}\right] = a \tag{823.4}$$

which provides for trapping to be negligible when $N \ll |\bar{N}|$. Using the definition (823.3), the solution of (823.4) is

$$S = (2\gamma)^{-1}\{[(\gamma-a)-(\gamma+a)(N/\bar{N})] + \surd\{[(\gamma-a)-(\gamma+a)(N/\bar{N})]^2 + 4a\gamma\}\} \tag{823.5}$$

8.3 LIFETIME FOR A SMALL FLAW DENSITY (THE S–R MODEL)

When the flaw density is small, $N_f \ll p_0\bar{N}$, the excess densities n_e and p_e are the same. Under these circumstances, Eqs. (812.6) and (812.7) can be replaced by a single continuity equation

$$g_E - \frac{\mathrm{d}n_e}{\mathrm{d}t} = \frac{n_e(n_0+p_0+n_e)}{\tau_{n0}(p_0+p_1+n_e)+\tau_{p0}(n_0+n_1+n_e)} \tag{830.1}$$

which corresponds with the pair lifetime†

$$\tau_n = \tau_p = \tau = \frac{\tau_{n0}(p_0+p_1+n_e)+\tau_{p0}(n_0+n_1+n_e)}{(n_0+p_0+n_e)} \tag{830.2}$$

† The more general expression for the electron lifetime with arbitrary flaw density [of which Eq. (830.2) is a special case] is given in Section 8.4.

This expression for carrier lifetime was derived by Hall (1952:**8**) and independently by Shockley and Read (1952:**7**). The latter authors considered the consequences of this model in some detail, and since their names are so closely associated with the subject, we shall refer to recombination through a small density of flaws as constituting the *S–R* model.

Equation (830.2) serves as a reminder that electron–hole annihilation by *S–R* recombination involves the capture first of an electron then of a hole (or vice versa). The first term in Eq. (830.2) indicates the time constant for electron capture, and the second term the time required for emptying the flaw again by hole capture. The relative importance of the two terms depends on the semiconductor doping, flaw energy and asymmetry of capture coefficients, temperature, etc.

8.3.1 Small-modulation Lifetime

As the modulation of the carrier populations tends towards zero, the lifetime approaches

$$\tau_0 = \tau_{n0}\left(\frac{p_0+p_1}{p_0+n_0}\right)+\tau_{p0}\left(\frac{n_0+n_1}{n_0+p_0}\right) \tag{831.1}$$

Fig. 83.1 shows how this zero-modulation lifetime varies with the Fermi energy in a semiconductor supposing a small density of donor-like flaws at an energy in the lower half of the intrinsic gap. This figure is adapted from one given by Shockley and Read, and as in their figure, indicates the two components which add up to τ_0.

For the case illustrated, donor-like flaws are supposed; thus $\tau_{p0} > \tau_{n0}$. Even so, the term in τ_{n0} dominates the right side of Eq. (831.1) for all p-type material and for mildly n-type cases up to a Fermi energy which coincides with $\zeta = [2\phi_i - E_f + kT\ln(\gamma)]$. It will be noted in the figure that ζ is actually a little lower than $(2\phi_i - E_f)$ with donor-like flaws. If acceptor-like centers had been supposed (for which $\gamma > 1$), the change-over point would have been for a Fermi energy *higher* than $(2\phi_i - E_f)$.

The features of Fig. 83.1 can be described in terms of four ranges for the Fermi level:

(a) $\phi < E_f$. The rate-determining process is that of capture of excess free electrons by empty flaws. Since $\phi < E_f$, the flaws are *all* empty, and this process has its minimum time constant of τ_{n0}. Any flaw which becomes filled empties itself by hole capture in a time very much shorter than τ_{n0} because the free hole density is so large.

(b) $E_f < \phi < \phi_i$. Now only a fraction $[1-f(E_f)]$ or $(1+p_1/p_0)^{-1}$ of the flaws are empty and available for electron trapping; thus the time

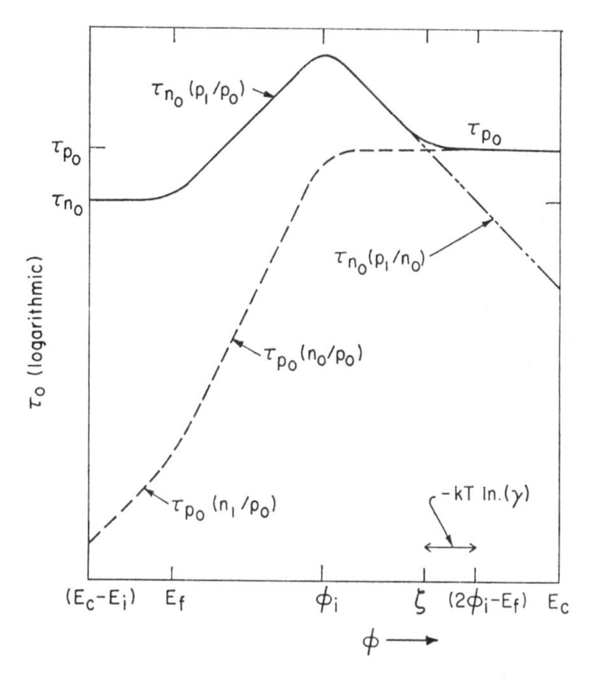

FIG. 83.1. Zero-modulation lifetime as a function of Fermi energy for a semiconductor with donor-like flaws in the lower half of the gap. The solid line shows τ_0, while the two broken curves give the contributions arising from electron and hole capture times.

constant for this process is forced to increase. The free hole density is still sufficiently large to keep the time constant for hole capture negligibly small.

(c) $\phi_i < \phi < \zeta$. Holes are now the minority carriers. Since the flaws are now all full, there is a time constant τ_{p0} for hole capture. But an even larger contribution to the time constant is provided by the subsequent process of electron capture, this contribution being $\sim \tau_{n0}(p_1/n_0)$. When n_0 is still rather small, this process is much slower than hole capture. As Shockley and Read put it, there are not enough electrons to recombine with every trapped hole before most of the latter are re-emitted to the valence band.

(d) $\zeta < \phi$. Hole capture still provides a time constant τ_{p0} and this is now the major contribution to τ_0. The electron density is now large enough to make electron capture speedy.

We shall not discuss the corresponding arguments for a flaw level located in the upper half of the energy gap, since it is obvious that a simple mirror transposition of the above description would cover the situation. However, it is interesting to show the dependence of τ_0 on flaw energy for a particular free carrier density. This is illustrated in Fig. 83.2, supposing a p-type semiconductor and donor-like flaws. As in

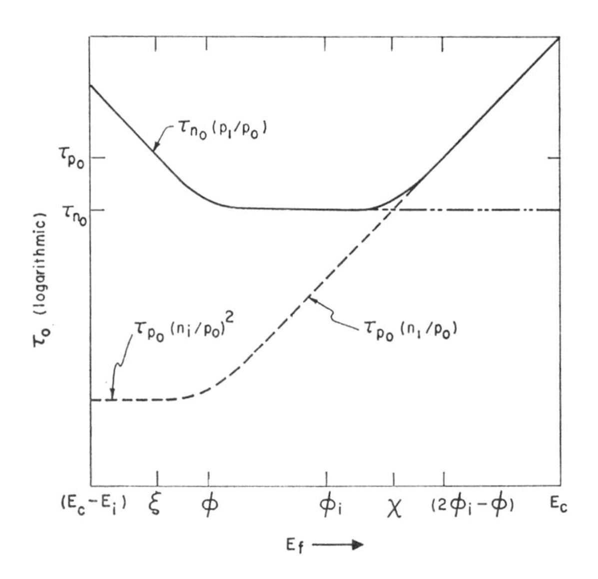

FIG. 83.2. Zero-modulation lifetime τ_0 as a function of flaw energy for a p-type semiconductor. Donor-like flaws are supposed, so that $(\xi - \phi) = (\chi + \phi - 2\phi_i) = kT \ln(\gamma)$ is a negative quantity. The solid line shows the complete lifetime, and the two broken curves the contributions arising from electron and hole capture times.

Fig. 83.1, the two contributions to τ_0 are shown as broken curves, and their sum as a solid line. The two contributions are equal when $\gamma = a(=n_1/p_0)$. This happens when the flaw level has the energy $\chi = [2\phi_i - \phi + kT\ln(\gamma)]$.

This position for a flaw level has been called the "level of equality" by Shockley (1958:**16**), and the "demarcation level" by Rose (1957:**20**). Nomura and Blakemore (1961:**1**) have suggested that conditions might be called those of "semi-permanent trapping" when $E_f = \chi$; for under these conditions half of the captured electrons are re-excited to the conduction band and half remain in the flaws until holes can be captured. Trapping is a very temporary affair when $E_f > \chi$ for then an electron is likely to be trapped and re-excited several times before a free hole can be procured with which to annihilate it.† When $E_f < \chi$, most trapped electrons are retained by the flaws until they can find free holes, and in this sense, trapping is of a more "permanent" character.

From both Figs. 83.1 and 83.2 it is obvious that τ_0 will depend on temperature, but the precise form of the dependence cannot be seen too readily. This is clarified in the next group of figures. As a purely arbitrary choice, these figures are based on a model of a p-type semiconductor. It will be assumed that the major impurities remain completely ionized over the range of interest, so that $N_r = (p_0 - n_0)$ does not depend on temperature. A further assumption is that τ_{n0} and τ_{p0} are themselves not functions of temperature. When these quantities *do* depend on temperature, the additional trends must be superimposed on those of Figs. 83.4 and 83.5.

Fig. 83.3 shows how p_0 and n_0 will themselves depend on temperature for this model, the material becoming intrinsic at the temperature T_1. The broken lines in the figure show the behavior of p_1 and n_1 for a (Class I) situation in which $E_f < \phi_i$. At a temperature T_2, p_1 and p_0 are equal—the Fermi level is coincident with E_f.

The temperature dependence of τ_0 (and its two constituents) for this Class I model is illustrated in Fig. 83.4. Since n_0 and n_1 are both very small at low temperatures, the term $\tau_{p0}[(n_0+n_1)/(n_0+p_0)]$ of Eq. (831.1) is negligible all through the extrinsic range.

† This is particularly prone to happen with very asymmetric flaws for which $\gamma \ll 1$, such as those reported in silicon by Hornbeck and Haynes (1955:**36**). Section 9.3 considers the Hornbeck–Haynes model of a semiconductor containing extremely asymmetric flaws when a second recombinative mechanism exists in the material.

The term in Eq. (831.1) dependent on τ_{n0} is essentially equal to τ_{n0} itself at low temperatures but increases when $T > T_2$, since then $p_1 > p_0$. The activation energy for this rise of τ_0 is the energy separation of the flaw state from the top of the valence band. A maximum lifetime

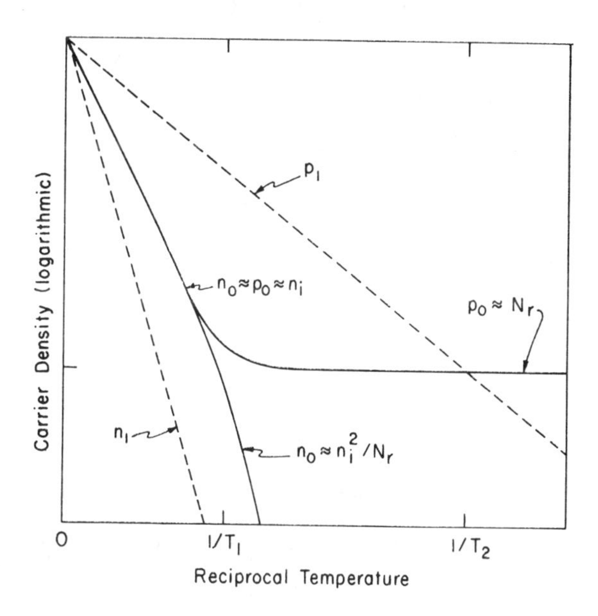

FIG. 83.3. Temperature dependence of free hole and electron densities in a p-type semiconductor with a net excess of ionized acceptors over ionized donors of $N_r = (n_0 - p_0)$. The broken lines indicate the behavior of p_1 and n_1 when flaw levels are in the lower half of the gap.

is reached at the intrinsic transition point T_1; and the electron capture term $\tau_{n0}[(p_0+p_1)/(p_0+n_0)]$ declines on further heating,† characterized by an activation energy $(\phi_i - E_f)$.

It was decided to draw Fig. 83.4 for donor-like flaws. Had acceptor-like flaws $(\tau_{n0} > \tau_{p0})$ been used, the contribution of $\tau_{p0}[(n_0+n_1)/(n_0+p_0)]$

† It will be noted from Fig. 83.4 that this contribution to the lifetime is marked as $\tau_{n0}(p_1/2n_i)$ for temperatures higher than T_1, since $p_1 > n_i$ at any finite temperature. The line curves to reach τ_{n0} rather than $\tau_{n0}/2$ at infinite temperature, since n_i, n_0, p_0, n_1 and p_1 must all coincide for $T = \infty$.

to the lifetime would have been negligible at *all* temperatures. However, with the donor-like flaws adopted for Fig. 83.4, the hole capture time contribution to τ_0 does become the larger one at temperatures higher than the value T_3 (for which $n_i = \gamma p_1$). The zero-modulation lifetime τ_0 will exhibit a plateau of $\frac{1}{2}\tau_{p0}$ for a wide range of temperature extending

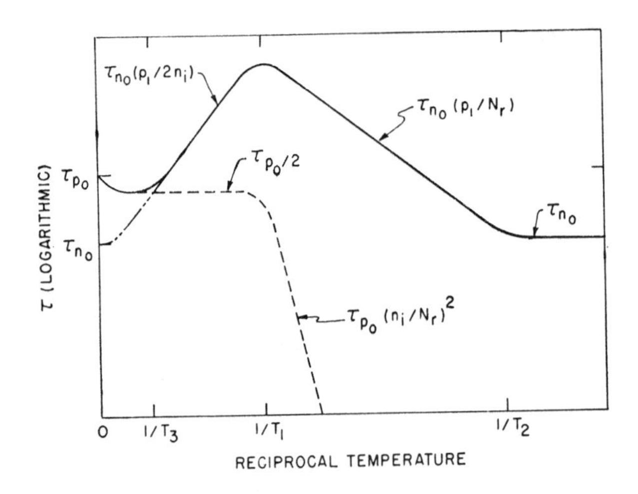

FIG. 83.4. Temperature dependence of τ_0 for a Class I situation, involving a p-type semiconductor with flaws in the lower half of the gap. These flaws are supposed to be donor-like, $\tau_{n0} < \tau_{p0}$.

upwards from T_3, but it will eventually rise† to become τ_{p0} at infinite temperature.

Fig. 83.5 illustrates the corresponding temperature dependence of τ_0 (and its two components) for a p-type Class II situation—one for which flaw levels are in the upper half of the gap. Then $n_1 > n_i > p_1$ at any *finite* temperature. Once again, donor-like flaws are supposed for this figure.

In this kind of situation, the behavior of the electron capture term $\tau_{n0}[(p_0+p_1)/(p_0+n_0)]$ is very simple. It reduces to τ_{n0} throughout the extrinsic range ($T < T_1$), and to $\frac{1}{2}\tau_{n0}$ in the intrinsic range (except for an approach to τ_{n0} again† at the highest temperatures). With the donor-

† Because, as previously noted, n_i, n_0, p_0, n_1 and p_1 are all the same for infinite temperature, irrespective of the doping and flaw position.

like flaws supposed here, electron capture is the rate-controlling process only below the temperature T_4 for which $n_1 = \gamma N_r$.

The hole capture term $\tau_{p0}[(n_0+n_1)/(n_0+p_0)]$ comprises the majority of τ_0 for $T > T_4$. In the extrinsic range this term rises, characterized by an activation energy $(E_c - E_f)$. The maximum lifetime occurs for the

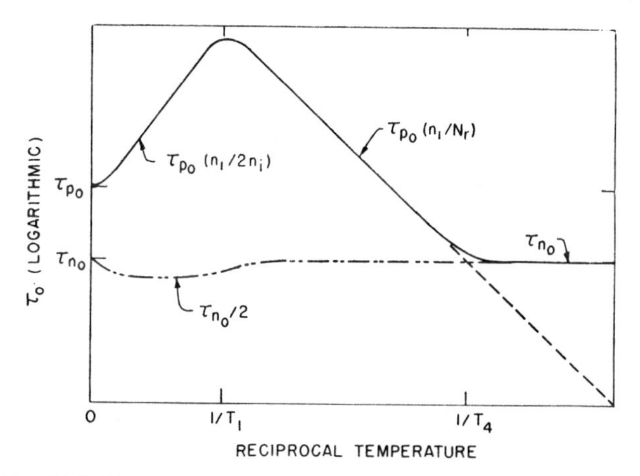

FIG. 83.5. Temperature dependence of τ_0 for a Class II situation, involving a p-type semiconductor with donor-like flaws in the upper half of the intrinsic gap.

intrinsic transition point, $T = T_1$, and the activation energy for the subsequent decline of $\tau_{p0}[(n_i+n_1)/(2n_i)]$ is $(E_f - \phi_i)$.

Note that for acceptor-like flaws $(\gamma > 1)$ the electron capture will control the lifetime again for temperatures in the intrinsic range above a point for which $n_1 = (\gamma-1)n_i$. Indeed if γ is sufficiently large compared with unity, electron capture can be the rate-determining process over the entire range of temperature.†

8.3.2 Variation of Lifetime with Modulation

The discussion in this section has so far been centered on the lifetime τ_0 for an infinitesimal modulation, showing that this is a function of

† This will be the case if n_1 is smaller than γN_r at the temperature T_1.

flaw energy, doping, temperature, etc. But it will be noted from Eq. (830.2) that the lifetime for infinitely large modulation is not explicitly dependent on any of these factors, being simply

$$\tau_\infty = (\tau_{n0} + \tau_{p0})$$
$$= \tau_{n0}(1 + 1/\gamma) \quad (832.1)$$

In terms of τ_0 and τ_∞, the lifetime for any carrier modulation can be expressed as

$$\tau = \frac{(n_0 + p_0)\tau_0 + n_e\tau_\infty}{n_0 + p_0 + n_e} \quad (832.2)$$

Thus whether the lifetime rises or falls with increasing modulation depends on whether the ratio (τ_∞/τ_0) is larger or smaller than unity;

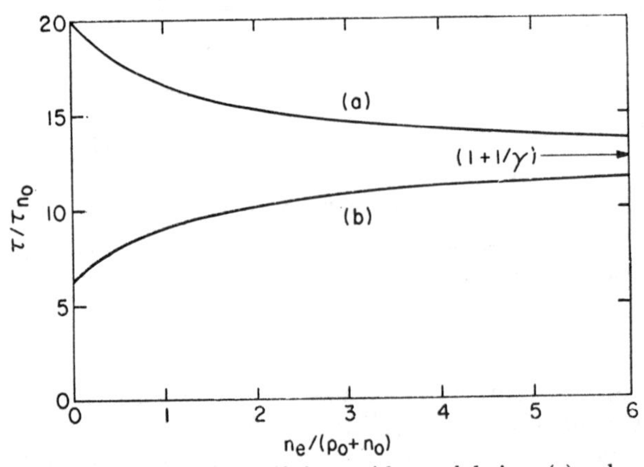

FIG. 83.6. Variation of lifetime with modulation (a) when $\tau_0 > \tau_\infty$ (b) when $\tau_0 < \tau_\infty$. Donor-like flaws are supposed for which $\gamma \sim 0{\cdot}085$.

and this *does* depend on doping, temperature, etc. Fig. 83.6 indicates the way the lifetime varies with n_e for the two alternatives.

In either case, the quantity $\tau[1 + n_e/(n_0 + p_0)]$ increases with n_e, and the increase is a linear one:

$$\tau[1 + n_e/(n_0 + p_0)] = \tau_0 + \tau_\infty[n_e/(n_0 + p_0)] \quad (832.3)$$

Then if experimental data on lifetime is expected to satisfy a *S–R* model, the quantities τ_0 and τ_∞ can be determined from the intercept and slope of a plot such as that given in Fig. 83.7. A lack of linearity in the relationship between $\tau[1+n_e/(n_0+p_0)]$ and n_e indicates (1957:**25**, 1957:**26**) that the simple *S–R* model is inadequate. This can be because the flaw density is large enough to make trapping serious or

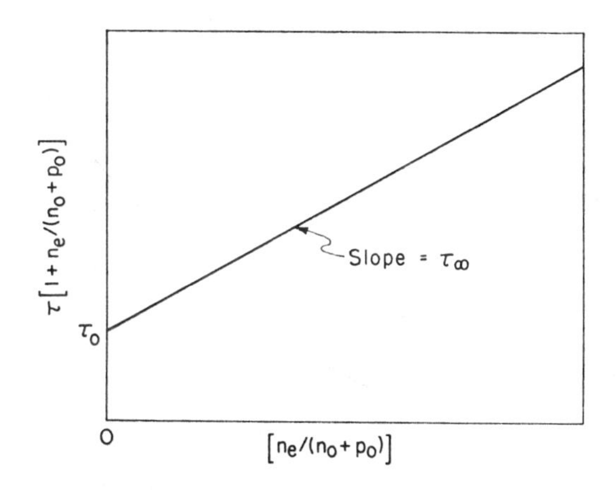

FIG. 83.7. Determination of τ_0 and τ_∞ from the intercept and slope when the *S–R* lifetime is plotted in accordance with Eq. (832.3).

because more than one species of flaw is active (1958:**17**). The plot of Fig. 83.7 is also likely to be non-linear when capture is in accordance with the Auger model of Bess (1957:**17**).

8.3.3 Variation of Excess Density with Steady State Excitation Rate

Under conditions of steady state generation, the term dn_e/dt in Eq. (830.1) vanishes, and the equation which results for the excess density n_e maintained by any generation rate g_E is

$$n_e^2 + n_e(n_0+p_0-\tau_\infty g_E) = (n_0+p_0)\tau_0 g_E \tag{833.1}$$

This can be solved in the customary fashion for a quadratic equation, and the solution has some rather curious features. For the special case of $\tau_0 = \tau_\infty$, the relationship of n_e to g_E is a completely linear one over the entire range of modulation, but when $\tau_0 \neq \tau_\infty$, either sub-linear or super-linear behavior occurs in some part of the range.

The behavior when $\tau_0 > \tau_\infty$ is indicated by the double logarithmic plot of Fig. 83.8. For small modulation, the relationship is a linear one,

$$n_e = \tau_0 g_E \quad \text{when} \quad \left(\frac{n_e}{n_0+p_0}\right) \ll 1 \tag{833.2}$$

As the generation rate is increased, a range of sub-linear response is

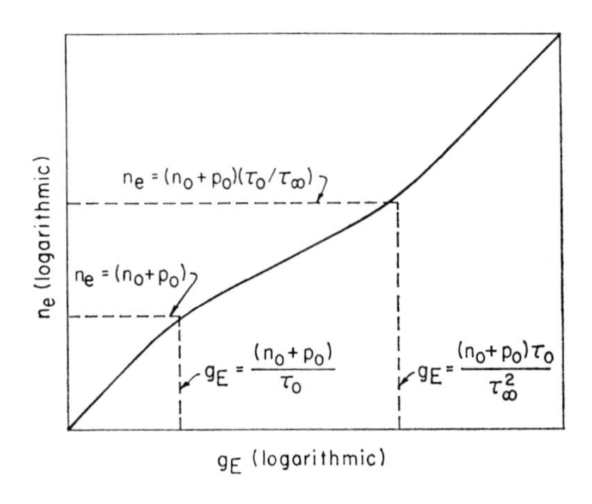

FIG. 83.8. The variation of excess density with steady state generation rate for the *S–R* model when $\tau_0 > \tau_\infty$.

entered, for which n_e varies as the square root of g_E,

$$n_e \approx [g_E \tau_0(n_0+p_0)]^{1/2} \quad \text{when} \quad 1 < \left(\frac{n_e}{n_0+p_0}\right) < \frac{\tau_0}{\tau_\infty} \tag{833.3}$$

For a generation rate larger than $(n_0+p_0)(\tau_0/\tau_\infty^2)$, the response becomes linear again,

$$n_e = \tau_\infty g_E \quad \text{when} \quad \left(\frac{n_e}{n_0+p_0}\right) \gg \frac{\tau_0}{\tau_\infty} \tag{833.4}$$

When τ_0 is very much larger than τ_∞, the range of generation rate for which $n_e \propto g_E^{1/2}$ will be considerable. This is a point to bear in mind when experimental observations show that the dependence of excess density on generation rate is at first linear and then a square root one. Such behavior is possible for any of the three direct recombination processes described in Chapters 5 and 6 as well as for the *S–R* model. However, the response becomes linear again at very high modulation for the *S–R* model and does *not* for direct recombination.

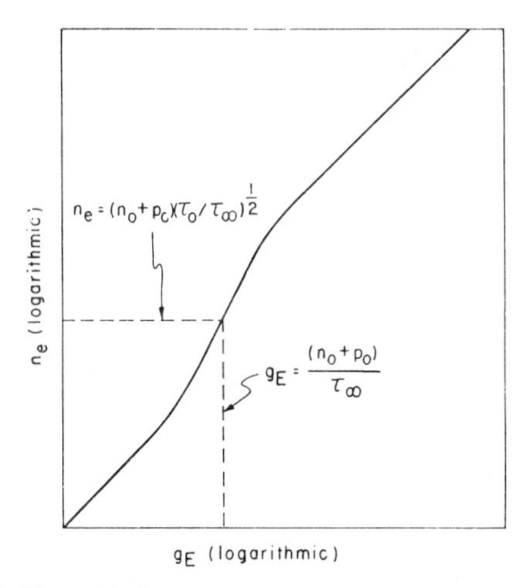

FIG. 83.9. The variation of excess density with steady state generation rate for the *S–R* model when $\tau_0 < \tau_\infty$. The slope at the point of inflection is $s_{\max} = \frac{1}{2}[1 + (\tau_\infty/\tau_0)^{1/2}]$, which is equal to 2 in the above curve ($\tau_\infty = 9\tau_0$).

We now consider the characteristic of n_e vs. g_E for an *S–R* model when τ_0 is smaller than τ_∞. Fig. 83.9 shows the appropriate double logarithmic plot. The relationship is a linear one for small modulation and for large modulation,

$$n_e = \tau_0 g_E \quad \text{when} \quad g_E \ll \frac{n_0 + p_0}{\tau_\infty} \tag{833.5}$$

while

$$n_e = \tau_\infty g_E \quad \text{when} \quad g_E \gg \frac{n_0 + p_0}{\tau_\infty} \tag{833.6}$$

There is, however, an intermediate region for which n_e varies superlinearly with g_E, centered on a point of inflection at the indicated position in the figure. Thus for a considerable range, $n_e \propto g_E^s$ with $s > 1$. The maximum slope, s_{max}, occurs at the inflection point; its value depends on the ratio (τ_∞/τ_0).

A general expression for

$$s = \left(\frac{g_E}{n_e}\right)\left(\frac{dn_e}{dg_E}\right)$$

can be obtained by differentiation and manipulation of Eq. (833.1). This is rather unwieldy in the general case, but simplifies at the point of inflection to

$$s_{max} = \tfrac{1}{2}[1+(\tau_\infty/\tau_0)^{1/2}] \quad \text{when} \quad \begin{cases} n_e = (n_0+p_0)(\tau_0/\tau_\infty)^{1/2} \\ g_E = \dfrac{(n_0+p_0)}{\tau_\infty} \end{cases} \tag{833.7}$$

The maximum slope of 2 in Fig. 83.9 is thus consistent with $(\tau_\infty/\tau_0) = 9$. It will presumably not often happen that τ_∞ can exceed τ_0 by a much larger factor. Thus it will not usually be expected that super-linear behavior for an *S–R* model will involve a very large value of s or extend over a range of more than a decade or so. This contrasts with the possibilities which can arise for multi-level models (e.g. 1951:**17**, 1958:**23**). Such models are especially interesting for insulating photoconductors, as discussed extensively by Rose (1955:**15**, 1955:**16**, 1957:**20**) and Bube (1960:**10**). In these materials it is not uncommon to find a super-linear response occurring over a range of many decades (e.g. 1957:**31**).

8.3.4 Transient Decay

When the externally provoked generation rate g_E in Eq. (830.1) is terminated, this equation can be integrated to describe the relationship of n_e and t during the ensuing decay. It seems more natural to express n_e as a function of time, but the form of (830.1) requires the integral to be performed in a manner which expresses time as a function of n_e. The procedure is then quite straightforward, and yields

$$t = \frac{\tau_{n0}(p_0+p_1)+\tau_{p0}(n_0+n_1)}{(n_0+p_0)} \ln\left[\frac{n_{e0}}{n_e}\right] + \\ + \frac{\tau_{n0}(n_0-p_1)+\tau_{p0}(p_0-n_1)}{(n_0+p_0)} \ln\left[\frac{n_{e0}+n_0+p_0}{n_e+n_0+p_0}\right] \tag{834.1}$$

where n_{e0} denotes the excess density at the origin of the time scale. Using Eqs. (831.1) and (832.1), this is simply

$$t = \tau_0 \ln\left[\frac{n_{e0}}{n_e}\right] + (\tau_\infty - \tau_0) \ln\left[\frac{n_{e0}+n_0+p_0}{n_e+n_0+p_0}\right] \tag{834.2}$$

Thus the decay is not usually a simple exponential from start to finish. When the excess carrier density at the start of the decay is large compared with (n_0+p_0), there is an early region of exponential decay:

$$\left.\begin{aligned} t &\approx \tau_\infty \ln\left[\frac{n_{e0}}{n_e}\right] \\ n_e &\approx n_{e0} \exp(-t/\tau_\infty) \end{aligned}\right\} \quad \text{while } n_e \gg (n_0+p_0) \tag{834.3}$$

Of course, this region cannot be seen if decay starts from a more modest amplitude.

The final stages of decay, once n_e has become small compared with (n_0+p_0), are again exponential:

$$\left.\begin{aligned} t &\approx \tau_0 \ln\left[\frac{n_{e0}}{n_e}\right] + (\tau_\infty - \tau_0) \ln\left[\frac{n_{e0}+n_0+p_0}{n_0+p_0}\right] \\ n_e &\approx n_{e0} \,.\, \exp(-t/\tau_0)\left[\frac{n_0+p_0}{n_{e0}+n_0+p_0}\right]^{(1-\tau_\infty/\tau_0)} \end{aligned}\right\} \quad \text{when } n_e \ll (n_0+p_0) \tag{834.4}$$

Under most circumstances, a plot of $\ln(n_e)$ as a function of time will exhibit a curvature as the effective time constant, $-n_e(dt/dn_e)$, approaches its small modulation value τ_0.

This curvature fails to develop only if the positions of the Fermi level and flaw level are related in such a way that $\tau_0 = \tau_\infty$. There are two positions for the flaw level which make this occur:

(a) When $E_f = \xi$. For this position of the flaws, $\gamma b = 1$, or $\tau_{n0}p_1 = \tau_{p0}p_0$, $\tau_{n0}n_0 = \tau_{p0}n_1$.

(*b*) When $E_f = (2\phi_i - \phi)$. Under these circumstances $a = 1$, or $n_1 = p_0$, $n_0 = p_1$.

Then in either of these circumstances

$$n_e = n_{e0} \exp\left(\frac{-t}{\tau_{n0}+\tau_{p0}}\right), \quad \left\{\begin{array}{l} \text{if } E_f = \xi \\ \text{or } E_f = (2\phi_i - \phi) \end{array}\right. \tag{834.5}$$

Otherwise, the decay either speeds up or slows down as it proceeds.

When the flaw levels lie towards the center of the energy gap, $\xi < E_f < (2\phi_i - \phi)$, the infinite modulation lifetime τ_∞ is larger than τ_0; decay then becomes more rapid as it proceeds.

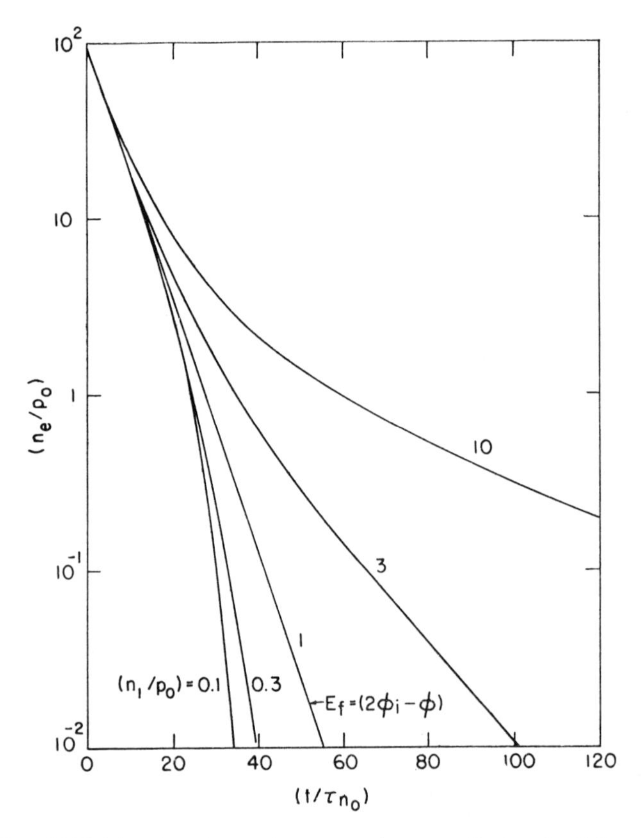

Fig. 83.10. Transient decay of excess carriers according to the *S–R* model, for a Class II situation of a *p*-type semiconductor with donor-like flaws ($\gamma = 0{\cdot}2$) in the upper half of the gap. The curves follow Eq. (834.1) for various values of n_1, assuming both p_1 and n_0 to be negligibly small.

For flaw levels rather close to one band or the other, $E_f < \xi$ or $E_f > (2\phi_i - \phi)$, we have $\tau_\infty < \tau_0$; the decay then slows down as it proceeds.

Examples of both forms of behavior are shown in Fig. 83.10. This supposes a Class II situation of a p-type semiconductor with donor-like flaws ($\gamma = 0{\cdot}2$) in the upper half of the gap. Curves are drawn for various values of the parameter $a = (n_1/p_0)$. The curve for $a = 1$ is completely linear, indicating a pure exponential decay of time constant $6\tau_{n0}(=\tau_{n0}+\tau_{p0})$. The most rapidly descending curve, that for $n_1 = 0{\cdot}1\, p_0$, has a final time constant of only $1{\cdot}5\,\tau_{n0}$. In contrast, the curve for $a = 10$ must eventually reach a limiting slope characteristic of $\tau_0 = 51\tau_{n0}$.

Decay curves for Class I conditions show the same qualitative features.

8.4 STEADY STATE CONDITIONS FOR ARBITRARY FLAW DENSITY

When generation of hole–electron pairs is externally provoked at a steady rate, the terms $\mathrm{d}n_e/\mathrm{d}t$ and $\mathrm{d}p_e/\mathrm{d}t$ in Eqs. (812.6) and (812.7) can be dropped. Thus

$$\frac{n_e}{\tau_n} = \frac{p_e}{\tau_p} = g_E = \frac{1}{\tau_{n0}}\left[\frac{(n_0+n_1+n_e)(n_e-p_e)}{N_f}+\frac{n_e n_1}{n_0+n_1}\right]$$
$$= \frac{1}{\tau_{p0}}\left[\frac{(p_0+p_1+p_e)(p_e-n_e)}{N_f}+\frac{p_e p_1}{p_0+p_1}\right] \qquad (840.1)$$

N_f can be eliminated by substitution from one of the expressions on the right into the other. This gives

$$g_E = \frac{n_e}{\tau_n} = \frac{p_e}{\tau_p} = \frac{p_0 n_e + n_0 p_e + n_e p_e}{\tau_{p0}(n_0+n_1+n_e)+\tau_{n0}(p_0+p_1+p_e)} \qquad (840.2)$$

If attention is focused on the electron lifetime for the present, then we have

$$\tau_n = \frac{\tau_{p0}(n_0+n_1+n_e)+\tau_{n0}(p_0+p_1+p_e)}{(n_0 p_e/n_e)+p_0+p_e} \qquad (840.3)$$

By utilizing Eq. (811.7) and working through an extensive reorganization, this can be expressed in the form

$$\tau_n = \frac{\tau_{p0}(n_0+n_1+n_e)+\tau_{n0}(p_0+p_1+n_e)+\tau_{n0}N_f P_e(E_f)}{(n_0+p_0+n_e)+N_f(1+p_1/p_0)^{-1}P_e(E_f)} \qquad (840.4)$$

which is the source of a number of well known equations.

Thus when N_f is sufficiently small, Eq. (840.4) reduces to the form (830.2) of the *S–R* model. For this model, of course, $n_e \approx p_e$ and $\tau_n \approx \tau_p$. The bulk of Shockley and Read's paper (1952:**7**) was concerned with the model for small flaw density, and only in an appendix did they permit the generalization to large values of N_f. Even then, they restricted the discussion to infinitesimal modulation. A number of more recent papers on steady state and transient phenomena [e.g. (1957:**18**, 1957:**24**, 1960:**14**)] indicate a fascination with the simplification which results for sufficiently small modulation. This is not altogether warranted, since for steady state conditions a solution is possible for modulation of any magnitude (and even transient conditions for arbitrary n_e and N_f are not wholly intractable).

It is still, however, useful to start with consideration of a very small steady state generation rate.

8.4.1 Small-modulation Lifetime

When the externally provoked generation rate is sufficiently small, not only can terms in Eq. (840.4) involving n_e be dropped, but also $P_e(E_f)$ simplifies to $f(E_f)$, or $(1+p_0/p_1)^{-1}$ [see Eq. (811.6)]. Then the electron lifetime is

$$\tau_n = \frac{\tau_{p0}(n_0+n_1)+\tau_{n0}(p_0+p_1)+\tau_{n0}N_f(1+p_0/p_1)^{-1}}{n_0+p_0+N_f(1+p_1/p_0)^{-1}(1+p_0/p_1)^{-1}}, \quad n_e \to 0 \quad (841.1)$$

The corresponding hole lifetime is

$$\tau_p = \frac{\tau_{p0}(n_0+n_1)+\tau_{n0}(p_0+p_1)+\tau_{p0}N_f(1+p_1/p_0)^{-1}}{n_0+p_0+N_f(1+p_1/p_0)^{-1}(1+p_0/p_1)^{-1}}, \quad p_e \to 0 \quad (841.2)$$

Eqs. (841.1) and (841.2) are identical with (A7) of Shockley and Read.

It might at first seem that τ_n of Eq. (841.1) is a function of N_f apart from the dependence of τ_{n0} and τ_{p0} on N_f. However, when electrons are the minority carriers in p-type material, the terms in N_f drop out or cancel out (except for the hypothetical case of almost intrinsic material with $N_f \gg p_0$ or n_1 or p_1). The terms in N_f do remain when we consider majority electron lifetime in n-type material. This is illustrated by the set of expressions in Table 84.1. A corresponding table can readily be prepared for the hole lifetime under Class I and Class II n-type and p-type conditions; the most involved expression for the low-modulation

Table 84.1. Small modulation electron lifetime for steady state conditions

	Minority electrons in p-type material $p_0 > n_i > n_0$	Majority electrons in n-type material $n_0 > n_i > p_0$
Flaw levels in upper half of gap $n_1 > n_i > p_1$	*Class II* $\tau_n \approx \tau_{n0} + \tau_{p0}(n_1/p_0)$	*Class I* $\tau_n \approx \tau_{p0}(1+n_1/n_0)\left[\frac{\gamma n_0 N_f + (n_0+n_1)^2}{n_1 N_f + (n_0+n_1)^2}\right]$
Flaw levels in lower half of gap $p_1 > n_i > n_1$	*Class I* $\tau_n \approx \tau_{n0}(1+p_1/p_0)$	*Class II* $\tau_n \approx \tau_{p0} + \tau_{n0}\left(\frac{p_1+N_f}{n_0}\right)$

lifetime is then found for p-type Class I conditions. Thus Eqs. (841.1) and (841.2) can be readily assimilated, for the supposition of small disturbance of equilibrium.

8.4.2 Finite Modulation

When the excess carrier densities are finite, the electron lifetime of Eq. (840.4) presents more of a problem. It is still possible to obtain an expression for τ_n with n_e as the only variable, but this expression is by no means compact.

It is useful at this point to recall the dimensionless notation set out in Sub-section 8.1.3. In terms of this notation, the conditions of steady state equilibrium can be described by the two cubic equations of (814.1) and (814.2). Eq. (814.1) yields the small-modulation lifetime of Eq. (841.1) when all terms in x^3, x^2, xG_E and G_E^2 are dropped; and Eq. (814.2) similarly contains Eq. (841.2) as its limiting case.

For modulation of arbitrary magnitude, it is not exactly a simple proposition to find the real positive roots of the cubics (814.1) and (814.2) which give the values of x and y corresponding with a given generation coefficient G_E. On the other hand, these equations can be written as quadratic equations for G_E in terms of x and y:

$$G_E^2 N - G_E\{[x+a(1+b)][x(1+1/\gamma)+(1+b)(1+a/\gamma)] + \\ + N[ab+x(2+b)/(1+b)]\} + \\ + x\{[x+a(1+b)][x+1+ab]+N(x+ab)/(1+b)\} = 0 \quad (842.1)$$

and

$$G_E^2 N - \gamma G_E\{[y+1+b][y(1+\gamma)+(1+b)(a+\gamma)]+ \\ +N[1+y(1+2b)/(1+b)]\}+ \\ +\gamma^2 y\{[y+1+b][y+1+ab]+Nb(y+1)/(1+b)\} = 0 \quad (842.2)$$

These become linear as $N \to 0$, with ratios (G_E/x) and (G_E/y) in conformity with Eq. (830.2). For non-zero N, the solutions of Eqs. (842.1) and (842.2) are obvious in form but complicated so far as the actual terms go. Thus if as a temporary abbreviation we denote

$$\left.\begin{aligned} A &= \{[x+a(1+b)][x(1+1/\gamma)+(1+b)(1+a/\gamma)]+ \\ &\qquad +N[ab+x(2+b)/(1+b)]\} \\ B &= \{[x+a(1+b)][x+1+ab]+N(x+ab)/(1+b)\} \end{aligned}\right\} \quad (842.3)$$

the solution of the excess electron equation (842.1) is

$$G_E = \frac{2Bx}{A+\sqrt{(A^2-4NBx)}} \quad (842.4)$$

The positive sign preceding the square root in the denominator is appropriate for the physically required condition that there will be no excess generation when $x = 0$. From Eq. (842.4), a simple step takes us to the expression for excess electron lifetime under any steady state conditions. For (G_E/x) is equal to (τ_{n0}/τ_n). Thus

$$\tau_n = \tau_{n0}\left(\frac{x}{G_E}\right) = \tau_{n0}\left(\frac{A}{B}\right)\left\{\frac{1}{2}+\sqrt{\left(\frac{1}{4}-\frac{NBx}{A^2}\right)}\right\} \quad (842.5)$$

The leading terms of the expression for τ_n can be expressed in more familiar language as

$$\tau_{n0}\left(\frac{A}{B}\right) = \frac{\tau_{p0}(n_0+n_1+n_e)+\tau_{n0}(p_0+p_1+n_e)+\tau_{n0}N_f\left[\dfrac{p_1(n_0+n_1+n_e)+2p_0n_e}{(n_0+n_1+n_e)(p_0+p_1)}\right]}{(n_0+p_0+n_e)+N_f\left[\dfrac{p_0(n_0+n_e)}{(n_0+n_1+n_e)(p_0+p_1)}\right]} \quad (842.6)$$

Now the factor $\{\frac{1}{2}+\sqrt{(\frac{1}{4}-NBx/A^2)}\}$ converges on unity for small modulation; $\tau_{n0}(A/B)$ is then the electron lifetime itself, and it will be seen that Eq. (842.6) reduces under such conditions to the form of Eq. (841.1). For very large modulation also, $\{\frac{1}{2}+\sqrt{(\frac{1}{4}-NBx/A^2)}\}$ will be very close to unity; indeed it never departs very far from unity for any intermediate modulation unless flaws are extremely numerous. Then it may be assumed that the right side of Eq. (842.6) is in itself usually quite a good approximation to the electron lifetime. Conditions will occasionally require the general and laborious expansion of Eq. (842.5) to be used.

A completely similar treatment can be used for expressing the hole lifetime τ_p corresponding to any arbitrary values of n_e and N_f. When the secondary factor for this case is assumed to be essentially unity, we have

$$\tau_p \approx \frac{\tau_{p0}(n_0+n_1+p_e)+\tau_{n0}(p_0+p_1+p_e)+\tau_{p0}N_f\left[\dfrac{p_0(p_0+p_1+p_e)+2p_1p_e}{(p_0+p_1)(p_0+p_1+p_e)}\right]}{(n_0+p_0+p_e)+N_f\left[\dfrac{p_1(p_0+p_e)}{(p_0+p_1)(p_0+p_1+p_e)}\right]} \tag{842.7}$$

which is the expected elaboration of Eq. (841.2).

It is obvious that there must be an expressible relationship between n_e and p_e. When the two expressions on the right side of (840.1) are equated, the result can be expressed using the previously introduced dimensionless notation:

$$\frac{x}{y} = \frac{x+\gamma y+(1+b)(a+\gamma)+\gamma bN/(1+b)}{x+\gamma y+(1+b)(a+\gamma)+N/(1+b)} \tag{842.8}$$

This emphasizes that there is no trapping ($x=y$) when $b\gamma = 1$. The solution of Eq. (842.8) is

$$x = \left\{\tfrac{1}{4}\left[(1+b)(a+\gamma)+y(1+\gamma)+\frac{N}{(1+b)}\right]^2 - yN\left(\frac{1-\gamma b}{1+b}\right)\right\}^{1/2} - \\ -\tfrac{1}{2}\left[(1+b)(a+\gamma)-y(1-\gamma)+\frac{N}{(1+b)}\right] \tag{842.9}$$

or a similar result for y in terms of x.

It is instructive to illustrate this by a numerical example. Consider a p-type Class I situation involving donor-like flaws, when $b=1$,

$\gamma = 0{\cdot}05$, $a \approx 0$. Then

$$x = \{[0{\cdot}05+0{\cdot}525y+0{\cdot}25N]^2-0{\cdot}475Ny\}^{1/2}-[0{\cdot}05-0{\cdot}475y+0{\cdot}25N] \tag{842.10}$$

Curves illustrating this relationship for various values of N are shown in Fig. 84.1. Since $\gamma b < 1$ with the parameters selected, this is a situation of electron trapping. When flaws are present in very small quantities, $x \approx y$ at any level of modulation. For more numerous flaws,

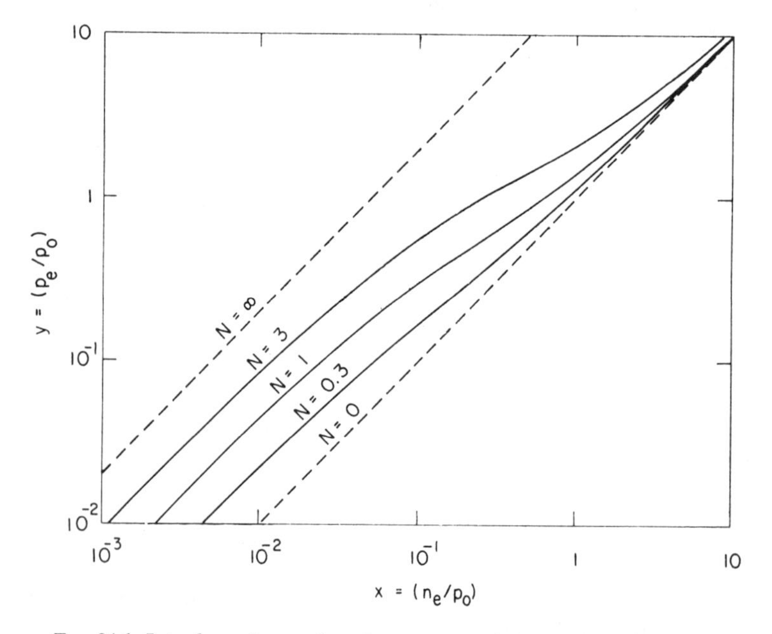

FIG. 84.1. Interdependence of steady state excess hole and electron densities for a markedly extrinsic p-type Class I situation. It is supposed that $b = (p_1/p_0)$ is unity, and that the flaws are donors for which $\gamma = (\tau_{n0}/\tau_{p0}) = 0{\cdot}05$. Curves for several values of $N = (N_f/p_0)$ are shown, which satisfy Eq. (842.10).

the disparity of n_e to p_e becomes progressively more marked, particularly for small modulation. The figure shows the limiting case of *infinite* flaw density, for which $x = b\gamma y$ with any finite excess concentrations of carriers.

8.5 TRANSIENT DECAY FOR ARBITRARY FLAW DENSITY

When excess electrons and holes are present in a semiconductor as a result of some excitation which has terminated, n_e and p_e will usually be different and have different temporal dependences. However both tend to fall towards zero. According to Eqs. (812.6) and (812.7), these decay schemes satisfy

$$\frac{n_e}{\tau_n} = -\frac{\mathrm{d}n_e}{\mathrm{d}t} = \frac{1}{\tau_{n0}}\left[\frac{(n_0+n_1+n_e)(n_e-p_e)}{N_f} + \frac{n_e n_1}{n_0+n_1}\right] \tag{850.1}$$

and

$$\frac{p_e}{\tau_p} = -\frac{\mathrm{d}p_e}{\mathrm{d}t} = \frac{1}{\tau_{p0}}\left[\frac{(p_0+p_1+p_e)(p_e-n_e)}{N_f} + \frac{p_e p_1}{p_0+p_1}\right] \tag{850.2}$$

We shall find it useful to refer to the decay equations when they are written in the dimensionless notation of Sub-section 8.1.3, viz.

$$-x' = \frac{(x-y)[x+a(1+b)]}{N} + \frac{x}{1+b} \tag{850.3}$$

and

$$-y' = \frac{\gamma(y-x)[y+1+b]}{N} + \frac{\gamma b y}{1+b} \tag{850.4}$$

Eqs. (850.1)–(850.4) present a far from simple problem, and it will be necessary to consider the various attributes of the decay process one by one. As noted in Sub-section 8.1.4, the separate non-linear equations (814.4) and (814.5) can be obtained from Eqs. (850.3) and (850.4), but analytic solutions are known only for restrictive values of the parameters N, γ, b and a; or when x and y are either very large or very small. Perturbation methods fail when the variables x or y are comparable in magnitude to the normalized flaw density N, for then all terms in Eqs. (814.4) and (814.5) are of importance.

A number of approaches have been followed by previous writers on this subject. Sandiford (1957:**18**), Adirovich and Goureau (1956:**16**), Clarke (1957:**24**) and van Roosbroeck (1960:**14**) consider only the solutions for very small excess carrier densities (thus removing the nonlinearities in the differential equations). This small modulation solution is certainly of interest, and it is discussed in Sub-section 8.5.2, but it is important to observe at the outset that it is often satisfactory for the excess minority carriers when their density has become *extremely* small. Wertheim (1958:**14**) concentrates primarily on this "zero-modulation" solution, but does consider an extension to moderate modulation when flaws are numerous.

Goureau (1957:**19**) allows for arbitrary densities of excess carriers, but places a restriction on the value of N. Isay (1953:**14**) has used a rather different approach in permitting any values of the variables and parameters, but requiring the solution to be in terms of specific functions. This is not always satisfactory.

Nomura and Blakemore (1958:**13**, 1961:**1**) concede that no general analytic procedure is likely to be wholly successful, but show how Eqs. (850.3) and (850.4) reveal the form which will be taken by the decay in various ranges. The information which can be extracted is sufficient to build up a picture of how n_e and p_e should vary with time for Class I and Class II decay.

Eqs. (850.3) and (850.4) are of a type which can be solved numerically by a digital computer for any desired set of the parameters N, γ, b, and a, and of the initial carrier disturbances x_0 and y_0. Curves obtained by computation were used by Nomura and Blakemore to verify their conclusions about the courses of x and y during decay. Such computed curves for particular values of the parameters are not a *substitute* for analytic examination of the differential equations, but a *supplement* to them. Several computed curves are used to illustrate the remarks of the following pages.

8.5.1 The Initial Stages of Decay

In this section, transient decay is deemed to start at the moment when externally inspired excess generation stops. The initial values n_{e0}, p_{e0} of the excess electron and hole densities† depend on the intensity and duration of the previous generation. If this duration has been finite, n_{e0} and p_{e0} will be unequal (unless $\gamma b = 1$ and/or $N \ll |\bar{N}|$) since either electrons or holes will have been trapped during the excitation period. For a delta function pulse of generation, $n_{e0} = p_{e0}$, and the initial stages of the decay are likely to resemble the pattern shown in Fig. 85.1. This figure is shown for a situation of electron trapping, $\gamma b < 1$. Part (A) of the figure shows a semilogarithmic plot

† The corresponding dimensionless notation given is x_0 for (n_{e0}/p_0) and y_0 for (p_{e0}/p_0).

of excess carrier densities against time, and part (B) the corresponding time constants.

The reasons for the behavior shown are as follows. Before any trapping has commenced, a fraction $(1+b)^{-1}$ of the flaws are empty and a

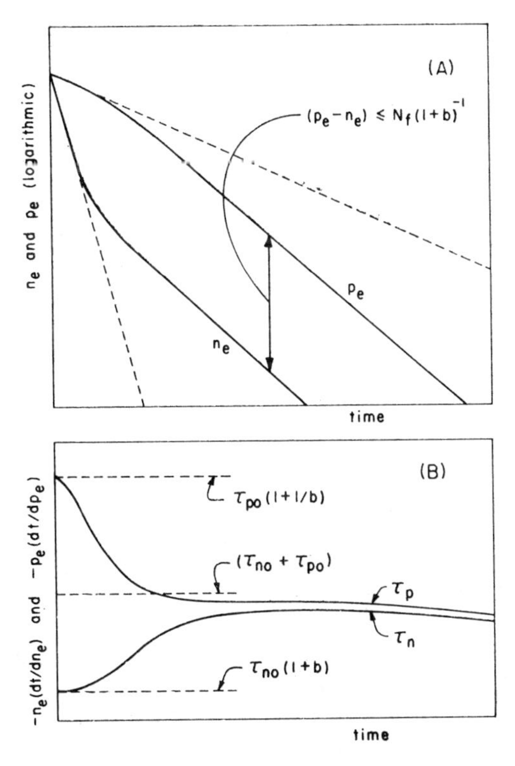

FIG. 85.1. General appearance of the initial stages of electron and hole decay when $n_{e0} = p_{e0}$. (A) The variation of the excess densities with time. (B) The corresponding time constants. Drawn for an electron trapping case, $\gamma b < 1$, so that $\tau_{p0}(1+1/b) > (\tau_{n0}+\tau_{p0}) > \tau_{n0}(1+b)$.

fraction $(1+1/b)^{-1}$ full [see Eqs. (811.6, 811.7)]. From the definitions (811.10) and (811.12) of τ_{n0} and τ_{p0}, it follows that the *initial* decay of n_e must correspond with a time constant $\tau_{n0}(1+b)$. Such behavior is extended as the steepest dashed line in Fig. 85.1(A). Similarly, the initial decay of p_e is characterized by a time constant $\tau_{p0}(1+1/b)$, which is extended as the gently sloping dashed line in Fig. 85.1(A). Note that in this initial region, $(\tau_n/\tau_p) = \gamma b$.

The time constants become modified from their initial values when $(p_e - n_e)$ has become a large enough fraction of N_f to exert an influence on Eqs. (850.1) and (850.2). It will be seen that these equations provide for the above-mentioned time constants whenever $n_e = p_e$, but for a modification of the decay scheme when n_e and p_e have become sufficiently unbalanced to make the first terms on the right side of the equations important.

The termination of this initial phase is not so much a matter of n_e and p_e becoming different as it is a sign that the fraction of empty flaws has shifted considerably from $(1+b)^{-1}$. When N_f is extremely large, the behavior

$$\left.\begin{aligned} n_e &= n_{e0} \exp\left[\frac{-t}{\tau_{n0}(1+b)}\right] \\ p_e &= n_{e0} \exp\left[\frac{-t}{\tau_{p0}(1+1/b)}\right] \end{aligned}\right\} \tag{851.1}$$

persists for a long time; though as will be seen in the next sub-section, both carrier densities eventually have the *longer* of the two time constants $\tau_{n0}(1+b)$, $\tau_{p0}(1+1/b)$ when the decay is far advanced.

Fig. 85.1 is drawn supposing the initial value of n_e to be rather large, so that when the initial transient has subsided, both n_e and p_e have time constants not far short of the infinite modulation value† $\tau_\infty = (\tau_{n0} + \tau_{p0})$ [see Eq. (832.1)]. The trapped electron density $(p_e - n_e)$ has reached its maximum value [which obviously cannot exceed $N_f(1+b)^{-1}$] within the first third of the time range in the figure, and $(p_e - n_e)$ gradually declines again as time goes on. When the initial value of n_e is rather small, the maximum of $(p_e - n_e)$ is likely to be considerably less than $N_f(1+b)^{-1}$.

For the latter part of the time range in Fig. 85.1, the behavior of n_e and p_e does not depend on the initial conditions, but follows a course which would have resulted for *any other starting conditions* at some time

† The infinite modulation lifetime τ_∞ is larger than $\tau_{n0}(1+b)$ but smaller than $\tau_{p0}(1+1/b)$ when the electron trapping condition $\gamma b < 1$ holds. For the hole trapping situation of $\gamma b < 1$, $\tau_{p0}(1+1/b) < \tau_\infty < \tau_{n0}(1+b)$. The three time constants are identical when $E_f = \xi$ and trapping disappears.

in the past. This statement can be confirmed by examining the curves of Fig. 85.2, obtained by Nomura and Blakemore through computer solutions of the differential equations. The dimensionless variables x and y are plotted as functions of the dimensionless time variable

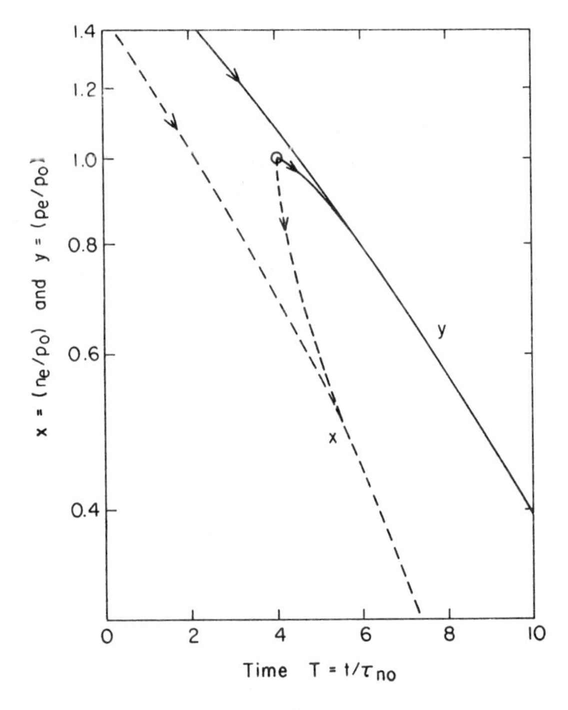

FIG. 85.2. Decay of excess holes (solid curves) and electrons (broken curves) for a p-type Class II situation of donor flaws ($\mathcal{N} = 0{\cdot}5$, $\gamma = 0{\cdot}1$, $a = 0{\cdot}02$, $b \approx 0$). Note that decay starting from $x_0 = y_0 = 1$ at time $\mathcal{T} = 4$ rapidly coalesces with the curves which originate from $x_0 = y_0 = 100$ at time $\mathcal{T} = -40$. After Nomura and Blakemore (1961:**1**).

$\mathcal{T} = t/\tau_{n0}$ for a given set of values for the parameters $\mathcal{N}$, γ, a and b. The figure shows decay from a supposed initial condition $x_0 = y_0 = 1$ at time $\mathcal{T} = 4$; it will be seen that following an initial rapid separation of the curves for x and y, they coalesce with curves of the same variables for decay which has started from $x_0 = y_0 = 100$ at time $\mathcal{T} = -40$. Thus only a trivial change in the origin of the time scale is required to bring all decay curves for the same *parameters* into alignment. When decay starts from a condition $n_{e0} \neq p_{e0}$, the curves show a similar brief transient and then join the universal curves.

8.5.2 The Final Stages of Decay

When the excess carrier densities have become sufficiently small, the terms which make Eqs. (850.3) and (850.4) non-linear can be dropped. Under the worst circumstances, this can be done when $p_e \ll (p_0 + p_1)$ and $n_e \ll (n_0 + n_1)$, though the condition for the kind of carrier which becomes trapped can be less stringent when N_f is not too large. At any rate, when x and y are *sufficiently* small, the linearized forms of Eqs. (850.3) and (850.4) yield identical second-order linear differential equations for x and y:

$$\left.\begin{aligned} x'' + \alpha x' + \beta x &= 0 \\ y'' + \alpha y' + \beta y &= 0 \end{aligned}\right\} \tag{852.1}$$

where

$$\alpha = \left[\frac{(1+b)(a+\gamma)}{N} + \frac{(1+\gamma b)}{(1+b)}\right] \tag{852.2}$$

and

$$\beta = \left[\frac{\gamma(1+ab)}{N} + \frac{\gamma b}{(1+b)^2}\right] \tag{852.3}$$

The solution of Eq. (852.1) is well known to be of the form

$$\left.\begin{aligned} x &= A \exp\left(\frac{-t}{\tau_+}\right) + B \exp\left(\frac{-t}{\tau_-}\right) \\ y &= C \exp\left(\frac{-t}{\tau_+}\right) + D \exp\left(\frac{-t}{\tau_-}\right) \end{aligned}\right\} \tag{852.4}$$

The integration constants A, B, C, D depend on the previous conditions. The two time constants $\tau_{\pm}$ are given by

$$\tau_{\pm} = \frac{\tau_{p0}(1+b)(a+\gamma)+\tau_{p0}N\left(\dfrac{1+\gamma b}{1+b}\right)}{1+ab+\dfrac{Nb}{(1+b)^2}} \cdot \left\{\frac{1 \pm \sqrt{(1-R)}}{2}\right\}$$

$$= \frac{\tau_{p0}[n_0+n_1+N_f(1+p_1/p_0)^{-1}]+\tau_{n0}[p_0+p_1+N_f(1+p_0/p_1)^{-1}]}{p_0+n_0+N_f(1+p_1/p_0)^{-1}(1+p_0/p_1)^{-1}} \times$$

$$\times \left\{\frac{1 \pm \sqrt{(1-R)}}{2}\right\} \qquad (852.5)$$

where

$$R = \frac{4\gamma N\left[(1+ab)+\dfrac{Nb}{(1+b)^2}\right]}{\left[(1+b)(a+\gamma)+N\left(\dfrac{1+\gamma b}{1+b}\right)\right]^2} \qquad (852.6)$$

It is obvious that the decay of both x and y must *eventually* be controlled by the longer of the two time constants, τ_+. That the two types of excess carrier must always decay with the same final time constant is dictated by the result (823.5) that the ratio (x/y) eventually assumes a steady value,

$$S = \lim_{x\to 0,\, y\to 0} (x/y)$$

$$= \frac{[(\gamma-a)-(\gamma+a)N/\bar{N}]+\sqrt{\{[(\gamma-a)-(\gamma+a)N/\bar{N}]^2+4a\gamma\}}}{2\gamma}$$

$$= \frac{2a}{[(a-\gamma)+(a+\gamma)N/\bar{N}]+\sqrt{\{[(a-\gamma)+(a+\gamma)N/\bar{N}]^2+4a\gamma\}}} \qquad (852.7)$$

The sign and magnitude of $\bar{N}$ relative to that of N determines which of the two expressions for S is more useful.

As observed by Sandiford (1957:**18**), the two time constants τ_+, τ_- are widely separated when $R \ll 1$, since then

$$\left\{\frac{1+\sqrt{(1-R)}}{2}\right\} \approx 1$$

whereas

$$\left\{\frac{1-\sqrt{(1-R)}}{2}\right\} \ll 1$$

For a set of parameters which make R small, if decay is initiated from a small value of $x_0 = y_0$, the curves for x and y will diverge only during an exceedingly brief period, comparable with τ_- (which will be $\ll \tau_{n0}$ and $\ll \tau_{p0}$). Following this extremely brief adjustment, both x and y will decay with time constant τ_+.

Sandiford remarks that the situation of $R \ll 1$ will "nearly always be the case", a statement which is not supported by more detailed scrutiny of the form of R. As may easily be verified, R can be much smaller than unity only when $N \ll |\bar{N}|$; but for such small flaw densities the simple S–R model suffices. It is for flaw densities comparable with or larger than $p_0|\bar{N}|$ that trapping produces a marked disparity of the two excess carrier densities, and R can then never be neglected by comparison with unity.

It is useful to review some of the simplified forms taken by τ_+ and S for certain ranges of the parameters.

(a) *Very Large Flaw Density*

When N_f is very large, R simplifies to $\approx 4\gamma b(1+b)^{-2}$. Two possible values must be quoted for the final decay time constant of electrons and holes, since the larger value of τ_+ in Eq. (852.5) now depends on whether electrons are trapped ($\gamma b < 1$) or holes trapped ($\gamma b > 1$). These values are

$$\left.\begin{aligned} \tau_+ &\approx \tau_{+1} = \tau_{n0}(1+p_1/p_0) \quad \text{for} \quad \gamma b > 1 \\ \tau_+ &\approx \tau_{+2} = \tau_{p0}(1+p_0/p_1) \quad \text{for} \quad \gamma b < 1 \end{aligned}\right\} \text{large } N_f \qquad (852.8)$$

Similarly, two values must be specified for the ratio of electron density to hole density during this final decay:

$$\left.\begin{aligned} S &\approx \frac{a(1+b)^2}{N(1-\gamma b)} \quad \text{for} \quad \gamma b < 1 \\ S &\approx \frac{N(\gamma b-1)}{\gamma(1+b)^2} \quad \text{for} \quad \gamma b > 1 \end{aligned}\right\} \text{large } N_f \qquad (852.9)$$

Since $C_n = 1/\tau_{n0}$ and $C_p = 1/\tau_{p0}$ are proportional to N_f, the time constants of Eq. (852.8) are inversely proportional to the flaw density, an entirely natural result. Such proportionality is also obeyed when N_f is small; but as shown below, there can be an intermediate range of flaw density for which the zero-modulation time constant is relatively insensitive to N_f.

(b) *P-type Class I Situation*

This is a situation for which the Fermi level and flaw level are both in the lower half of the intrinsic gap. The parameter $b = (p_1/p_0)$ may be either larger or smaller than unity, but $a = (n_1/p_0) \ll 1$. For this form of simplification of the problem

$$R = \frac{4\gamma N[Nb+(1+b)^2]}{[N(\gamma b+1)+\gamma(1+b)^2]^2} \tag{852.10}$$

so that

$$\sqrt{(1-R)} = \frac{N(\gamma b-1)+\gamma(1+b)^2}{N(\gamma b+1)+\gamma(1+b)^2} \tag{852.10}$$

It is interesting to note that for electron trapping situations ($\gamma b < 1$), the right side of (852.10) changes sign when N passes through the value $\gamma(1+b)^2/(1-\gamma b)$ [which a comparison with Eq. (823.3) will show is just $\bar{N}$ for Class I conditions]. In hole trapping situations all values of N correspond with $\sqrt{(1-R)} > 0$. Then the description of the final time constant must be given in two forms:

$$\tau_+ = \tau_{+1} = \tau_{n0}(1+b) \quad \text{for} \quad \begin{cases} \gamma b > 1 \\ \text{or} \quad \gamma b < 1 \quad \text{but} \quad N < \bar{N} \end{cases} \tag{852.11}$$

while

$$\left.\begin{aligned} \tau_+ = \tau_{+3} &= \frac{\tau_{+1}}{\gamma b+(\bar{N}/N)(1-\gamma b)} \\ &= \frac{\tau_{p0}N(1+b)}{Nb+(1+b)^2} \end{aligned}\right\} \quad \text{for} \quad \gamma b < 1, \quad N > \bar{N} \tag{852.12}$$

For majority hole trapping situations the situation is very simple, and the zero-modulation lifetime is inversely proportional to N_f over the entire range. The lifetime of Eq. (852.11) is completely unchanged from that of an *S–R* model when a Class I p-type semiconductor is considered.

The behavior is less simple when the flaw energy is far enough from the valence band to provoke electron trapping. The S–R result is then obeyed for small flaw densities, but when the quantity τ_{+3} becomes appropriate, lifetime is relatively insensitive to flaw density while $\bar{N} < N < \bar{N}[(\gamma b)^{-1} - 1]$. For a *sufficiently* large flaw density, τ_{+3} approaches the form of τ_{+2} and is again inversely proportional to N_f. This behavior is illustrated in Fig. 85.3, shown for a p-type Class I case

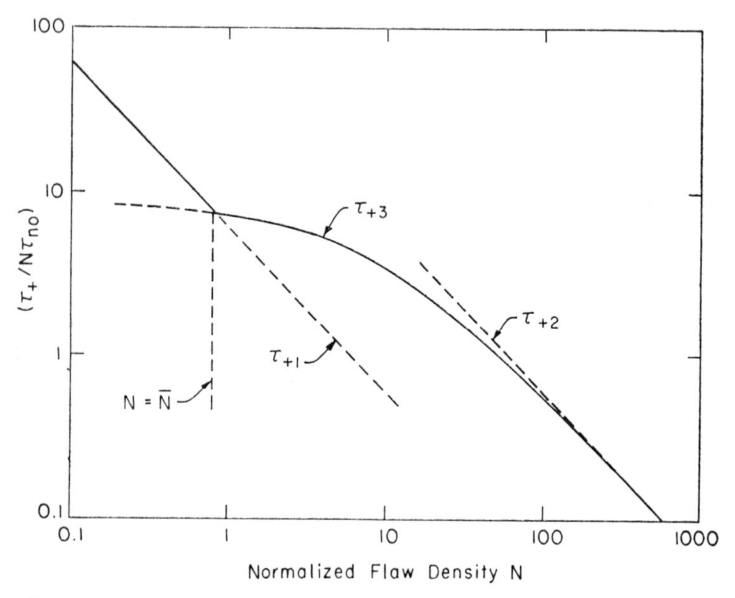

FIG. 85.3. Variation of the final decay time constant τ_+ with flaw density for a p-type Class I situation involving donor-like flaws. Plotted for the parameters $a \approx 0$, $b = 5$, $\gamma = 0{\cdot}02$.

when $a \approx 0$, $b = 5$, and $\gamma = 0{\cdot}02$. This choice of parameters makes $(\tau_{+1}/\tau_{+2}) = \gamma b = 0{\cdot}1$, and $\bar{N} = 0{\cdot}8$ for the normalized flaw density at which the lifetime breaks away from the pattern of τ_{+1}.

When $E_f < \xi$ and majority holes tend to be trapped, the ratio (n_e/p_e) will not usually become much larger than unity even in the final stages of decay. As flaw energies closer and closer to the valence band are considered, the flaw density which can be tolerated without serious trapping becomes progressively larger, as indicated in Fig. 82.2. The situation is more acute when E_f is high enough to induce minority electron trapping. Nomura and Blakemore (1958:**13**) have suggested that the terms "weak" and "strong" be applied to electron trapping depending on whether N is less than or greater than $\bar{N}$. In the latter case, the limiting ratio S of n_e to p_e will be very much smaller than unity for an extrinsic semiconductor.

One expression for S can be used in hole trapping and weak electron trapping Class I situations, but a different expression applies for strong trapping situations. These come from the two expressions for S in Eq. (852.7) when the Class I simplification of $a \ll 1$ is applied:

$$S = 1 + \frac{N(\gamma b - 1)}{\gamma(1+b)^2} \quad \begin{cases} \text{for hole trapping, } \gamma b > 1 \\ \text{for weak electron trapping, } \gamma b < 1,\ N < \bar{N} \end{cases} \tag{852.13}$$

whereas

$$\left.\begin{aligned} S &= \frac{a(1+b)^2}{N(1-\gamma b) - \gamma(1+b)^2} \\ &= \frac{a\bar{N}}{\gamma(N-\bar{N})} \end{aligned}\right\} \quad \begin{aligned} &\text{for strong electron trapping,} \\ &\qquad \gamma b < 1 \text{ and } N > \bar{N} \end{aligned} \tag{852.14}$$

When N is actually equal to $\bar{N}$, $S \approx (a/\gamma)^{1/2}$, which is already rather small, but as will be noted from the form of (852.14), S is exceedingly small for a markedly extrinsic semiconductor if $N > \bar{N}$.

The final time constant τ_{+3} of strong trapping situations becomes effective for holes when $p_e \ll (p_0 + p_1)$, but not for the minority electrons until n_e is much smaller than the very small quantity $(n_0 + n_1)$.

Strong electron trapping is impossible if $N \leqslant \gamma$, but for any larger value of the normalized flaw density, strong trapping can be expected at low temperatures, disappearing above a certain temperature. The influence of temperature comes in through the parameter

$$b = (p_1/p_0) = \exp\left(\frac{\phi - E_f}{kT}\right)$$

which increases with temperature. Fig. 85.4 shows the variation of τ_+ with b for a p-type Class I model involving donor-like flaws like those of the preceding figure ($\gamma = 0{\cdot}02$). Curves for several values of N are shown, some too small to permit strong trapping and others which provide for strong trapping when b is less than a critical value. In the weak trapping regions, the time constant is $\tau_{+1} = \tau_{n0}(1+b)$, and this behavior makes a marked contrast with the strong trapping regions, for which the time constant τ_{+3} decreases with increasing b.

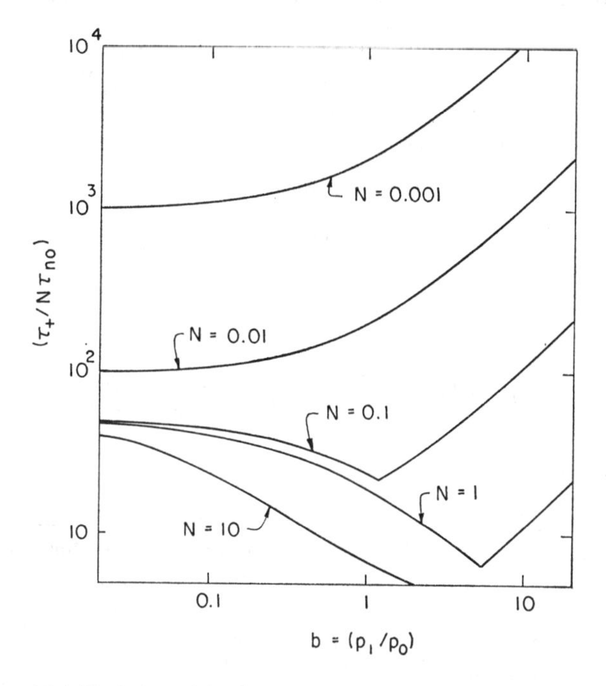

Fig. 85.4. Variation of the final time constant τ_+ with the parameter b for several values of the normalized flaw density. Drawn supposing p-type Class I conditions ($a \approx 0$) with donor-like flaws ($\gamma = 0{\cdot}02$).

When b reaches the value $\gamma^{-1} = 50$ (just off to the right of Fig. 85.4), trapping must automatically be non-existent for any flaw density: there will be very weak hole trapping for larger values of b.

Class I conditions have been described here for a p-type semiconductor; b finite but $a \approx 0$. These arguments can easily be inverted to discuss a Class I n-type semiconductor for which b is finite but $a^{-1} \approx 0$.

(c) *P-type Class II Situation*

With a p-type semiconductor containing flaw levels in the upper half of the gap, $a = (n_1/p_0)$ may be larger or smaller than unity but $b = (p_1/p_0) \ll 1$. For this simplification of the problem, the quantity R in Eq. (852.6) reduces to

$$R \approx \frac{4\gamma N}{(a+\gamma+N)^2} \tag{852.15}$$

Then the small-modulation lifetime τ_+ of Eq. (852.5) is

$$\tau_+ \approx \frac{\tau_{p0}\{(a+\gamma+N)+\sqrt{[(a-\gamma+N)^2+4a\gamma]}\}}{2(1+bN)} \tag{852.16}$$

The apparently insignificant quantity bN is retained in the denominator in order that the lifetime should tend to $\tau_{p0}(p_0/p_1)$ for sufficiently numerous flaws, as required by Eq. (852.8). For any reasonable flaw density this refinement can be dispensed with, leaving the lifetime as

$$\begin{aligned}\tau_{+4} &= \tfrac{1}{2}\tau_{p0}\{(a+\gamma+N)+\sqrt{[(a-\gamma+N)^2+4a\gamma]}\} \\ &= \tfrac{1}{2}\tau_{p0}\{(a+\gamma+N)+\sqrt{[(a+\gamma+N)^2-4\gamma N]}\}\end{aligned} \tag{852.17}$$

From Eq. (852.7), the corresponding final ratio S of excess electrons to excess holes is

$$S = (2\gamma)^{-1}\{(\gamma-a-N)+\sqrt{[(\gamma-a-N)^2+4a\gamma]}\} \tag{852.18}$$

It is evident that τ_{+4} cannot be larger than $[\tau_{n0}+\tau_{p0}(a+N)]$, nor can it be smaller than τ_{n0}. Where it lies between those limits depends on the relative magnitudes of the parameters a, N and γ. Whereas the excess carrier ratio S depends primarily on the flaw density, the functional behavior of the time constant is very sensitive to the ratio of a to γ. The value of this ratio is significant in differentiating between what has been called temporary and permanent trapping (1961:**1**).

With Class I conditions, a trapped minority electron has virtually no chance of re-excitation to the conduction band. Thus in this sense, Class I electron trapping is always "permanent", the proceedings being terminated by the subsequent capture of a hole. With Class II conditions, the flaw levels are much closer to the conduction band, and electron capture can be followed either by hole capture or electron emission. As Shockley (1958:**16**) points out, the four processes of electron and hole capture and emission all go on at the same rate in thermal equilibrium when the flaw energy E_f coincides with the position χ, which Shockley calls the "level of equality" and Rose (1957:**20**) the "demarcation level". This is the condition that $\gamma = a$.

When conditions depart from equilibrium, the ratio of electron emission to hole capture rates is $a/\gamma(1+y)$; thus for any reasonably small modulation the rates of these two processes are the same when $E_f = \chi$. Nomura and Blakemore (1961:**1**) think of trapping as a temporary phenomenon when flaws are closer to the conduction band than χ, since then an electron is likely to be trapped and re-excited several times before a free hole can be procured with which to annihilate it. This is particularly prone to happen with very asymmetric flaws for which $\gamma \ll 1$ (1955:**36**).

For lower lying flaws, $a < \gamma$, the probability of electron re-emission is less than 50%. The trapping of an electron is then usually "permanent"—until the flaw captures a hole and fulfils its function as a recombination center.

8.5.3 The Course of Class I Decay

The character of the very early and very late stages of Class I decay has been exposed in the two previous sub-sections. The intermediate region of the decay can less easily be described in analytic terms, and the general course of decay is illustrated here by some of the computed curves of Nomura and Blakemore (1958:**13**).

(a) *Majority Hole Trapping*, $\gamma b > 1$

When decay is initiated from a position of equal excess densities, $n_{e0} = p_{e0}$, the electron decay must have a time constant $\tau_{+1} = \tau_{n0}(1+b)$ for a very short initial period. The corresponding initial hole lifetime is $\tau_{+2} = \tau_{p0}(1+1/b)$. The sequence of time constants is $\tau_{+1} > \tau_{\infty} > \tau_{+2}$ whenever $\gamma b > 1$, and this requires holes to become trapped in the early stages of decay. For the electron and hole decay curves† of Fig. 85.5, this period of initial adjustment is too brief to be clearly visible, but the disparity of n_e and p_e which is produced during that period establishes the pattern for the remaining decay.

† Note that the abscissa is expressed in units of τ_{n0}, i.e. it is a scale of $\mathscr{T}$ rather than t. This permits a comparison of curves for differing flaw densities with the provisions of the *S–R* model. The *S–R* curve for the same values of γ and b does in fact lie between the inner pair of curves for x and y. Thus, compared with an *S–R* model, hole decay is speeded up and electron decay slowed down when flaws are numerous.

The figure confirms previous remarks that even with rather numerous flaws, the ratio (n_e/p_e) does not become much larger than unity, and that the form of the decay does not deviate seriously from Eq. (834.1) of the *S–R* model.

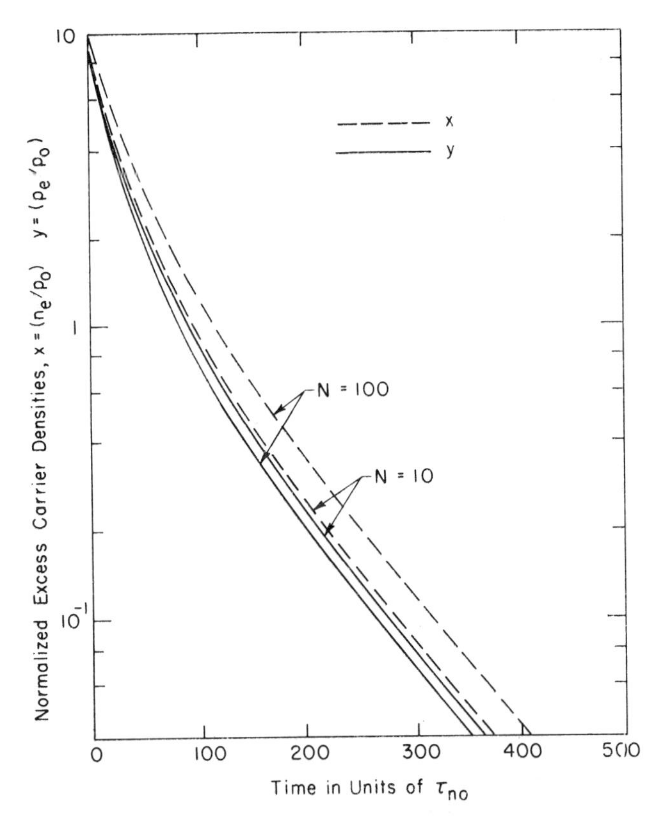

FIG. 85.5 Decay showing majority hole trapping. For donor-like flaws well below ξ so that $\gamma = 0{\cdot}05$, $b = 100$, $a \ll 1$.

(b) *Minority Electron Trapping*, $\gamma b < 1$

The decay of excess populations is a rather more complicated matter when $\gamma b < 1$. This is especially true of the final stages, when the time constant becomes either τ_{+1} (for $N < \bar{N}$) or τ_{+3} (for $N > \bar{N}$).

Fig. 85.6 shows the course of electron and hole decay for several flaw densities when the flaw properties are appropriate for electron trapping. The parameters selected make $\bar{N} = 0{\cdot}21$; thus the pair of

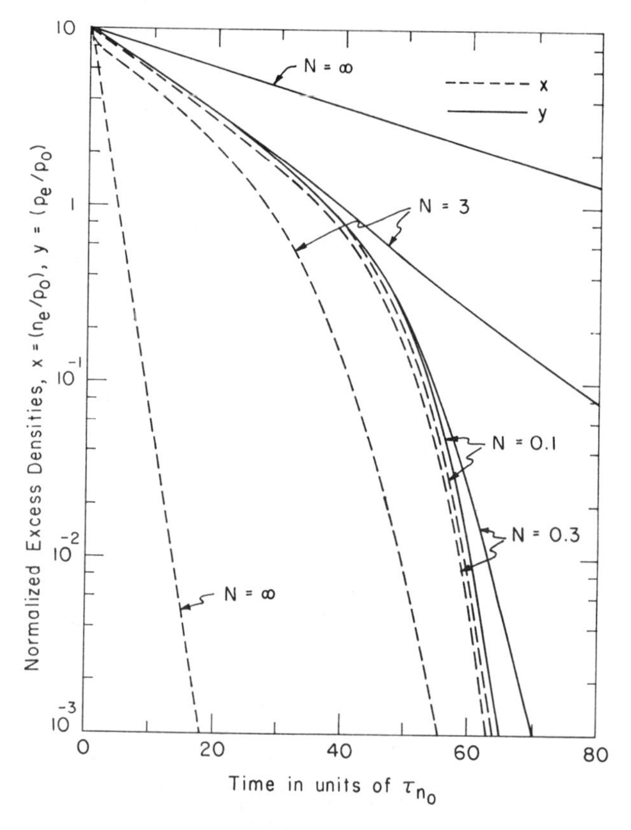

Fig. 85.6. Electron and hole decay when minority electron trapping occurs, supposing various densities of flaws for which $\gamma = 0{\cdot}05$, $b = 1$, $a = 5\times10^{-7}$.

curves shown for $N = 0{\cdot}1$ conform reasonably well to the *S–R* model, with a final time constant $\tau_{n0}(1+b)$. As larger values of N are considered, the disparity of p_e and n_e becomes more pronounced. It will also be noted that the final hole lifetime for $N = 0{\cdot}3$ is perceptibly larger than τ_{+1}, while for $\mathcal{N} = 3$, τ_{+3} is considerably larger than the small-modulation lifetime of an *S–R* model.

For strong trapping cases, the final electron lifetime must also be τ_{+3}, but there is no sign of this in Fig. 85.6. When the curves for $\mathcal{N} = 3$ are extended to very much smaller modulation, as is done in Fig. 85.7,

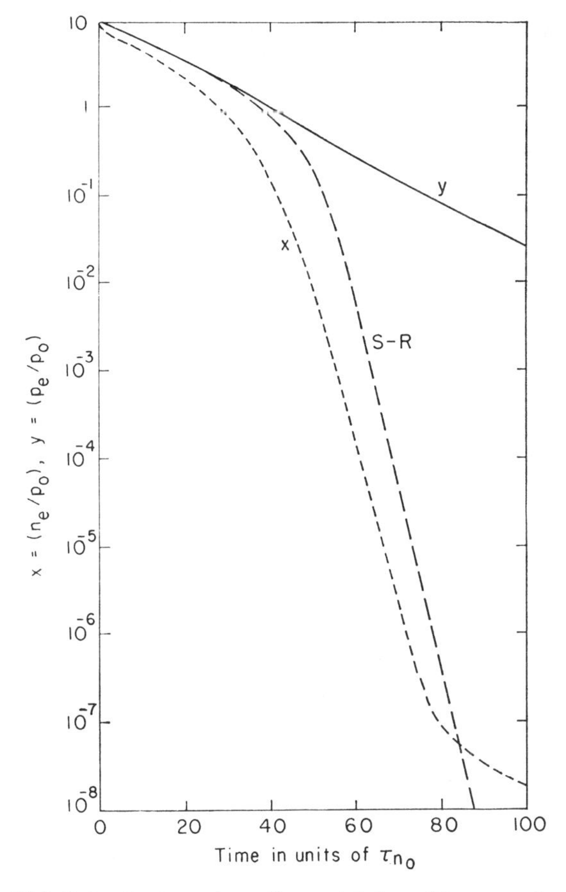

Fig. 85.7. Extension towards smaller modulation of the curves for $\mathcal{N} = 3$ in Fig. 85.6 ($\gamma = 0{\cdot}05$, $b = 1$, $a = 5 \times 10^{-7}$). Showing how electrons as well as holes eventually have the time constant τ_{+3}. The single curve of the *S–R* model is shown for comparison.

it will be seen that the electron decay does indeed assume the expected form when $x \ll a(1+b)$. The value of S is extremely small with the parameters chosen, in accordance with Eq. (852.14).

(c) *Variation with Temperature*

For some kinds of flaw, τ_{n0} and τ_{p0} are functions of temperature. This cannot be taken into account in any generally useful fashion, since the

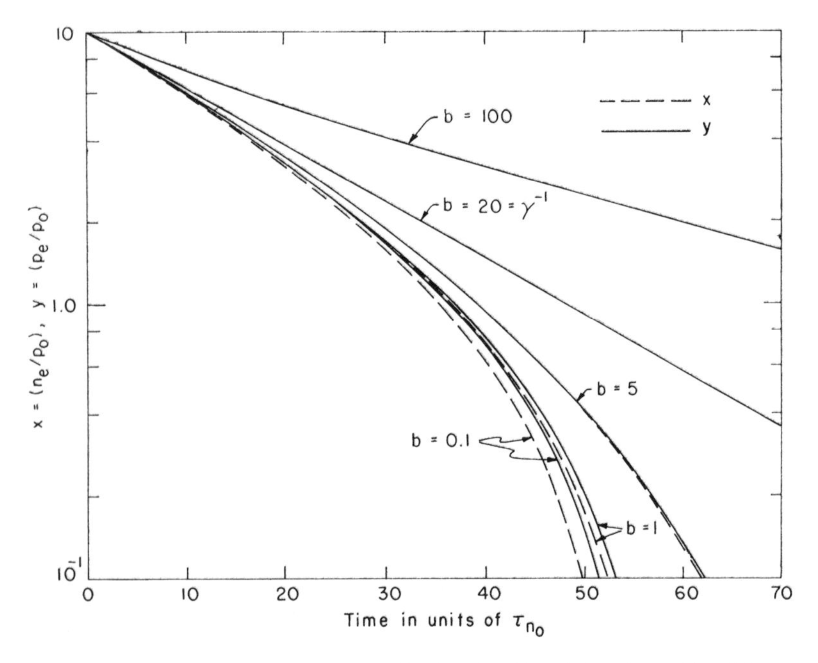

Fig. 85.8. Variation of x and y with time for Class I situations ($\mathcal{N} = 0{\cdot}1$, $\gamma = 0{\cdot}05$, $a \ll 1$) with various values for the temperature-dependent parameter b.

possible forms of cross-section temperature dependence are rather varied.

However, as a first approach to the problem of temperature variation, it may be supposed that the variation of b is the most important for a Class I process. Fig. 85.8 shows how the shape of the decay changes as successively larger values of b are considered. The pair of curves for $b = 0{\cdot}1$ represent a strong trapping situation, but this changes to weak trapping for $b > 0{\cdot}4$. Weak trapping is the rule for the curves of $b = 1$

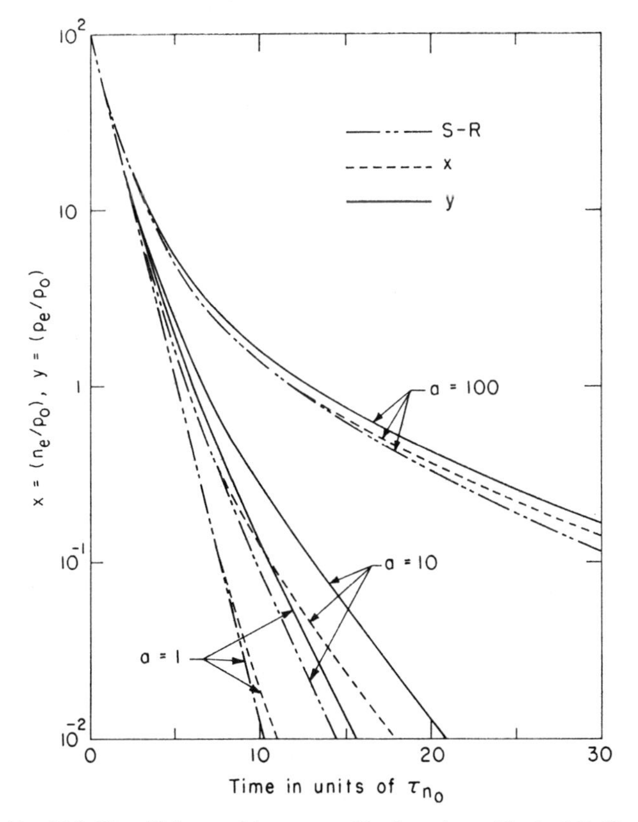

FIG. 85.9. Class II decay with acceptor-like flaws ($\gamma = 10$, $ab \ll 1$). Showing the decay prescribed by the S–R model for three values of a, and the separate behavior of x and y when flaws are numerous [$\mathcal{N} = 20$].

and $b = 5$, and of course there is no trapping at all for $b = 20 = \gamma^{-1}$. The final curve of $b = 100$ should show extremely mild hole trapping. The variation of the final time constant with b follows a pattern which has already been described (see the discussion concerning Fig. 85.4).

8.5.4 The Course of Class II Decay

When equal numbers of excess electrons and holes are created in a p-type semiconductor with flaws in the upper half of the intrinsic gap,

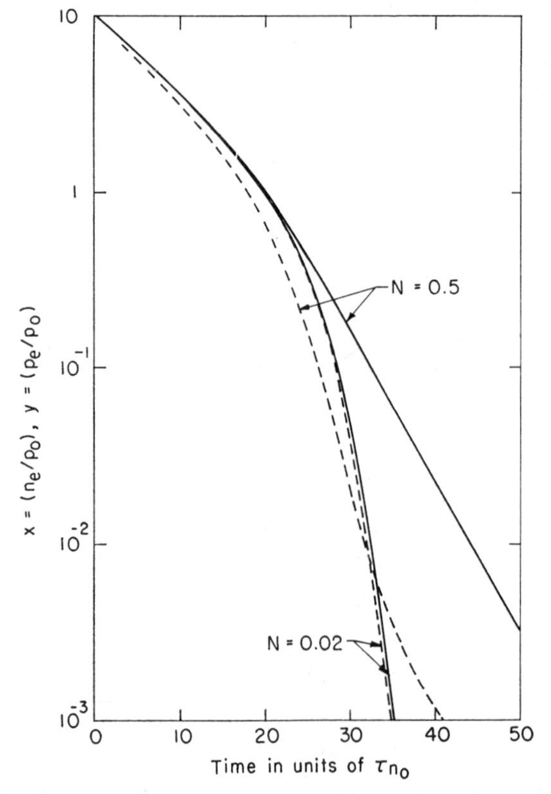

Fig. 85.10. The shape of decay in a Class II situation involving donor-like flaws ($\gamma = 0{\cdot}1$, $a = 0{\cdot}02$, $ab \ll 1$). For a small flaw density, when the decay is little different from the *S–R* model; and for a much larger flaw density.

no hole capture is possible until some electrons have been trapped—since the flaws must start out completely empty. This can be seen in the initial shapes of the curves in Fig. 85.2.

The final behavior of both n_e and p_e is dictated by the lifetime τ_{+4} of Eq. (852.17), which depends on the values of the quantities $\mathcal{N}$, γ and a. It is convenient to consider the decay associated with acceptor-like and donor-like flaws separately.

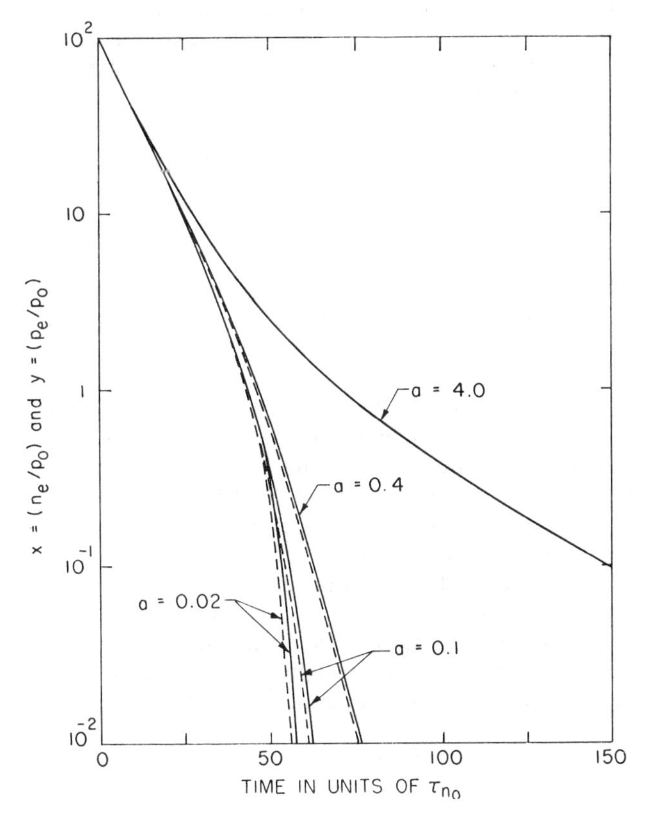

FIG. 85.11. The transformation from permanent to temporary electron trapping when the density of donor-like flaws is moderate ($\mathcal{N} = 0{\cdot}1$, $\gamma = 0{\cdot}1$, $ab \ll 1$).

(a) *Decay when Flaws are Acceptor-like*

The essential features of Class II decay via acceptor-like flaws can be seen in Fig. 85.9. One trio of curves shows the result for the *S–R* model (small flaw density) when three values for a are considered (corresponding with different temperatures). An increase of a changes the situation from one of "permanent trapping" into the "temporary trapping" range, the borderline being for $a = \gamma = 10$.

As expected from Eqs. (852.17) and (852.18), the inclusion of a large flaw density results in a separation of the decay curves for x and y, and in making τ_{+4} a larger multiple of τ_{n0}. Thus for flaws at the level of equality, the final time constant is $2\tau_{n0}$ when N is small, but it becomes $3{\cdot}4\tau_{n0}$ for $N = 20$.

The separation between curves of x and y diminishes as larger values of a are considered, since trapping always becomes less effective when the temperature rises.

(b) *Decay through Donor-like Flaws*

Fig. 85.10, based on a Class II model of donor-like flaws ($\gamma = 0{\cdot}1$, $a = 0{\cdot}02$, $ab \ll 1$) demonstrates that the *S–R* model is satisfied rather well when $N < (a+\gamma)$, but not for larger flaw densities. The curves for $N = 0{\cdot}5$ have a resemblance to those of Fig. 85.7 for Class I decay with many flaws. The main difference is that the excess electron curve assumes its final slope without waiting for n_e to become less than the very small quantity n_0. For of course Eq. (852.1) becomes valid when n_e is small compared with (n_0+n_1). This is not a severe restriction for Class II decay, since n_1 may be quite large.

The effect of increasing temperature can be simulated by considering successively larger values of a. The typical form of result is shown in Fig. 85.11. For the parameters used in this figure, the borderline between permanent and temporary trapping occurs when $a = 0{\cdot}1 = \gamma$. As expected, the electron–hole ratio approaches unity for large values of a.

Chapter 9

MORE COMPLICATED EXAMPLES OF FLAW RECOMBINATION

THE model discussed in Chapter 8 was highly idealized in that only one type of flaw (and that a monovalent variety) was presumed to contribute to the recombination. Neglect of band-to-band recombination is probably justifiable under conditions which make the ratio (E_i/kT) rather large. But the flaw recombination which then dominates may receive significant contributions from several kinds of center. Moreover, some interesting kinds of flaw (copper in germanium, for example) are multivalent. This chapter comments on these and other complications of flaw recombination.

9.1 MULTIVALENT FLAWS §

A multivalent flaw may be said to "contain" anywhere between zero and a maximum of m electrons. If N_s denotes the number of flaws with s electrons, then

$$N_f = \sum_{s=0}^{m} N_s \tag{910.1}$$

The recombination rate when excess free carriers are present depends on the distribution of flaws between the various possible states of charge, and on the capture and emission coefficients for increasing or decreasing s by unity.

Sah and Shockley (1958:**11**) have studied this problem extensively for a semiconductor containing only one type of multivalent flaw, when external stimulation maintains a condition of steady state non-equilibrium. They point out that the non-equilibrium distribution of the various N_s cannot be characterized by a flaw "quasi-Fermi level" or electrochemical potential, in contrast to the situation for monovalent flaws.†

Thus the treatment of Landsberg (1957:**22**), in which a common value of ϕ_f is taken to indicate the occupation probability of the whole series of flaw states, is likely to be strictly correct only when the departure from thermal equilibrium is very small. Landsberg (1960:**1**) later removed this restriction in a generalized treatment which also allows for degeneracy of the distributions in the bands.

Sah and Shockley's approach should be valid for any departure from equilibrium provided that the distribution in the bands follows the Boltzmann form. Their paper (1958:**11**) is recommended for a comprehensive treatment of the subject, of which the following remarks provide merely a summary sketch.

Four series of capture and emission coefficients must be used to describe the probabilities of various transitions. Sah and Shockley set the rate of electron capture by flaws already holding s electrons as

† In thermal equilibrium, the Fermi level ϕ indicates the values of n_0 and p_0. It also characterizes the occupancy of all levels within the gap. Thus for monovalent flaws at energy E_f, we noted in Chapter 8 that

$$f(E_f) = \left[\frac{n_0}{n_0+n_1}\right] = \left[1+\exp\left(\frac{E_f-\phi}{kT}\right)\right]^{-1}$$

It was shown in Section 3.3 that the distribution of electrons over a set of multivalent or amphoteric impurities conformed with the same ϕ.

Now when conditions depart from equilibrium, the quantities ϕ_n and ϕ_p describe the conduction and valence band densities. The treatment of Chapter 8 referred to the fraction of "full" flaws as

$$P_e(E_f) = \left[\frac{n_0}{n_0+n_1} + \frac{p_e-n_e}{N_f}\right]$$

but this may be taken as defining an electrochemical potential ϕ_f for the flaws through

$$P_e(E_f) = \left[1+\exp\left(\frac{E_f-\phi_f}{kT}\right)\right]^{-1}$$

However, when multivalent flaws are in non-equilibrium, there is in general no value ϕ_f which can be substituted for ϕ in the thermal equilibrium expressions to describe the distribution of the various N_s.

$nN_s c(n, s)$. In the nomenclature of the capture coefficient $c(n, s)$, n denotes that an *electron* is being captured while s indicates the *initial* condition of the flaw. (The final condition for the reaction discussed obviously has $s+1$ electrons on the flaw.)

Transitions between the states s and $s+1$ of a flaw involve addition or removal of a bound electron at an energy $E(s+\frac{1}{2})$. The index here is the *average* of s and $s+1$ since the energy is associated with the transition between the two conditions but independent of the direction. In terms of $E(s+\frac{1}{2})$ two useful densities can be defined

$$\left.\begin{aligned} n(s+\tfrac{1}{2}) &= n_i \exp\left[\frac{E(s+\frac{1}{2})-\phi_i}{kT}\right] \\ p(s+\tfrac{1}{2}) &= n_i \exp\left[\frac{\phi_i - E(s+\frac{1}{2})}{kT}\right] \end{aligned}\right\} \tag{910.2}$$

which are analogous to the quantities n_1 and p_1 of the monovalent flaw model (see Chapter 8). The rate at which flaws undergo the transition $s+1 \rightarrow s$ by electron emission can be written as $N_{s+1}e(n, s+1)$, in terms of an "emission coefficient" $e(n, s+1)$. However, detailed balance requires that

$$e(n, s+1) = n(s+\tfrac{1}{2}) \,.\, c(n, s) \tag{910.3}$$

Hole capture for the transition $s+1 \rightarrow s$ is expressed in terms of a capture coefficient $c(p, s+1)$. The inverse process involves an emission coefficient $e(p, s)$ which must equal $p(s+\frac{1}{2}) \,.\, c(p, s+1)$ in order to satisfy the requirements of detailed balance. The four processes which contribute to transitions $s \leftrightarrow s+1$ are listed in Table 91.1.

Sah and Shockley consider *steady-state* non-equilibrium conditions. Then the rate of $s \rightarrow s+1$ transitions equals that of $s+1 \rightarrow s$ transitions, since the numbers of flaws in each of the possible charge conditions is time-invariant. Carrier lifetimes are defined in terms of the steady state recombination rate:

$$\frac{n_e}{\tau_n} = \frac{p_e}{\tau_p} = \sum_{s=0}^{m-1} u(s+\tfrac{1}{2}) \tag{910.4}$$

where

$$\left.\begin{aligned} u(s+\tfrac{1}{2}) &= c(n, s)[nN_s - n(s+\tfrac{1}{2})N_{s+1}] \\ &= c(p, s+1)[pN_{s+1} - p(s+\tfrac{1}{2})N_s] \end{aligned}\right\} \tag{910.5}$$

Table 91.1. Transition rates between conditions s and s+1 for multivalent flaws

Process	Flaw condition		Rate
	Initial	Final	
Electron capture	s	$s+1$	$nN_s c(n, s)$
Electron emission	$s+1$	s	$N_{s+1}e(n, s+1) = n(s+\frac{1}{2})N_{s+1}c(n, s)$
Hole capture	$s+1$	s	$pN_{s+1}c(p, s+1)$
Hole emission	s	$s+1$	$N_s e(p, s) = p(s+\frac{1}{2})N_s c(p, s+1)$

From Eq. (910.5), no great difficulty is involved in reaching Sah and Shockley's result

$$u(s+\tfrac{1}{2}) = \frac{(N_s + N_{s+1})(np - n_0 p_0)}{\left[\dfrac{p + p(s+\frac{1}{2})}{c(n, s)}\right] + \left[\dfrac{n + n(s+\frac{1}{2})}{c(p, s+1)}\right]} \tag{910.6}$$

This equation clearly adopts the proper form for the monovalent flaw model [see Eq. (840.2)] when the flaw is *monovalent* and only the charge conditions s and $s+1$ exist. For *multivalent* flaws, it will still usually happen that most states of the flaw will be either too high or too low in energy to make an appreciable contribution to the recombination rate; then the summation (910.4) usually contains two or three terms only.

Let $u^*(s+\frac{1}{2})$ denote the value taken by $u(s+\frac{1}{2})$ when the numerator on the right of Eq. (910.6) is $N_f(np - n_0 p_0)$. Suppose that a fraction α of the flaws are in the condition s and substantially all the remainder in the condition $s+1$. Then from Eqs. (910.4) and (910.6),

$$\frac{n_e}{\tau_n} = \frac{p_e}{\tau_p} = \alpha u^*(s-\tfrac{1}{2}) + u^*(s+\tfrac{1}{2}) + (1-\alpha)u^*(s+\tfrac{3}{2}) \tag{910.7}$$

This reduces to $u^*(s-\frac{1}{2}) + u^*(s+\frac{1}{2})$ when almost *all* flaws are in a single condition s (which is frequently likely to be the case).

The presence of many excess free carriers (electrons and holes) can tend to change the average occupancy of a flaw very considerably. It will depend on the relative magnitudes of electron and hole capture coefficients whether the flaw occupancy will tend to be guided by the electrochemical potential ϕ_n for free electrons, or the quantity ϕ_p for holes. If there is much asymmetry of capture coefficients, every flaw may change its charge by one or two units in attempting to respond to the situation. When this is the case, successive terms in the summation (910.4) assume importance in turn as the carrier modulation is increased.

9.2 MORE THAN ONE KIND OF FLAW §

Suppose that a semiconductor contains $\mathcal{N}_1$ flaws of type 1, $\mathcal{N}_2$ of type 2, and so on up to $\mathcal{N}_k$ of type k. Each set of flaws would (in the absence of the rest but with the Fermi level unchanged) provide a lifetime $\tau_1, \tau_2, \ldots \tau_k$. A question of obvious interest is: what lifetime τ results when the several sets of flaws act in concert?

Kalashnikov (1956:**34**) has considered this question for conditions of small modulation and steady state stimulation. His conclusion must be expressed that in general

$$\frac{1}{\tau} = \sum_{j=1}^{k} \frac{1}{\tau_j} - \nu_m \qquad (920.1)$$

where ν_m represents the mutual effect of the flaws. For large modulation (or small total flaw density) such that $n_e \approx p_e \gg \Sigma\mathcal{N}_j$, it can reasonably be expected that ν_m will be unimportant, but for conditions of small modulation, ν_m will vanish only in favorable circumstances.

The theoretical problems associated with simultaneous recombination by two or more kinds of flaw have been considered by several other authors, including Landsberg (1957:**22**), Wertheim (1958:**14**) and Rose (1955:**16**, 1957:**20**). The last author considers localized states distributed over a wide range of energies throughout the forbidden gap—a model which is capable of explaining the various complications of insulating photoconductors (superlinearity, quenching effects, etc.).

An important point which Kalashnikov brings out is that the development of a considerable term ν_m depends very much on the cross-section *asymmetry* of the various kinds of flaws present. He notes that when free carriers are trapped by one kind of flaw, the remaining flaws must attempt to carry out their recombinative duties in the face of a considerable imbalance of n_e and p_e. The *absolute* magnitudes of the capture cross-sections for the flaws which cause all the trouble may both be small; it is their *ratio* which determines by how much the recombinative action of the other flaws can be hindered.

This aspect of the composite effect of recombination mechanisms is amplified in the next section, which considers the competition between a purely recombinative process and a set of flaws which are so asymmetric that they can be deemed not to capture one kind of carrier at all.

9.3 THE HAYNES–HORNBECK TRAPPING MODEL

Chapter 8 described how flaws can engage in both recombination and trapping. Haynes and Hornbeck (1955:**36**, 1955:**37**) have considered the model of a semiconductor in which recombination proceeds via some unspecified mechanism (at a rate n_e/τ_r) while a set of flaws is active in trapping but very weak in recombination ($\gamma \ll a$). They developed this model to describe the behavior of very asymmetric flaws found in some kinds of silicon. The model should be of interest for any semiconductor containing flaws for which γ is either very large or very small. Fan (1953:**16**) has discussed a similar type of trapping model.

9.3.1 Flaws Which Do Not Capture Holes

As an initial simplification, suppose that the semiconductor is p-type and contains flaws for which γ is so small that they capture virtually no holes at all. Then the attenuation rate of excess holes after the cessation of any excess generation follows

$$-\frac{dp_e}{dt} = \frac{n_e}{\tau_r} \qquad (931.1)$$

For excess electrons under the same conditions†

$$-\frac{dn_e}{dt} = \frac{n_e}{\tau_r} + \frac{n_e}{\tau_{n0}}\left[\frac{n_1}{n_0 + n_1} - \frac{n_t}{N_f}\right] - \frac{(n_0 + n_1)n_t}{\tau_{n0}N_f} \qquad (931.2)$$

Here n_t denotes $(p_e - n_e)$, the excess density of occupied flaws. The first term on the right of Eq. (931.2) is the recombination rate, the second

† The adaptation of Eq. (931.2) from Eq. (812.6) should need no explanation.

is the rate of trapping, and the third is the rate of release from flaws. Haynes and Hornbeck use the symbol τ_g for $N_f\tau_{n0}(n_0+n_1)^{-1}$, the mean time an electron spends trapped at a flaw.† They further use τ_t to signify $\tau_{n0}(1+n_0/n_1)$, the time taken (for small modulation) to trap an electron.

When trapping is rather vigorous, it will often happen that $n_t \approx p_e \gg n_e$. An observed quantity such as photoconductive response is then dominated by the behavior of $p_e \approx n_t$ free holes. This provides an impetus for studying the time-dependence of n_t itself. From Eqs. (931.1) and (931.2).

$$-\frac{dn_t}{dt} = \frac{n_t(n_0+n_1)}{\tau_{n0}N_f} - \frac{n_e}{\tau_{n0}}\left[\frac{n_1}{n_0+n_1} - \frac{n_t}{N_f}\right] \tag{931.3}$$

Second-order non-linear equations in terms of one dependent variable and its time derivatives can be obtained by simultaneous solution of Eqs. (931.2) and (931.3). Thus:

$$\frac{d^2n_e}{dt^2}(n_0+n_1+n_e) - \left(\frac{dn_e}{dt}\right)^2 + \left(\frac{dn_e}{dt}\right)\left[\frac{(n_0+n_1)}{\tau_r} + \frac{n_1}{\tau_{n0}} + \frac{(n_0+n_1+n_e)^2}{\tau_{n0}N_f}\right] + $$
$$+\frac{n_e(n_0+n_1+n_e)^2}{\tau_r\tau_{n0}N_f} = 0 \tag{931.4}$$

A similar type of equation describes the decay of n_t. Eqs. (931.2)–(931.4) can be made to yield some useful approximate solutions. The necessary procedures depend on the excess densities and on the relative magnitudes of τ_r, τ_g and τ_t.

9.3.2 Small-modulation Decay

Eq. (931.4) can be linearized when $n_e \ll (n_0+n_1)$. This may appear to be a severe restriction for a p-type semiconductor with flaws rather a long way below the conduction band—but such a configuration tends to make n_e small rather rapidly, with n_t considerably larger. The criterion for linearizing the second-order equation in n_t is that

$$n_t \ll N_f(1+n_0/n_1)^{-1},$$

the density of normally empty flaws.

† The product $N_f\tau_{n0}$ is of course independent of flaw density, being the reciprocal of the electron capture coefficient $\langle c_n\rangle$. Thus $(1/\tau_g) = \langle c_n\rangle(n_0+n_1)$.

For appropriately small modulation, the decay schemes are

$$\left.\begin{aligned} \frac{d^2 n_e}{dt^2} + \alpha\frac{dn_e}{dt} + \beta n_e &= 0 \\ \frac{d^2 n_t}{dt^2} + \alpha\frac{dn_t}{dt} + \beta n_t &= 0 \end{aligned}\right\} \qquad (932.1)$$

with

$$\begin{aligned} \alpha &= \left[\frac{1}{\tau_r} + \frac{n_1}{\tau_{n0}(n_0+n_1)} + \frac{(n_0+n_1)}{\tau_{n0}N_f}\right] \\ &= \left[\frac{1}{\tau_r} + \frac{1}{\tau_t} + \frac{1}{\tau_g}\right] \end{aligned} \qquad (932.2)$$

and

$$\beta = \frac{(n_0+n_1)}{\tau_r\tau_{n0}N_f} = \frac{1}{\tau_r\tau_g} \qquad (932.3)$$

The complete solution for an equation with the form of (932.1) is the sum of two exponentially decaying terms, but the important term after a sufficiently long time is always the one with the longer time constant, τ_0. The standard procedure for Eq. (932.1) shows that

$$\begin{aligned} \tau_0 &= \left\{\frac{\alpha - \sqrt{(\alpha^2 - 4\beta)}}{2\beta}\right\} \\ &= \frac{\tau_r\tau_g}{2}\left\{\left[\frac{1}{\tau_r} + \frac{1}{\tau_t} + \frac{1}{\tau_g}\right] + \sqrt{\left[\left(\frac{1}{\tau_r} + \frac{1}{\tau_t} + \frac{1}{\tau_g}\right)^2 - \frac{4}{\tau_r\tau_g}\right]}\right\} \end{aligned} \qquad (932.4)$$

Three characteristic modes of behavior for the small-modulation region of the decay can be distinguished.

(a) *Decay Limited by Recombination,* $\tau_0 \approx \tau_r$

It is possible for a small density of asymmetric flaws to be present, yet not intrude appreciably on the final decay; provided that the flaw properties satisfy two conditions. These are that

$$(n_0+n_1) > \frac{1}{\langle c_n\rangle\ \tau_r} \qquad [\tau_g < \tau_r] \qquad (932.5)$$

and that

$$\mathcal{N}_f < \frac{(n_0 + n_1)^2}{n_1} \qquad [\tau_g < \tau_t] \qquad (932.6)$$

The first of these conditions means that the flaw level and/or Fermi level must not be too far below the conduction band. The limit on flaw density placed by Eq. (932.6) is again dependent on the relationship of flaw energy to Fermi level.

It is a general rule that trapping is more pronounced for small modulation than for large; then it may be concluded that flaws which satisfy Eqs. (932.5) and (932.6) will cause negligible interference for any excess densities. This enables us—when we are considering *S–R*, radiative or some other recombination mechanism in a semiconductor—to ignore levels lying very close to the minority carrier band. For example, in semiconductors such as *p*-type Ge or Si, the donor levels introduced by Group V elements are too close to the conduction band (n_1 too large) for appreciable trapping effects. It further follows that such levels will not be effective in recombination either (especially when, as in the case of donor centers, the hole capture cross-section is small).

For τ_0 to approximate to τ_r, it makes no difference whether τ_r is larger or smaller than τ_t, though naturally the mechanics are different in the two cases. With a very small flaw density located such that $\tau_t > \tau_r$, only a minor fraction of the excess electrons can ever be trapped. If the flaws are more numerous but very close to the conduction band, making $\tau_t < \tau_r$, most excess electrons will be trapped at least once and perhaps several times. But the release rate from flaws is then so rapid that the overall decay is not appreciably affected.

For flaws which are low lying and numerous—or competing with a more vigorous recombination system—trapping must influence the final time constant. It will depend on whether Eq. (932.5) or Eq. (932.6) fails first as to whether single or multiple trapping develops.

(b) *Single Trapping*, $\tau_0 \approx \tau_g$

When the flaw energy is far below the conduction band, then against the background of any reasonable recombination rate it is impossible to disguise the fact that flaws are withholding electrons for a considerable time. The final time constant τ_0 will approximate to τ_g (the time an electron has to wait before release from a flaw) if

$$(n_0 + n_1) < \frac{1}{\langle c_n \rangle \, \tau_r} \qquad [\tau_r < \tau_g] \qquad (932.7)$$

yet flaws are not very numerous, so that

$$N_f < \frac{(1 + n_0/n_1)}{\langle c_n \rangle \, \tau_r} \qquad [\tau_r < \tau_t] \qquad (932.8)$$

The latter provision ensures that only a minor fraction of the excess electrons are ever trapped, and re-trapping is unlikely; yet the period for which these few are held is long enough to impede the decay.

It might at first seem a paradox that the final decay time constant is now independent of flaw *density*, yet these flaws are supposed to be controlling the behavior. This is not in fact a paradox, since the ability of a flaw to release an electron is not contingent on the presence of other flaws. For flaws of such a character that $\tau_r < \tau_g$, then *some* trapping will occur for appropriately low modulation *no matter how small* N_f *may be*. But this is only required to be noticeable when n_t becomes small compared with the empty flaw density. If N_f is small, then the "single trapping" phenomenon is preceded by a lengthy period of pure recombination.

An increase of flaw density eventually forces a failure of the condition (932.8), bringing on multiple trapping.

(c) *Multiple Trapping*, $\tau_0 \approx (\tau_r \tau_g / \tau_t)$

When flaws are sufficiently numerous, both the conditions (932.6) and (932.8) fail; τ_t is shorter than both τ_r and τ_g. An excess electron is then likely to be trapped several times before it is accepted for recombination, and the detention time in the flaw can be rather long. The flaws now exert a profound influence on the decay, particularly for small modulation, where the appropriate simplification of Eq. (932.4) is

$$\tau_0 \approx \frac{\tau_r \tau_g}{\tau_t} = \tau_r \cdot \frac{N_f n_1}{(n_0 + n_1)^2} \qquad (932.9)$$

Of course, there is no formal boundary between single and multiple trapping. Provided that τ_g is long enough to make the effect of the flaws noticeable, Eq. (932.4) provides for a small-modulation time constant

$$\tau_0 = \tau_g[1 + \tau_r/\tau_t] \quad \text{if} \quad \tau_g \gg \tau_r \quad \text{or} \quad \tau_t \tag{932.10}$$

This contains τ_g and $(\tau_g\tau_r/\tau_t)$ as limiting forms.

The next sub-section illustrates an approximate solution for moderate modulation which approaches the time constant of Eq. (932.10) at very long times.

9.3.3 Finite Modulation Trapping Solution

An approximate solution which should be valid for moderate densities of trapped electrons is again due to Haynes and Hornbeck. They point out that if τ_g is large compared with either τ_r or τ_t (or both), then the term (dn_e/dt) in Eq. (931.2) will be very small compared with the other terms of that equation. Thus if the right side of Eq. (931.2) is set as zero,

$$n_e\left\{\frac{1}{\tau_r} + \frac{1}{\tau_t}[1 - (n_t/N_f)(1 + n_0/n_1)]\right\} \approx n_t/\tau_g \tag{933.1}$$

This may be used to express Eq. (931.3) as an equation involving only n_t and its first derivative:

$$\frac{-dn_t}{dt} \approx \frac{n_e}{\tau_r} \approx \frac{n_t}{\tau_g\{1 + (\tau_r/\tau_t)[1 - (n_t/N_f)(1 + n_0/n_1)]\}} \tag{933.2}$$

Such a procedure is obviously not valid when the modulation is large enough to fill almost all the normally empty flaws $[n_t \to N_f(1 + n_0/n_1)^{-1}]$; but for more moderate excess populations it should satisfactorily describe trapping situations. Note from Eq. (933.2) that at any stage of decay, the time constant for further decay is

$$-\frac{1}{n_t} \cdot \left(\frac{dt}{dn_t}\right) = \tau_g\{1 + (\tau_r/\tau_t)[1 - (n_t/N_f)(1 + n_0/n_1)]\} \tag{933.3}$$

which approaches the result (932.10) for very small modulation.

9.3.4 Solution When There is Some Hole Capture

It was pointed out in Section 7.3 that *any* kind of flaws must have *some* kind of interaction with both bands, even though the cross-section for interaction with one band may be many orders of magnitude smaller than that for the other band. When the trapping flaws do have a non-zero (but small) probability of capturing free holes, the equations for (dp_e/dt) and (dn_t/dt) contain additional terms. Eq. (931.1) must be generalized to

$$\frac{-dp_e}{dt} = \frac{n_e}{\tau_r} + \frac{p_e}{\tau_{p0}}\left[\frac{p_1}{p_1+p_0} + \frac{n_t}{N_f}\right] + \frac{(p_0+p_1)n_t}{\tau_{p0}\,N_f} \tag{934.1}$$

Our present interest is in flaws for which $\gamma = (\tau_{n0}/\tau_{p0})$ is quite small, since trapping disappears when $\gamma \to (p_0/p_1)$. Let us concentrate on a case for which trapping is still very much in evidence, so that $n_t \approx p_e \gg n_e$. Then Eq. (934.1) can be approximated by

$$\frac{-dp_e}{dt} \approx \frac{n_e}{\tau_r} + \frac{n_t}{\tau_h} \tag{934.2}$$

where the hole capture time τ_h is quite long.

These conditions again permit (dn_e/dt) to be neglected in Eq. (931.2). When n_e is substituted from Eq. (933.1) into the revised equation for (dn_t/dt), it follows immediately that the free excess hole and trapped excess electron populations decay with a rate constant

$$\frac{1}{\tau} = \frac{1}{\tau_h} + \frac{1}{\tau_g\{1+(\tau_r/\tau_t)[1-(n_t/N_f)(1+n_0/n_1)]\}} \tag{934.3}$$

When multiple trapping is the vogue $(\tau_t \ll \tau_r)$, the last term of Eq. (934.3) varies essentially as $[1-(n_t/N_f)(1+n_0/n_1)]^{-1}$; then a plot of τ^{-1} against this quantity should be linear, with intercept and slope given by τ_h^{-1} and $(\tau_t/\tau_r\tau_g)$, respectively. This method was used by Haynes and Hornbeck in their studies of trapping flaws in silicon (1955:**36**, 1955:**37**); their discovery that τ_h^{-1} for the deep flaws varied as the square of the majority density showed that the very weak capture was of an Auger type.

9.4 RECOMBINATION AND TRAPPING AT DISLOCATIONS §

A considerable weight of experimental evidence attests to the recombinative action of dislocations in semiconductors. Such observations have been made for instance with germanium and silicon (1957:**35**, 1957:**37**), lead sulfide (1957:**36**) and tellurium (1960:**20**).

An edge-type dislocation marks the termination of a half-plane in the crystal lattice.† Read (1954:**22**) has pointed out that this kind of dislocation in some structures (including the zincblende structure) will present a line source of "dangling bond" acceptor levels. If there are d such levels per unit length, then a dislocation will represent a line charge of $-q/d$ per unit length when the Fermi level is sufficiently high to ionize every acceptor. In general, the number of ionized dislocation acceptors per unit length may be written $\mathcal{Z} \leqslant (1/d)$. The occupancy factor $\mathcal{Z}d$ cannot be described by a Fermi–Dirac probability function since the occupancy of a dangling bond site depends on the charge condition of neighboring sites. (This happens since d may be in excess of 10^7 cm^{-1}.) However, some calculations (1954:**22**, 1960:**21**) suggest that the departure from a Fermi–Dirac occupancy factor is not a very large one.

Morrison (1956:**35**) has suggested a simple model for recombination by this kind of dislocation in an n-type semiconductor, which contains a uniform volume density of isolated impurity atoms [effectively, $\mathcal{N}_r = (\mathcal{N}_d - \mathcal{N}_a)$] in addition to $\mathcal{N}_D$ cm^{-2} dislocations. Under these conditions, each dislocation line is likely to be appreciably charged, producing a cylindrically symmetric space-charge region which sets up a potential barrier against electron capture. The radius r_0 of this space-charge region will be $r_0 = (\mathcal{Z}/\pi\mathcal{N}_r)^{1/2}$, and the height V of the potential barrier is

$$V \approx (q\mathcal{Z}/2\pi\kappa)\ln(r_0/\lambda) \tag{940.1}$$

from solution of Poisson's equation, where λ is a small quantity related to the electron wavelength. If (qV/kT) is denoted as $b\mathcal{Z}$, then Morrison suggests that the electron capture rate by dislocations (in the face of this potential barrier) should be of the form

$$R_e = \frac{1}{\tau_D}[n\exp(-b\mathcal{Z}) - n_0\exp(-b\mathcal{Z}_0)] \tag{940.2}$$

This disappears at thermal equilibrium when $n = n_0$, $\mathcal{Z} = \mathcal{Z}_0$. An analogous (but not equivalent) expression for hole capture is

$$R_h = \frac{1}{\tau_D}\{p - p_0\exp[b(\mathcal{Z}_0 - \mathcal{Z})]\} \tag{940.3}$$

Strictly speaking, the time constants in Eqs. (940.2) and (940.3) should

† See any modern textbook on physical metallurgy. Dislocations are discussed extensively by Cottrell (1953:**17**).

not be the same, but Morrison points out that the important effects are still demonstated by a simplified model in which a common τ_D is used for the two equations.

The essential result of this model is that the dislocations will have a primarily recombinative effect if bZ_0 is small, but will introduce trapping when bZ_0 is large. The conditions may be summarized as $\theta < 1$ for recombination (lifetime $\sim \tau_D$) but $\theta > 1$ for trapping; where

$$\theta = \frac{N_D}{bp_e} \cdot \ln\left\{1 + \frac{p_e}{N_r \exp(-bZ_0)}\right\} = \frac{N_D(Z - Z_0)}{p_e} \tag{940.4}$$

When $\theta \gg 1$, the effective lifetime is approximately $\theta\tau_D$.

Chapter 10

SPATIAL DISTRIBUTION OF EXCESS CARRIERS

THE recombination models of Chapters 5 through 9 were developed assuming that n_e and p_e were spatially invariant. It was noted in Section 4.2 that such a procedure was idealistic, but that it would be followed for the sake of simplicity.

At this point it is recognized that continuity equations usually contain terms describing the movement of carriers in a semiconductor. These terms cannot be completely ignored in a realistic discussion, since neither the manner of excess carrier introduction nor of recombination is indifferent to spatial considerations.

This chapter obviously cannot discuss contact or junction aspects of the spatial problem with any measure of completeness, and Section 10.2 merely gives reference to one or two of the more extensive accounts of these complicated subjects. The main part of the chapter is still concerned with homogeneous semiconductors—for which the *equilibrium* densities n_0 and p_0 are spatially invariant.

10.1 APPROACH TO THE SPACE-DEPENDENT PROBLEM

10.1.1 THE CONTINUITY EQUATIONS

The kinetics of electrons and holes are expressed by a pair of continuity equations. These equations were developed in Section 4.2 and are repeated here:

$$\frac{\partial n_e}{\partial t} = g_E - \frac{n_e}{\tau_n} + q^{-1}\nabla \cdot \mathbf{I}_n \tag{1011.1}$$

$$\frac{\partial p_e}{\partial t} = g_E - \frac{p_e}{\tau_p} - q^{-1}\nabla \cdot \mathbf{I}_p \tag{1011.2}$$

The electron current density $\mathbf{I}_n$ can be written as the sum of a diffusion term (proportional to ∇n) and a drift term (proportional to the electric field $\mathbf{E} = q^{-1}\nabla\phi_i$). Alternatively this can be expressed as a single term [see for instance (1950:**1**) or (1953:**8**)] controlled by the gradient of the electron electrochemical potential:

$$\mathbf{I}_n = [n\mu_n\nabla\phi_i + qD_n\nabla n] = n\mu_n\nabla\phi_n \tag{1011.3}$$

Similarly for the hole current

$$\mathbf{I}_p = [p\mu_p\nabla\phi_i - qD_p\nabla p] = p\mu_p\nabla\phi_p \tag{1011.4}$$

When departures occur from electrical neutrality, Poisson's equation requires that $\nabla^2\phi_i$ cannot vanish, but must satisfy

$$\nabla^2\phi_i = \frac{4\pi q^2}{\kappa}[n_e - p_e + \Delta n_f] \tag{1011.5}$$

where Δn_f denotes the number of flaw levels occupied in excess of that required for equilibrium and neutrality.

Whenever excess carrier populations are spatially dependent, the problem must be solved using Eqs. (1011.1) through (1011.5), with the nature of surfaces and contacts setting the boundary conditions. Since several recombination mechanisms operate simultaneously inside many semiconductors, it is obvious that any attempt at a general treatment will usually become hopelessly lost in a maze of mathematics. Greater insight can be gained by a careful examination of the solutions obtained when the less vital parts of the problem are simplified.

It was for this reason that spatial effects were deliberately excluded in Chapters 5–9. When now it is *required* to consider carrier flow, some compromise is called for in the description of the recombination process.

10.1.2 Assumption of a Constant Lifetime

When the spatial variations of n_e have certain forms, it is possible to solve Eq. (1011.1) for some specific and rather simple variation of τ_n with n_e; however, this does not happen too frequently. In a much larger number of cases, it is possible to examine the phenomena of spatial dependence only on the basis of a very simplified model, for which τ_n does not depend on carrier densities at all.

When this simplified model is adopted, an attempt may subsequently be made to fuse the results of the enquiry (assuming constant τ) with knowledge about the behavior of the bulk lifetime (when there is no spatial dependence problem.) Such attempts will not be too satisfactory if carrier densities change drastically through a sample *and* the dominant recombination mechanism is very sensitive to carrier density. But it may work out quite well if either of the following extremes is the case.

(1) The important problem is the distribution of carriers in space and the current carried by them—allowance for the concentration dependence of lifetime slightly perturbs this result.

(2) Spatial effects have a small perturbing influence on the study of the recombination mechanism.

The first of these alternatives is likely to be the case for the situations mentioned briefly in Section 10.2, but the subsequently discussed situation of homogeneous material affected by surface recombination and non-uniform generation does not necessarily fall into one camp or the other.

10.2 SITUATIONS INVOLVING JUNCTIONS AND CONTACTS

10.2.1 Inhomogeneous Semiconductors

When the equilibrium carrier densities n_0 and p_0 are themselves functions of the spatial variables, it is reasonable to expect complications in the description of excess carriers. Section 2.5.2 comments on displacements of the bands with respect to the Fermi level for a semiconductor (in thermal equilibrium) throughout which accidental variations of N_d and N_a occur. Now the fluctuations due to purely random placement of impurities should not usually be severe, but problems of an entirely different magnitude arise when there is a massive and systematic progression of doping through a crystal.

The arch-typical result of such a deliberate change of doping within a crystal is a p–n junction—or the arrangement of neighboring p–n junctions which forms a junction transistor. The consequences of carrier injection across junctions form an immense subject which it is impossible to give justice to in a few words. Since Shockley outlined his junction theory (1949:**5**, 1950:**1**), this has been elaborated and expounded in a very large number of papers and more than a few books (e.g. 1957:**34**, 1960:**17**).

The *p–n* junction is a good example of category (1) in Sub-section 10.1.2. Its behavior is keenly sensitive to the spatial distribution of impurities, and depends in a less drastic fashion on the details of the dominant recombination mechanism. That the recombinative behavior does influence junction properties to some extent is well exemplified by the work of Hall (1951:**18**) with germanium *p–n* junctions. Hall's analysis of the forward characteristic indicated that a constant lifetime was enjoyed for a wide range of large injected carrier densities. This showed that flaw recombination must dominate over band-to-band processes in germanium, contrary to the ideas previously current.

10.2.2 Contact Effects

Even when n_0 and p_0 have the same values throughout a crystal of semiconducting material, the distribution of excess carriers will be highly non-uniform when current is applied from an external circuit by means of contacts. Rectifying contacts can inject or extract minority carriers (depending on the polarity of the current); the density of excess carriers falls off with increasing distance from the place of injection. A comprehensive account of rectifying contact behavior has been given by Henisch (1957:**32**). As with the *p–n* junction problem, complexities in the behavior of τ_n are likely to be of secondary importance.

Rittner (1956:**13**) has considered a number of rather different end contact problems. These occur when excess carriers are created (by illumination) within the body of a sample of homogeneous material, but are influenced by an appreciable voltage applied between the two end contacts. When this voltage is sufficiently large, many of the optically created excess carriers will be swept out of the sample before they have time to experience recombination in the bulk. These "sweep-out" problems have been discussed also by Stöckmann (1956:**33**). For any of these problems, the differential equations which must be solved assume a very intractable form (even for one-dimensional geometry) when allowance is made for any influence of n_e on τ.

10.3 RESIDUAL SPATIAL INFLUENCES IN HOMOGENEOUS SAMPLES §

It might be supposed that spatial effects would be at a minimum for a sample of homogeneous semiconducting material with essentially no electrical current externally impressed upon it.† Yet even though n_0 and p_0 may be constant throughout the volume, the same can never be said of the excess populations. The two reasons for this are (a) that recombination occurs on all the surfaces of a sample as well as in the bulk, and (b) that the creation of an excess population in the first place can never be completely freed from problems of spatial non-uniformity.

10.3.1 Surface Recombination

The earliest experiments on the motion of excess minority carriers in a single crystal [summarized in Shockley's book (1950:**1**)] indicated that electron–hole recombination occurs on crystal surfaces. This surface recombination is associated with localized surface flaw levels, and the kinetics can be described (1954:**20**) in the same manner as for a bulk S–R model. Thus the surface recombination rate depends on the relationship of the Fermi level to the surface flaw energy, which in turn depends on whether a surface barrier exists or not (1947:**3**). These properties of the surface are sensitive to both the physical condition of the surface region and the chemical nature of its environment.‡ Reports of two international conferences (1957:**33**, 1960:**18**) probably bring together the most complete reviews available of these properties of semiconducting surfaces.

When recombination is going on at a semiconductor surface, there is a flow of electrons and holes towards the surface (a current $\mathbf{I}_p$ *towards* the surface and a conventional current $\mathbf{I}_n$ *away* from the surface). Shockley (1950:**1**) defines a quantity with dimensions (length/time) as the *surface recombination velocity* $\mathbf{s}(x, y, z, t)$, which is related to the surface-directed current of excess minority carriers and their density *at the surface*. Thus for p-type material,

$$\mathbf{I}_n = -qn_e\mathbf{s} \qquad \textit{at the surface} \tag{1031.1}$$

For n-type material the important boundary condition is $\mathbf{I}_p = qp_e\mathbf{s}$.

Excess carriers recombine immediately upon colliding with a surface in very poor mechanical or chemical condition, when the surface state

† A very small current might be used to record the photoconductance of excess carriers. If this current is sufficiently small, it will not perturb the carrier distribution to any important extent (1955:**39**).

‡ The nature of the environment determines what types of atoms or atomic groupings are likely to be adsorbed, influencing the electronic equilibrium.

density (1947:**3**) is very large. Since the flow towards the surface remains finite even under these circumstances, such a surface is said to have an infinite recombination velocity.

For a less voracious surface, the numerical value of **s** depends on n_0, p_0, the height of the surface barrier, and the density of surface states. In germanium at room temperature, values from $\sim$ 50 cm/sec up to more than 10^5 cm/sec have been reported.

This recombinative behavior of any semiconductor surface—to a greater or lesser extent, dependent on the magnitude of **s**—means that even when excess carrier pairs are created reasonably uniformly through the volume of a sample, the outer regions become preferentially depleted. Diffusion from the heart of the sample towards active surfaces persists so long as any excess carriers remain.

The kind of distribution which becomes set up can be illustrated rather simply by considering a sample in the form of a large sheet, whose principal faces are the planes $x = 0$, $x = 2A$. The continuity equation (1011.1) can be simplified if:

(a) The sample is well on the p-type side of extrinsic. Carrier flow is then controlled by the diffusion rate of electrons.

(b) Excess generation occurs at a rate which is independent of time or of position in the sample. Then diffusion maintains a steady state profile, which occurs exclusively in the x-direction.

With these assumptions, the terms remaining in the continuity equation are

$$D_n \frac{d^2 n_e}{dx^2} - \frac{n_e}{\tau_n} + g_E = 0 \tag{1031.2}$$

It is not necessary to assume that τ_n is completely independent of n_e in order to solve Eq. (1031.2). Nomura† has shown that when the lifetime is of the form $\tau_n = \tau_0(1+\beta n_e)^{-1}$ (which is the case for direct radiative recombination and is essentially correct for some conditions of flaw recombination), Eq. (1031.2) can be solved in terms of the Weierstrassian elliptic function.

However, a good deal of mathematical detail can be obviated by assuming a concentration-independent bulk lifetime τ_n. The solution of (1031.2) can then be written in general as

$$n_e = \tau_n g_E \left\{1 - G \exp\left[\frac{x}{(D_n \tau_n)^{1/2}}\right] - H \exp\left[\frac{-x}{(D_n \tau_n)^{1/2}}\right]\right\} \tag{1031.3}$$

† Private communication from K. C. Nomura.

where the quantities G and H depend on the boundary conditions at $x = 0, 2A$. For surfaces which are completely inactive in recombination, $G = H = 0$ and $n_e = \tau_n g_E$ throughout.

The quantity $(D_n \tau_n)^{1/2}$ has the dimensions of length, and is often referred to in the literature as the *electron diffusion length* L_n. A companion quantity $L_p = (D_p \tau_p)^{1/2}$ is used in equations describing the movement of holes.

Another useful quantity is the so-called "diffusion velocity", which for electrons may be designated $v_{dn} = (D_n/\tau_n)^{1/2}$.

In terms of these parameters, the solution of Eq. (1031.2) subject to the boundary conditions $s = s_1$ at $x = 0$ and $s = s_2$ at $x = 2A$ is

$$n_e = \tau_n g_E \{1 - G \exp(x/L_n) - H \exp(-x/L_n)\} \qquad (1031.4)$$

with

$$\left.\begin{aligned} G &= \frac{s_2(v_{dn}+s_1)\exp(2A/L_n) + s_1(v_{dn}-s_2)}{(v_{dn}+s_1)(v_{dn}+s_2)\exp(4A/L_n) - (v_{dn}-s_1)(v_{dn}-s_2)} \\ H &= \frac{s_2(v_{dn}-s_1)\exp(2A/L_n) + s_1(v_{dn}+s_2)\exp(4A/L_n)}{(v_{dn}+s_1)(v_{dn}+s_2)\exp(4A/L_n) - (v_{dn}-s_1)(v_{dn}-s_2)} \end{aligned}\right\} \qquad (1031.5)$$

Simplifications occur in the expressions for G and H when s becomes infinite at either surface (or both).

Fig. 103.1 shows how n_e (expressed in units of $\tau_n g_E$) varies with x when the diffusion length is one quarter of the sample thickness $2A$. For each of the curves it is assumed that $s_2 = \infty$ on the rear surface; the curves correspond with three values for the front surface recombination velocity. Note that even when $s_1 \approx 0$, the carrier density is smaller than $\tau_n g_E$ near to the front face. This occurs because there is a continuous and vigorous diffusion of carriers towards the rear of the sample†; however, most of the carrier adjustment to surface conditions occurs within a diffusion length of a surface.

It should be remembered that the curves seen in this figure will have rather different shapes if τ_n is a function of n_e. When τ_n *increases* with n_e (as happens for some kinds of flaw recombination), the curve for $s = \infty$ on both faces will be more sharply peaked at $x = A$. Other consequences of variable τ_n on the depth distribution of carriers can

† It is conceded that such an effect would be much less severe if the sample were supposed to be ten or twenty diffusion lengths thick. The thickness considered here, four diffusion lengths, will be 0·4 cm for p-type germanium in which $\tau_n \sim 100$ μsec.

easily be predicted—at least semiquantitatively; and as noted, some cases can be solved in closed form.

Before going too far with such predictions, and corresponding ones for different geometric arrangements, it is well to remember that spatially uniform generation is an ideal which can be but imperfectly approached.

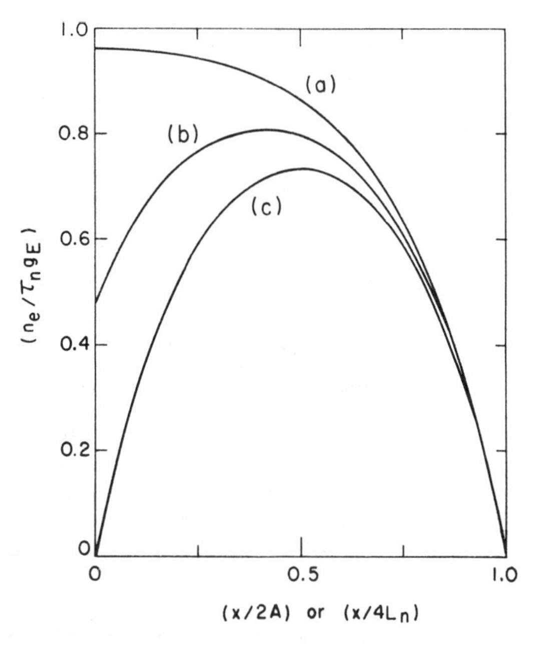

FIG. 103.1. Excess carrier density as function of depth in a plate-like sample of thickness $2A$. Supposed that generation occurs at a rate g_E independent of time or position, and that τ_n is a constant. Curves are drawn for a sample four diffusion lengths thick. (a) $s_1 = 0$, $s_2 = \infty$. (b) $s_1 = v_{dn}$, $s_2 = \infty$. (c) $s_1 = s_2 = \infty$.

10.3.2 Spatial Distribution of Generation

Excess carriers may appear in a semiconductor either because they have been injected electrically or because the material has been exposed to an ionizing influence. In neither case is it possible to set up an initial distribution which is *completely* uniform through any volume.

It was noted in Sub-section 10.2.2 that the density of carriers injected at a contact decreases with increasing distance from the contact. Similarly, when carrier pairs are "photo-injected" by the use of ionizing radiation (photons or atomic particles), the generation rate decreases with increasing thickness of semiconductor penetrated.

Suppose that a flux J_0 (cm^{-2} sec^{-1}) of photons is incident on the front face ($x = 0$) of a semiconducting slab $2A$ thick. Let K (cm^{-1}) denote the absorption coefficient and R the reflection coefficient. Then the excess generation rate at depth x is

$$g_E(x) = (1-R)J_0K\exp(-Kx)\left\{\frac{1+R\exp[-2K(2A-x)]}{1-R^2\exp[-4KA]}\right\} \quad (1032.1)$$

when allowance is made for multiple reflections. This can be simplified to $(1-R)J_0K\exp(-Kx)$ if there is no reflection from the rear surface.

In either case it is apparent that g_E can be made independent of x only if $K \ll (2A)^{-1}$ for the incident photons. But almost none of this type of radiation is absorbed by the sample—the generation rate, though uniform in depth, is vanishingly small. This is the case when $h\nu \leqslant E_i$.

For photons of progressively higher energy, K becomes larger than $(2A)^{-1}$, and most incident photons create hole–electron pairs. It would seem from Eq. (1032.1) that the number of excess pairs maintained per unit area of sample by unit photon flux should reach an upper limiting value

$$\int_0^{2A} \frac{n_e(x)\,.\,dx}{J_0} = \frac{\tau_n}{J_0}\int_0^{2A} g_E(x)\,.\,dx$$

$$\rightarrow \tau_n(1-R) \quad \text{as} \quad K \rightarrow \infty \quad (1032.2)$$

for large photon energies. As deVore (1956:**32**) has pointed out, this objective is frustrated when there is any surface recombination—for the high-energy (readily absorbed) photons create hole–electron pairs in large numbers close to the front surface, and the surface has an opportunity to promote rapid recombination.

Fig. 103.2 shows schematically how the integral of Eq. (1032.1) might vary with photon energy when s is zero, rather small or quite large. The actual shapes of such curves depend of course on what function K is of $h\nu$, and on whether the bulk lifetime varies with n_e (a factor not taken into account by deVore).

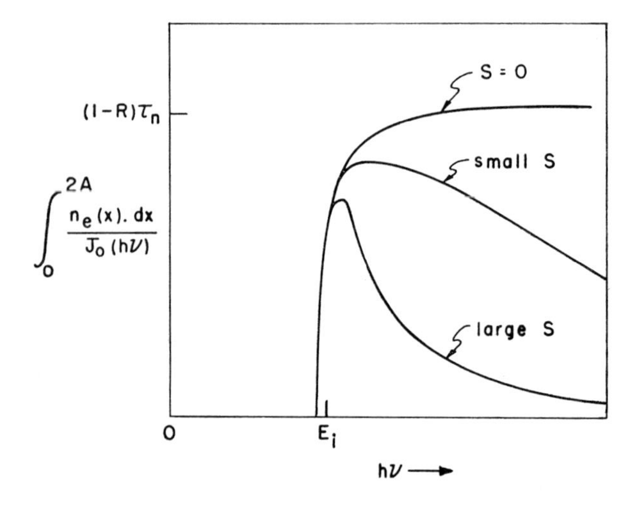

FIG. 103.2. The ordinate is the number of excess carriers maintained per unit area of a plate-like sample for unit of photon flux incident on one face. The curves show how this should vary with photon energy for zero, small or large recombination velocity on the front face.

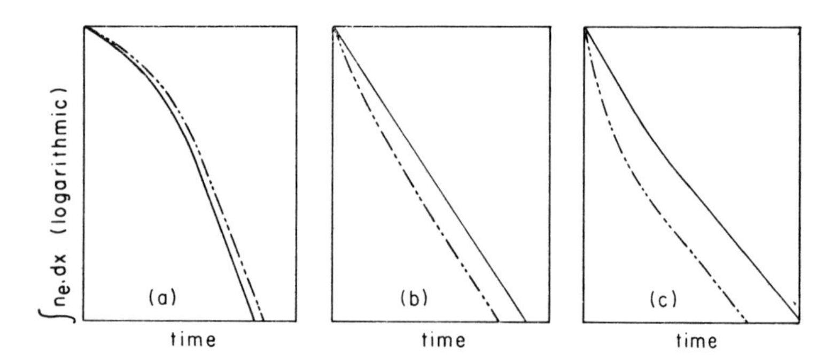

FIG. 103.3. Schematic decay of total excess population (a) when bulk lifetime τ increases with n_e; (b) when τ is independent of n_e; (c) when τ decreases for increasing n_e. Solid curve applies when n_e is spatially uniform. Broken curve applies when most carriers have been created in a thin frontal layer of the sample.

Effect of Concentration-Dependent Bulk Lifetime

It is useful to consider the consequences of creating excess carriers within a thin frontal zone, rather than more uniformly through the volume of a sample, in terms of any possible change of *bulk* recombination rate. When generation is concentrated in a shallow region (and the excess density there made rather large), the surface recombination rate is necessarily increased, but the bulk rate may be either decreased, increased, or not affected at all. These possibilities are indicated by the decay curves of Fig. 103.3.

This figure supposes a given number of excess carriers at time $t = 0$, distributed either uniformly in space (subsequent decay marked by a solid line) or in a thin frontal region (decay shown by a broken curve). In part (*b*), τ_n is supposed constant. When the carriers are clustered near the front surface, only the surface recombination rate is affected, and this is greatly speeded in the initial stages.

In part (c) of the same figure (for a semiconductor in which τ_n decreases as n_e increases), both surface and bulk recombination are speeded when electrons are constricted to a shallow surface zone. In part (a) it is assumed that τ_n increases with n_e; then the bulk recombination is slowed when a given number of electrons is confined to a small part of the total sample volume. The figure is drawn as though this bulk slow-down is only partly compensated by an increase of surface recombination, but it can easily happen that the acceleration of surface recombination will outweigh all other factors (1958:**17**).

Polychromatic Radiation—the Use of Filters

The generation rate of Eq. (1032.1) may be applicable when a semiconductor is exposed to monochromatic radiation, but more usually a light source will provide an output over a considerable range of photon energies.

Some of the preceding discussion indicates that it is often desirable to filter out those spectral components which are most heavily absorbed near to the front surface. One of the most useful kinds of filter is a polished slice of the semiconductor itself. This kind of filter stops all photons for which $h\nu$ is much more than E_i; admits a fraction of the useful photons with $h\nu \approx E_i$; and passes all the longer wavelength radiation which has no effect on the sample.

The resultant form of the generation function depends on the shape of the intrinsic absorption edge—but not to a very marked degree.

When a filter of thickness W precedes the sample and multiple reflection effects are ignored, the generation rate at depth x in the sample takes the form

$$g_E(x) \propto (W+x)^{-m} \qquad 1 \leqslant m \leqslant 3 \tag{1032.3}$$

Moss (1959:**18**) notes that the absorption edge for a number of well known semiconductors is essentially exponential in form.† Whenever this is the case, $m = 1$. A larger value of m is found when K varies as some finite power of $(h\nu - E_i)$; indeed Eq. (1032.3) is consistent with absorption behavior $K \propto (h\nu - E_i)^{1/(m-1)}$.

When measuring the bulk lifetime in a semiconductor sample by the photoconductive decay method (1955:**39**), a filter of the same semiconductor is often used in an attempt to make excess generation more nearly uniform in depth. Unfortunately, such filters are often much too thin to do the required job. As this author has warned previously (1958:**17**), a filter should be at least as thick as the sample; and if the absorption edge is of such a nature that $m > 1$, a filter several times as thick as the sample is not out of order. This conclusion has subsequently been re-emphasized by Sim (1959:**17**).

The varying influences of surface recombination and non-uniform generation are considered further in the next section, where the transient decay of a population is considered as an eigenfunction problem.

10.4 LIFETIME IN FILAMENTS

The general solutions of the time-dependent differential equations can be handled most readily by supposing a material in which

(a) n_0 and p_0 are everywhere the same;
(b) there is no trapping, $n_e = p_e$;
(c) the bulk recombination rate $\nu_b = (1/\tau_n) = (1/\tau_p)$ does not depend on n_e.

Then the inhomogeneous partial differential equation

$$\frac{\partial n_e}{\partial t} = g_E - \nu_b n_e + q^{-1}\nabla \cdot \mathbf{I}_n \tag{1040.1}$$

is linear and separable, and has a solution which can be written as

† Absorption coefficient proportional to $\exp(C\nu)$, where the constant C controls the steepness of the edge.

products of separate functions of space and time. As has been shown by Shockley (1950:**1**) and Stevenson and Keyes (1955:**39**), the assumption of a constant electric field does not create any analytic difficulties, but since it gives no additional insight into the problem we shall assume here that $\mathbf{E} = 0$. A substantially p-type material is assumed, so that D_n is the important diffusion constant. Then

$$\frac{\partial n_e}{\partial t} = g_E - \nu_b n_e + D_n \nabla^2 n_e \tag{1040.2}$$

10.4.1 Homogeneous Equation. Decay Modes

At any moment in time when the generation rate g_E is zero throughout the sample, Eq. (1040.2) becomes a well known homogeneous equation:

$$\frac{\partial n_e}{\partial t} = -\nu_b n_e + D_n \nabla^2 n_e \tag{1041.1}$$

Quantum-mechanical problems (1949:**9**) and situations of heat conduction (1947:**4**) are concerned with this same type of equation, whose solutions are discussed extensively by Morse and Feshbach (1953:**15**). This is an eigenvalue problem; the solution subject to any required initial distribution of n_e and to any boundary conditions (set by surface recombination velocity on the various sample faces) can always be written as a linear combination of eigenfunctions.

Any set of separable co-ordinates may be used for this purpose. Thus excess carrier problems for a sample which is finite in only one direction have been considered by Visvanathan and Battey (1954:**21**), by Ridley (1958:**12**) and by Sim (1958:**24**). Sim also considered the problem of cylindrical symmetry, as did McKelvey (1958:**18**) and Kennedy (1960:**5**). Shockley (1950:**1**) first discussed carrier decay as an eigenfunction problem, using the normal three-dimensional Cartesian co-ordinate system; this system has been preserved in the subsequent discussions of Stevenson and Keyes (1955:**39**) and of Blakemore and Nomura (1960:**4**), and will be used here. Consider then a sample in the form of a rectangular parallelepiped, bounded by the planes $x = 0$, $x = 2A$; $y = 0, y = 2B$; $z = 0$, $z = 2C$. Suppose that while generation may have been going on at some time in the past, it ends completely at the time t^*. The most general type of solution for Eq. (1041.1) is

$$\begin{aligned} n_e &= \sum_{ijk} n_{ijk} \\ &= \sum_{ijk} \alpha_{ijk} \exp[-(t-t^*)(\nu_b+\nu_{ijk})] \times \\ &\qquad \times \sin\left[\left(\frac{\xi_i x}{A}\right)+\delta_i\right] \sin\left[\left(\frac{\eta_j y}{B}\right)+\delta_j\right] \sin\left[\left(\frac{\zeta_k z}{C}\right)+\delta_k\right] \\ &\qquad\qquad t \geqslant t^* \end{aligned} \tag{1041.2}$$

where

$$\nu_{ijk} = D_n\left[\frac{\xi_i^2}{A^2}+\frac{\eta_j^2}{B^2}+\frac{\zeta_k^2}{C^2}\right] \tag{1041.3}$$

The quantities ξ_i, η_j, ζ_k and the phase angles δ_i, δ_j, δ_k are determined by the condition $D_n\nabla n_e = \mathbf{s}n_e$ at the various boundaries. Thus the boundary conditions on the xz faces of the sample require that

$$\tan\delta_j = -\tan(2\eta_j+\delta_j) = D_n\eta_j/sB \tag{1041.4}$$

and entirely analogous conditions must be met for the other eigenvalues. There is a solution for η_j (and also for ξ_i and ζ_k) between zero and $\pi/2$, another between $\pi/2$ and π, and so on.

In Eq. (1041.2), n_{ijk} denotes the portion of the excess carrier density (dependent on position) which is described by a given eigenfunction or "mode". The total number of excess electrons in the sample associated with this mode can be signified as

$$N_{ijk} = \int_0^{2A}\int_0^{2B}\int_0^{2C} n_{ijk}\,\mathrm{d}x\mathrm{d}y\mathrm{d}z \tag{1041.5}$$

Both N_{ijk} and n_{ijk} decrease as time goes on, characterized by the decay rate $(\nu_b+\nu_{ijk})$. This is the sum of the *bulk recombination rate* ν_b (the same for all modes) and a *surface recombination rate* ν_{ijk} [which depends in accordance with Eq. (1041.3) on the eigenvalues characterizing the mode]. Thus the 111 mode (fundamental mode), which has the smallest possible set of values for the eigenvalues ξ_i, η_j, ζ_k, is characterized by a surface recombination rate ν_{111} which is smaller than that of any of the "higher order modes".

The coefficients α_{ijk} of the various modes must be chosen so that

$$\sum_{ijk} n_{ijk}(t^*)$$

fits the required form of $n_e(t^*)$ throughout the sample at the moment decay begins. As time goes on, the fundamental mode will become progressively more important than other modes, since it decays less rapidly. For some spatial distributions of generation, the fundamental mode is pre-eminent even in the initial stages of decay; but with less ideal spatial distributions which require large α_{ijk} for certain high-order modes, the 111 mode must still eventually dominate.

When the photoconductance of a complete sample is measured by monitoring a small applied current, the signal will be proportional to

$$\sum_{ijk} N_{ijk}$$

The decay rate may be expressed as $(\nu_b + \nu_s)$, where ν_s represents the composite effect of all surviving modes on the speed of surface recombination. The measured time constant $\tau_f = (\nu_b + \nu_s)^{-1}$ is often referred to as the "filament lifetime" for photoconductive decay. Then

$$\frac{1}{\tau_f} = (\nu_b + \nu_s) = \frac{-\int_0^{2A}\int_0^{2B}\int_0^{2C} (\partial n_e/\partial t)\,\mathrm{d}x\mathrm{d}y\mathrm{d}z}{\int_0^{2A}\int_0^{2B}\int_0^{2C} n_e\,\mathrm{d}x\mathrm{d}y\mathrm{d}z}$$

$$= \frac{-\sum_{ijk}(\partial N_{ijk}/\partial t)}{\sum_{ijk} N_{ijk}}, \quad t \geqslant t^* \qquad (1041.6)$$

For the consideration of excess carrier decay in finite samples, it has proved convenient (1960:**4**) to define the quantity

$$F(t) = \exp[\nu_b(t - t^*)] \frac{\sum_{ijk} N_{ijk}(t)}{\sum_{ijk} N_{ijk}(t^*)}, \quad t \geqslant t^* \qquad (1041.7)$$

This is the fraction of all the excess carriers present at time t^* which have been spared by surface recombination up to the time t. It is evident from Eqs. (1041.6) and (1041.7) that ν_s is the logarithmic decrement of $F(t)$:

$$\nu_s(t) = \frac{-1}{F(t)} \cdot \frac{dF(t)}{dt} \tag{1041.8}$$

When the interior of the sample is completely devoid of recombination mechanisms, $F(t)$ describes completely the course of the excess population (attenuated only by the surface recombinative action of the various modes). There is customarily some bulk recombination as well, but this is the same for every mode and can be described in a separate term outside the summation sign.

Consideration of the fate of excess carriers which are created in some (not necessarily spatially uniform) fashion in a sample can best be accomplished by following the progress of $F(t)$ and its logarithmic decrement ν_s. As already remarked, at a sufficiently late stage of the decay, high-order modes will become of negligible importance by comparison with the fundamental mode, and the right side of Eq. (1041.6) will reduce to $(\nu_b + \nu_{111})$. For some kinds of experiment—such as those involving measurement of bulk lifetime—suppression of the high-order modes is very desirable. The important question then is, how long must the decay go on before $(\nu_b + \nu_s)$ is satisfactorily close to $(\nu_b + \nu_{111})$? This is controlled by the relative magnitudes of the mode coefficients α_{ijk}, which as discussed in the next sub-section depend on the pattern of generation.

Many samples studied in experimental work are very long compared with the transverse dimensions. Then the actual length $2A$ has little bearing on the value of ν_{111}, which may in these circumstances be abbreviated to ν_{11}. Fig. 104.1 reproduces the result of Shockley (1950:**1**) for the dependence of this minimum surface decay rate ν_{11} on $\mathbf{s}$ for a long sample of square cross-section $(2B = 2C)$; the behavior varies between the limiting forms

$$\left.\begin{aligned} \nu_{11} &\approx \frac{2s}{B}, & s &\to 0 \\ \nu_{11} &\approx \frac{\pi^2 D_n}{2B^2}, & s &\to \infty \end{aligned}\right\} \tag{1041.9}$$

Apropos the result quoted above for infinite recombination velocity, it is interesting to note the specific forms taken by Eqs. (1041.2)–(1041.4) for a sample of arbitrary dimensions $2A$, $2B$, $2C$, when all the

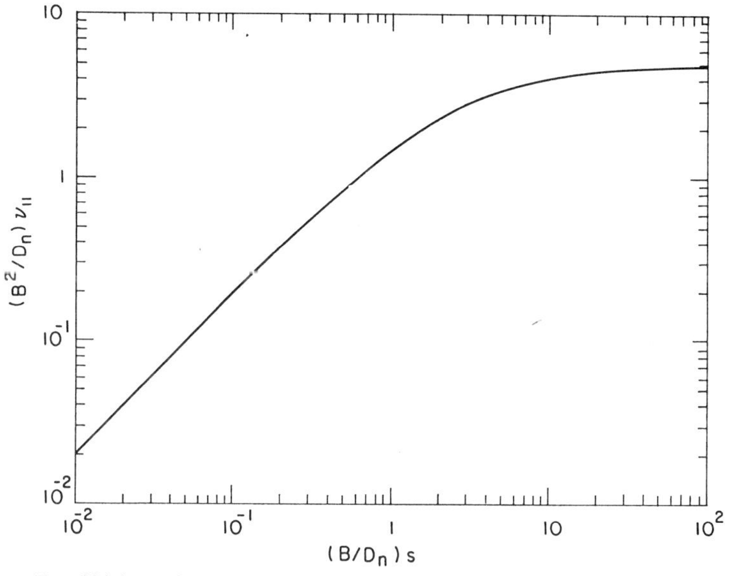

FIG. 104.1. Variation with surface recombination velocity **s** of the fundamental mode surface decay rate ν_{11} for a long sample of square cross-section. After Shockley (1950:**1**).

surfaces are extremely active in recombination. The boundary conditions (1041.4) are then satisfied by

$$\left.\begin{aligned} \delta_i,\ \delta_j,\ \delta_k &= 0 \\ \xi_i,\ \eta_j,\ \zeta_k &= \frac{\pi}{2},\ \pi,\ \frac{3\pi}{2},\ 2\pi\ldots \end{aligned}\right\} \quad s \to \infty \qquad (1041.10)$$

Accordingly, the excess carrier density can be described at any moment during the decay and at any position in the sample by

$$\left.\begin{aligned} n_e &= \sum_{ijk} n_{ijk} \\ &= \sum_{ijk} \alpha_{ijk} \exp[-(t-t^*)(\nu_b+\nu_{ijk})] \times \\ &\quad \times \sin\left(\frac{i\pi x}{2A}\right) \sin\left(\frac{j\pi y}{2B}\right) \sin\left(\frac{k\pi z}{2C}\right) \\ &\quad i,\ j,\ k = 1,\ 2,\ 3,\ 4,\ \ldots \end{aligned}\right\} \quad s \to \infty, \quad t \geqslant t^* \qquad (1041.11)$$

where

$$\left.\begin{aligned} \nu_{ijk} &= \frac{\pi^2 D_n}{4}\left[\frac{i^2}{A^2}+\frac{j^2}{B^2}+\frac{k^2}{C^2}\right] \\ i,\ j,\ k &= 1,\ 2,\ 3,\ 4,\ \ldots \end{aligned}\right\} \quad s \to \infty \qquad (1041.12)$$

It will be observed that the eigenfunction series has for the case of infinite **s** become a Fourier series. This offers a hope for analytic solution of a number of problems which are intractable for the eigenfunction series corresponding to a finite surface recombination velocity. The subject matter of the next sub-section demonstrates one such simplification.

10.4.2 The Amplitudes of Decay Modes

The coefficients α_{ijk} of the various modes of Eq. (1041.2) must satisfy the initial boundary condition that there is a certain distribution $n_e(x, y, z, t^*)$ of excess electrons at time t^*. When $n_e(x, y, z, t^*)$ is known as an analytic function of the spatial variables, it may be possible to determine each of the α_{ijk} in turn by Fourier's method, giving each coefficient as a ratio of triple integrals:

$$\alpha_{ijk} = \frac{\left\{\begin{aligned} &\int_0^{2A}\int_0^{2B}\int_0^{2C} n_e(x; y, z, t^*) \sin[(\xi_i x/A)+\delta_i] \times \\ &\qquad \times \sin[(\eta_j y/B)+\delta_j] \sin[(\zeta_k z/C)+\delta_k] \mathrm{d}x\mathrm{d}y\mathrm{d}z \end{aligned}\right\}}{\left\{\begin{aligned} &\int_0^{2A}\int_0^{2B}\int_0^{2C} \sin^2[(\xi_i x/A)+\delta_i] \sin^2[(\eta_j y/B)+\delta_j] \times \\ &\qquad \times \sin^2[(\zeta_k z/C)+\delta_k]\, \mathrm{d}x\mathrm{d}y\mathrm{d}z \end{aligned}\right\}} \qquad (1042.1)$$

The method is usually computationally very tedious if **s** is finite, requiring the roots of a series of transcendental equations.

However, a valuable simplification occurs in the limit of infinite surface recombination velocity. The triple integral in the denominator of Eq. (1042.1) reduces to ABC, and

$$\alpha_{ijk} = \frac{1}{ABC}\int_0^{2A}\int_0^{2B}\int_0^{2C} n_e(x, y, z, t^*) \times$$

$$\times \sin\left(\frac{i\pi x}{2A}\right) \sin\left(\frac{j\pi y}{2B}\right) \sin\left(\frac{k\pi z}{2C}\right) \, dx dy dz, \quad s \to \infty \qquad (1042.2)$$

Fourier integrals of this form have been studied extensively, and the solution for α_{ijk} can be written down immediately when $n_e(x, y, z, t^*)$ takes any one of several simple analytic forms.

The simplest case of all occurs when $\nabla n_e(t^*)$ vanishes; this will happen if generation is spatially uniform and a delta function $\delta(t-t^*)$ of time.† For this very simplified situation an elementary integration of (1042.2) yields

$$\left.\begin{aligned} \alpha_{ijk} &= \left(\frac{4}{\pi}\right)^3 \cdot \frac{n_e(t^*)}{ijk} \quad \text{when } i, j, k \text{ are all odd integers} \\ \alpha_{ijk} &= 0 \quad \text{if any of } i, j, k \text{ are even integers} \end{aligned}\right\} \qquad (1042.3)$$

It has been pointed out (1960:**4**) that recombination is *usually* assisted by modes for which i, j, and k are all odd integers. Some spatial distributions of the generative process cause certain odd modes to have $\alpha_{ijk} < 0$, and these modes will be *generative* in character.‡ For the example of spatially uniform generation which produces Eq. (1042.3), all odd numbered modes have $\alpha_{ijk} > 0$; thus in this case they all contribute to the recombination.

That Eq. (1042.3) should prohibit all modes involving even integers need come as no surprise, since these modes are antisymmetric and are required to assist in the description of an initial distribution only when one-half of the sample contains more carriers than the other. Even when the pattern of generation is of such a form that even numbered modes are brought into being, their role consists entirely of describing

† The supposition of spatially uniform generation and of a delta function generative pulse are both idealized, but the simple result which follows is adequate for the purposes of illustration.

‡ When $\alpha_{ijk} < 0$, then the total mode content N_{ijk} for an odd numbered mode is a *negative quantity* whose absolute magnitude *decreases* as time goes on. This is tantamount to a decaying generative effect.

diffusive tendencies, trying to make an excess carrier distribution more symmetrical. Even numbered modes do not contribute to the photoconductance of a sample and do not influence the photoconductive decay, since their N_{ijk} are zero at all times. This can readily be seen since

$$n_{ijk} = \alpha_{ijk} \exp[-(t-t^*)(\nu_b + \nu_{ijk})] \sin\left(\frac{i\pi x}{2A}\right) \sin\left(\frac{j\pi y}{2B}\right) \sin\left(\frac{k\pi z}{2C}\right) \quad \text{for} \quad \begin{matrix} s \to \infty \\ t \geqslant t^* \end{matrix} \tag{1042.4}$$

When n_{ijk} is integrated over the volume of the sample in accordance with Eq. (1041.5), the result is

$$\left.\begin{aligned} N_{ijk} &= \left(\frac{4}{\pi}\right)^3 \frac{ABC}{ijk} \alpha_{ijk} \exp[-(t-t^*)(\nu_b+\nu_{ijk})], \quad i, j, k \text{ all odd} \\ N_{ijk} &= 0, \quad \text{any of } i, j, k \text{ even} \end{aligned}\right\} \tag{1042.5}$$

The second result of Eq. (1042.5) demonstrates the remark just made that even numbered modes do not contribute to the photoconductance of a sample at any time. The first result, for odd modes, can be combined with the answer of Eq. (1042.2) to give the overall influence of each mode in a sample.

Thus for an initially uniform carrier distribution, Eqs. (1042.3) and (1042.5) can be combined to yield

$$N_{ijk} = \left(\frac{4}{\pi}\right)^6 \frac{ABC}{(ijk)^2} n_e(t^*) \exp[-(t-t^*)(\nu_b+\nu_{ijk})] \quad \left\{\begin{matrix} t \geqslant t^* \\ s \to \infty \\ \nabla n_e(t^*) = 0 \end{matrix}\right. \tag{1042.6}$$

In this particularly simple case,

$$F(t) = \frac{\sum_{ijk} (ijk)^{-2} \exp[-\nu_{ijk}(t-t^*)]}{\sum_{ijk} (ijk)^{-2}} \tag{1042.7}$$

and

$$\nu_s = \frac{\sum_{ijk} \nu_{ijk}(ijk)^{-2} \exp[-\nu_{ijk}(t-t^*)]}{\sum_{ijk} (ijk)^{-2} \exp[-\nu_{ijk}(t-t^*)]} \tag{1042.8}$$

Fig. 104.2 shows how $F(t)$ of Eq. (1042.7) varies with $(t-t^*)$ for a filament which is supposed to be of square cross-section $(2B = 2C)$ and of very great length. The surface decay rate for the fundamental mode is then

$$\nu_{11} = \tfrac{1}{2}\pi^2 D_n/B^2 \quad \begin{cases} 2B = 2C \ll 2A \\ s \to \infty \end{cases} \qquad (1042.9)$$

which is used to normalize the time scale of Fig. 104.2. The surface

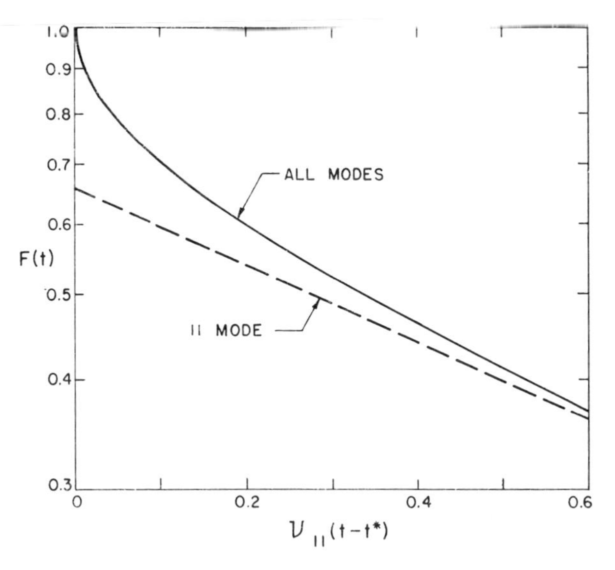

Fig. 104.2. Progression of $F(t)$ with time following a delta function pulse of generation which is uniform through the filament. (Calculated for a filament with square cross-section $2B \times 2B$ of semi-infinite length.) After Blakemore and Nomura (1960:**4**).

decay rate ν_s due to all modes is shown for the same normalized duration in Fig. 104.3. It will be seen that the fundamental mode initially comprises about two-thirds of all the excess carriers, and describes a progressively larger fraction as time goes on. The surface recombination rate ν_s is initially infinite, but does not take very long to approach its limiting value ν_{11}. Even so, attempts to measure ν_b from the decay of photoconductance can be frustrated by departure of ν_s from ν_{11} both when ν_b is comparable to ν_{11} and when it is much larger than ν_{11} (1960:**4**).

An assumption of initially uniform excess density is the simplest which can be made. The evaluation of mode amplitudes is less straightforward when the initial distribution takes other forms. Provided that generation is a delta function of time, the spatial distribution of $n_e(t^*)$

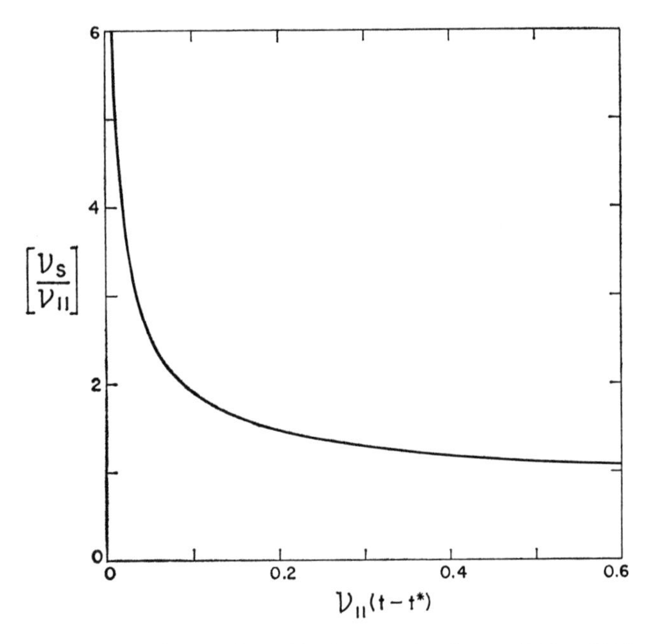

FIG. 104.3. Variation of ν_s with time for the decay of Fig. 104.2. After Blakemore and Nomura (1960:**4**).

is identical with that of g_E; this might for example have the form of Eq. (1032.1) or of (1032.3) with certain types of illumination, though more difficult problems are easy to imagine.

The difficulty of describing $n_e(x, y, z, t^*)$ in analytic terms is of a much higher order when generation has been going on for some time. Diffusion, bulk recombination and surface recombination combine to ensure that $n_e(t^*)$ will be a different function of position than g_E. The situation is ameliorated to some extent when the generation has been of constant intensity for a long time, for then $n_e(x, y, z)$ at $t \leqslant t^*$ can nominally be obtained by solving the steady state equation

$$D_n \nabla^2 n_e - \nu_b n_e + g_E(x, y, z) = 0 \tag{1042.10}$$

10.4.3 Inhomogeneous Equation. Green's Function Method

The situation of lengthy generation which results in Eq. (1042.10) will not usually lead to a very agreeable form for $n_e(x, y, z, t^*)$ to be substituted into Eq. (1042.1). The most general kind of case which must be considered, however, involves generation which varies with *both* space and time up until the instant t^*. It is then necessary to solve the inhomogeneous equation

$$\left.\begin{aligned} \frac{\partial n_e}{\partial t} + \nu_b n_e - D_n \nabla^2 n_e &= g_E(x, y, z, t), \quad & t < t^* \\ &= 0, & t \geqslant t^* \end{aligned}\right\} \tag{1043.1}$$

subject to the condition $D_n \nabla n_e = \mathbf{s} n_e$ at the various boundaries.

The most convenient method of solution is that of Green's functions, whereby the effect of each elementary act of generation is allowed for appropriately in terms of the time the generation occurred and the location of that generation relative to the locus point. The solution of (1043.1) in terms of a Green's function is

$$n_e = \int_0^{2A} \int_0^{2B} \int_0^{2C} \int_0^{t} g_E(x_0 y_0 z_0 t_0)\, G(xyzt | x_0 y_0 z_0 t_0)\, \mathrm{d}x_0 \mathrm{d}y_0 \mathrm{d}z_0 \mathrm{d}t_0 \tag{1043.2}$$

where

$$G = \frac{1}{ABC} \sum_{ijk} \omega_i(x)\, \omega_i(x_0)\, \omega_j(y)\, \omega_j(y_0)\, \omega_k(z)\, \omega_k(z_0) \exp[(t_0 - t)(\nu_b + \nu_{ijk})] \tag{1043.3}$$

where again

$$\nu_{ijk} = D_n \left[\frac{\xi_i^2}{A^2} + \frac{\eta_j^2}{B^2} + \frac{\zeta_k^2}{C^2} \right] \tag{1043.4}$$

The ω's and ξ_i, η_j, ζ_k are, respectively, the eigenfunctions and eigenvalues of the homogeneous part of Eq. (1043.1). As previously discussed in Sub-section 10.4.1, the ω's can be expressed as sine functions, which have an integral number of lobes within the sample dimension for the simplifying case of $s = \infty$.

The Green's function approach to equations with the form of (1043.1) has the advantage that boundary conditions are incorporated automatically. The coefficients of the eigenfunctions can in principle always be found by integration, even though the process may be rather laborious when g_E is a complicated function of space and time. A full treatment of this type of mathematical problem is given by Morse and Feshbach (1953:**15**), and some results have been applied to the question of excess carrier build-up and decay by Blakemore and Nomura (1960:**4**). The latter paper indicates the kinds of solution which occur (for infinite s) when g_E takes undesirable and desirable spatial forms; and examines the effect of a finite tail to the generative process.

Appendix A

THE FERMI–DIRAC DISTRIBUTION LAW

THE Fermi–Dirac form of quantum statistics is appropriate for particles which are *indistinguishable* and which occupy states in accordance with the Pauli principle—that is to say, a state characterized by three quantum numbers and a spin quantum number may be occupied by not more than one particle. Since we are interested in situations involving very large numbers of particles, the states of interest must also range from small to very large quantum numbers.

Let us now group these states according to their energy. Suppose that there are g_i states each characterized by an energy E_i, and that n_i of these are occupied (and hence $(g_i - n_i)$ empty). There are a large number of ways the particles could be distributed over the states, but not so large as may at first appear—since the particles are supposed to be indistinguishable from each other, and two distributions which differ from each other only by the interchange of pairs of particles must be regarded as equivalent. Thus the number of *distinguishable distributions* is

$$\omega_i = \frac{g_i!}{n_i!(g_i - n_i)!} \tag{A.1}$$

Comparable with our set of g_i states at the energy E_i are other sets of states at higher and lower energies helping to make up the whole system. Thus the total number of distinguishable distributions for the system as a whole is

$$\omega = \prod_r \omega_r = \prod_r \frac{g_r!}{n_r!(g_r - n_r)!} \tag{A.2}$$

When particles undergo transitions between states, this must occur subject to the condition that the total number of particles

$$n = \sum n_r \tag{A.3}$$

remains constant. Also, for a system in thermal equilibrium, transitions can only occur subject to the further condition that the total energy

$$n\bar{E} = \sum n_r E_r \tag{A.4}$$

remains constant.

We should like to find the most probable distribution of the particles over all the states, for this corresponds to the average behavior of a system in thermal equilibrium. This means that we should set up a distribution for which

$$\frac{\partial \omega}{\partial n_r} = 0 \tag{A.5}$$

subject to the conditions (A.3) and (A.4). Actually, it is more convenient to work in terms of $\ln \omega$ rather than ω itself. For we are dealing supposedly with very large numbers and can use Stirling's approximation

$$\ln y! \approx y \ln y - y, \qquad y \gg 1 \tag{A.6}$$

Using (A.6) and (A.2), we can express $\ln \omega$ as

$$\ln \omega = \sum_r [g_r \ln g_r - n_r \ln n_r - (g_r - n_r) \ln (g_r - n_r)] \tag{A.7}$$

In finding the maximum of $\ln \omega$ subject to the conditions (A.3) and (A.4) we adopt the method of Lagrangian undetermined multipliers. Thus we wish to have

$$\frac{\partial}{\partial n_r}\{\ln \omega + \alpha[n - \sum n_r] + \beta[n\bar{E} - \sum n_r E_r]\} = 0 \tag{A.8}$$

In view of (A.7), this requirement is that

$$\ln\left[\frac{g_r - n_r}{n_r}\right] = \alpha + \beta E_r \tag{A.9}$$

This means that for any of the g_r states at energy E_r, the probability that a state will be occupied is

$$f(E_r) = \left(\frac{n_r}{g_r}\right) = \frac{1}{1 + \exp(\alpha + \beta E_r)} \tag{A.10}$$

Now at sufficiently large energies when $f \ll 1$, this must approach a classical Maxwell–Boltzmann distribution. This will be the case if one of the Lagrangian multipliers has the value $\beta = 1/kT$. If we make the further substitution $\alpha = -(\phi/kT)$, Eq. (A.10) assumes the familiar form

$$f(E) = \frac{1}{1+\exp\left[\frac{E-\phi}{kT}\right]} \tag{A.11}$$

which we use in discussions of electronic equilibrium.

Appendix B

TABLES OF THE FERMI–DIRAC INTEGRALS

EXTENSIVE computations of the Fermi–Dirac integrals of order (3/2) and (1/2) were made by McDougall and Stoner (1938:**2**), who prepared tables for intervals of 0·1 in η over the range $-4 \leqslant \eta \leqslant +20$. Rhodes (1950:**3**) has given tabulations of the integrals when j is a small positive integer, as have Wright (1951:**3**) and Johnson and Shipley (1953:**3**). Beer *et al.* (1955:**4**) extended the work of McDougall and Stoner to higher half-integer values of j and Dingle (1956:**2**) has increased the scope of tabulations for the integrals when j is an integer.

Several of these authors did not tabulate the

$$\mathscr{F}_j(\eta) = \frac{1}{\Gamma(j+1)} \int_0^\infty \frac{\epsilon^j \, . \, d\epsilon}{1+\exp(\epsilon-\eta)} \tag{B.1}$$

but rather quoted values of

$$F_j(\eta) = \Gamma(j+1)\mathscr{F}_j(\eta) \tag{B.2}$$

However, there are several reasons which make it preferable to tabulate in terms of $\mathscr{F}_j$, as Dingle (1956:**2**) noted in his paper of tabulations for integer orders. Dingle observed that, unlike F_j, the $\mathscr{F}_j$ exist even for negative integer orders; and that in the classical limit of $\eta \ll 0$, $\mathscr{F}_j(\eta)$ is *independent of* the order j [in fact is just equal to $\exp(\eta)$]. This facilitates interpolation between *orders* as well as that between *arguments*.

Since the previously published tabulations are so scattered and expressed in such diverse forms, it was thought desirable to include a fairly comprehensive table of the more important $\mathscr{F}_j$. This information is collected in Tables B.1 and B.2, for the range of arguments

$$-4 \leqslant \eta \leqslant +10$$

The former table is for integer orders from $j = -1$ to $j = +4$, while Table B.2 covers half-integer orders from $j = -\frac{3}{2}$ to $j = +\frac{7}{2}$.

It may be queried at this point why functions other than $\mathscr{F}_{1/2}(\eta)$ should be tabulated. As discussed in Appendix C, a number of other integral and half-integral values of j are required for a discussion of transport phenomena in bands of standard form, while carrier statistics involve Fermi integrals of order $j \neq \frac{1}{2}$ when the bands are of non-standard form.

When a Fermi integral $\mathscr{F}_j(\eta)$ is desired of any order j, it is useful to have tables of $\mathscr{F}_{j-1}$ and $\mathscr{F}_{j-2}$ for interpolation. It was shown by McDougall and Stoner (1938:**2**) that

$$\mathscr{F}'_j(\eta) = \frac{\mathrm{d}}{\mathrm{d}\eta}\mathscr{F}_j(\eta) = \mathscr{F}_{j-1}(\eta) \tag{B.3}$$

as a relation between successive orders. Accordingly, if we want to know $\mathscr{F}_j(\eta_0+\Delta\eta)$ when the closest tabulated value is for η_0, an expansion can be written in terms of $\mathscr{F}_j(\eta_0)$ and its derivatives, i.e. of lower order integrals. Thus

$$\mathscr{F}_j(\eta_0+\Delta\eta) \approx \mathscr{F}_j(\eta_0) + \Delta\eta\,\mathscr{F}_{j-1}(\eta_0) + \tfrac{1}{2}\Delta\eta^2\,\mathscr{F}_{j-2}(\eta_0) \tag{B.4}$$

will prove accurate at least as far as the fourth significant figure for any part of the range, with the intervals of tabulation we have employed in Tables B.1 and B.2. Needless to say, Eq. (B.4) is valid both for positive and negative values of $\Delta\eta$.

For the process of inverse interpolation, when we require to know the $\eta = (\eta_0+\Delta\eta)$ corresponding with an untabulated $\mathscr{F}_j(\eta_0+\Delta\eta)$, the series of which Eq. (B.4) forms the first terms can be inverted. This yields

$$\begin{aligned}\eta &= \eta_0+\Delta\eta \\ &\approx \eta_0 + \frac{\mathscr{F}_j(\eta_0+\Delta\eta)-\mathscr{F}_j(\eta_0)}{\mathscr{F}_{j-1}(\eta_0)} - \frac{\mathscr{F}_{j-2}(\eta_0)[\mathscr{F}_j(\eta_0+\Delta\eta)-\mathscr{F}_j(\eta_0)]^2}{2[\mathscr{F}_{j-1}(\eta_0)]^3}\end{aligned} \tag{B.5}$$

taken to second order. It will not usually be necessary to consider terms of higher order, in view of the comparative closeness of spacing in Tables B.1 and B.2.

Table B.1 is based essentially on the tabular material of Dingle (1956:**2**) and Rhodes (1950:**3**). Table B.2 is derived from portions of the tables given by McDougall and Stoner (1938:**2**) and by Beer *et al.* (1955:**4**).

Table B.1. *Fermi–Dirac integrals of integer orders for negative arguments*

(The digit in parentheses is the power of ten by which an entry must be multiplied.)

η	$\mathscr{F}_{-1}$	$\mathscr{F}_0$	$\mathscr{F}_1$	$\mathscr{F}_2$	$\mathscr{F}_3$	$\mathscr{F}_4$
−4.0	1.799 (−2)	1.815 (−2)	1.8232 (−2)	1.8274 (−2)	1.8295 (−2)	1.8305 (−2)
−3.9	1.984 (−2)	2.003 (−2)	2.0140 (−2)	2.0191 (−2)	2.0216 (−2)	2.0229 (−2)
−3.8	2.188 (−2)	2.213 (−2)	2.2247 (−2)	2.2309 (−2)	2.2340 (−2)	2.2355 (−2)
−3.7	2.413 (−2)	2.442 (−2)	2.4572 (−2)	2.4648 (−2)	2.4686 (−2)	2.4705 (−2)
−3.6	2.660 (−2)	2.696 (−2)	2.7139 (−2)	2.7231 (−2)	2.7277 (−2)	2.7301 (−2)
−3.5	2.931 (−2)	2.975 (−2)	2.9972 (−2)	3.0084 (−2)	3.0141 (−2)	3.0169 (−2)
−3.4	3.230 (−2)	3.283 (−2)	3.3099 (−2)	3.3235 (−2)	3.3304 (−2)	3.3339 (−2)
−3.3	3.557 (−2)	3.625 (−2)	3.6549 (−2)	3.6715 (−2)	3.6799 (−2)	3.6841 (−2)
−3.2	3.917 (−2)	3.995 (−2)	4.0354 (−2)	4.0557 (−2)	4.0659 (−2)	4.0711 (−2)
−3.1	4.311 (−2)	4.407 (−2)	4.4552 (−2)	4.4800 (−2)	4.4924 (−2)	4.4986 (−2)
−3.0	4.743 (−2)	4.858 (−2)	4.9181 (−2)	4.9482 (−2)	4.9634 (−2)	4.9710 (−2)
−2.9	5.215 (−2)	5.356 (−2)	5.4284 (−2)	5.4651 (−2)	5.4836 (−2)	5.4929 (−2)
−2.8	5.732 (−2)	5.904 (−2)	5.9910 (−2)	6.0356 (−2)	6.0582 (−2)	6.0695 (−2)
−2.7	6.297 (−2)	6.504 (−2)	6.6109 (−2)	6.6652 (−2)	6.6927 (−2)	6.7066 (−2)
−2.6	6.914 (−2)	7.164 (−2)	7.2938 (−2)	7.3599 (−2)	7.3934 (−2)	7.4103 (−2)
−2.5	7.586 (−2)	7.889 (−2)	8.0459 (−2)	8.1263 (−2)	8.1671 (−2)	8.1877 (−2)
−2.4	8.317 (−2)	8.684 (−2)	8.8740 (−2)	8.9716 (−2)	9.0213 (−2)	9.0464 (−2)
−2.3	9.112 (−2)	9.555 (−2)	9.7852 (−2)	9.9038 (−2)	9.9643 (−2)	9.9949 (−2)
−2.2	9.975 (−2)	1.051 (−1)	1.0788 (−1)	1.0932 (−1)	1.1005 (−1)	1.1042 (−1)
−2.1	1.091 (−1)	1.155 (−1)	1.1890 (−1)	1.2065 (−1)	1.2154 (−1)	1.2200 (−1)
−2.0	1.192 (−1)	1.269 (−1)	1.3101 (−1)	1.3313 (−1)	1.3422 (−1)	1.3477 (−1)
−1.9	1.301 (−1)	1.394 (−1)	1.4432 (−1)	1.4689 (−1)	1.4821 (−1)	1.4888 (−1)
−1.8	1.419 (−1)	1.530 (−1)	1.5893 (−1)	1.6204 (−1)	1.6364 (−1)	1.6446 (−1)
−1.7	1.545 (−1)	1.678 (−1)	1.7496 (−1)	1.7872 (−1)	1.8067 (−1)	1.8166 (−1)
−1.6	1.680 (−1)	1.839 (−1)	1.9253 (−1)	1.9708 (−1)	1.9944 (−1)	2.0066 (−1)
−1.5	1.824 (−1)	2.014 (−1)	2.1178 (−1)	2.1728 (−1)	2.2015 (−1)	2.2162 (−1)
−1.4	1.978 (−1)	2.204 (−1)	2.3286 (−1)	2.3950 (−1)	2.4297 (−1)	2.4476 (−1)
−1.3	2.142 (−1)	2.410 (−1)	2.5592 (−1)	2.6392 (−1)	2.6812 (−1)	2.7029 (−1)
−1.2	2.315 (−1)	2.633 (−1)	2.8112 (−1)	2.9075 (−1)	2.9583 (−1)	2.9846 (−1)
−1.1	2.497 (−1)	2.873 (−1)	3.0863 (−1)	3.2022 (−1)	3.2636 (−1)	3.2955 (−1)
−1.0	2.689 (−1)	3.133 (−1)	3.3865 (−1)	3.5256 (−1)	3.5997 (−1)	3.6384 (−1)
−0.9	2.891 (−1)	3.412 (−1)	3.7135 (−1)	3.8804 (−1)	3.9698 (−1)	4.0166 (−1)
−0.8	3.100 (−1)	3.711 (−1)	4.0695 (−1)	4.2693 (−1)	4.3770 (−1)	4.4336 (−1)
−0.7	3.318 (−1)	4.032 (−1)	4.4564 (−1)	4.6953 (−1)	4.8249 (−1)	4.8933 (−1)
−0.6	3.543 (−1)	4.375 (−1)	4.8766 (−1)	5.1617 (−1)	5.3174 (−1)	5.4000 (−1)
−0.5	3.775 (−1)	4.741 (−1)	5.3322 (−1)	5.6718 (−1)	5.8587 (−1)	5.9584 (−1)
−0.4	4.013 (−1)	5.130 (−1)	5.8255 (−1)	6.2294 (−1)	6.4533 (−1)	6.5736 (−1)
−0.3	4.256 (−1)	5.544 (−1)	6.3590 (−1)	6.8382 (−1)	7.1063 (−1)	7.2510 (−1)
−0.2	4.502 (−1)	5.981 (−1)	6.9350 (−1)	7.5026 (−1)	7.8228 (−1)	7.9969 (−1)
−0.1	4.750 (−1)	6.444 (−1)	7.5561 (−1)	8.2267 (−1)	8.6088 (−1)	8.8179 (−1)
0.0	5.000 (−1)	6.932 (−1)	8.2247 (−1)	9.0154 (−1)	9.4703 (−1)	9.7212 (−1)

Table B.1. (contd.)—Fermi–Dirac integrals of integer order for small positive arguments

η	$\mathscr{F}_{-1}$	$\mathscr{F}_0$	$\mathscr{F}_1$	$\mathscr{F}_2$	$\mathscr{F}_3$	$\mathscr{F}_4$
0.0	5.000 (−1)	6.932 (−1)	8.2247 (−1)	9.0154 (−1)	9.4703 (−1)	9.7212 (−1)
0.1	5.250 (−1)	7.444 (−1)	8.9430 (−1)	9.8730 (−1)	1.0414 (0)	1.0715 (0)
0.2	5.498 (−1)	7.981 (−1)	9.7150 (−1)	1.0806 (0)	1.1448 (0)	1.1807 (0)
0.3	5.744 (−1)	8.544 (−1)	1.0541 (0)	1.1818 (0)	1.2578 (0)	1.3008 (0)
0.4	5.987 (−1)	9.130 (−1)	1.1424 (0)	1.2916 (0)	1.3814 (0)	1.4326 (0)
0.5	6.225 (−1)	9.7410 (−1)	1.2367 (0)	1.4105 (0)	1.5164 (0)	1.5774 (0)
0.6	6.457 (−1)	1.0375 (0)	1.3373 (0)	1.5391 (0)	1.6638 (0)	1.7363 (0)
0.7	6.682 (−1)	1.1032 (0)	1.4443 (0)	1.6782 (0)	1.8246 (0)	1.9106 (0)
0.8	6.900 (−1)	1.1711 (0)	1.5580 (0)	1.8282 (0)	1.9998 (0)	2.1017 (0)
0.9	7.110 (−1)	1.2412 (0)	1.6786 (0)	1.9900 (0)	2.1906 (0)	2.3111 (0)
1.0	7.311 (−1)	1.3133 (0)	1.8063 (0)	2.1642 (0)	2.3982 (0)	2.5404 (0)
1.1	7.503 (−1)	1.3873 (0)	1.9413 (0)	2.3515 (0)	2.6239 (0)	2.7913 (0)
1.2	7.685 (−1)	1.4633 (0)	2.0838 (0)	2.5527 (0)	2.8690 (0)	3.0658 (0)
1.3	7.858 (−1)	1.5410 (0)	2.2340 (0)	2.7685 (0)	3.1349 (0)	3.3658 (0)
1.4	8.022 (−1)	1.6204 (0)	2.3921 (0)	2.9997 (0)	3.4232 (0)	3.6936 (0)
1.5	8.176 (−1)	1.7014 (0)	2.5582 (0)	3.2472 (0)	3.7354 (0)	4.0513 (0)
1.6	8.320 (−1)	1.7839 (0)	2.7324 (0)	3.5116 (0)	4.0732 (0)	4.4415 (0)
1.7	8.455 (−1)	1.8678 (0)	2.9150 (0)	3.7939 (0)	4.4383 (0)	4.8668 (0)
1.8	8.582 (−1)	1.9530 (0)	3.1060 (0)	4.0949 (0)	4.8326 (0)	5.3301 (0)
1.9	8.699 (−1)	2.0394 (0)	3.3056 (0)	4.4154 (0)	5.2580 (0)	5.8344 (0)
2.0	8.808 (−1)	2.1269 (0)	3.5139 (0)	4.7563 (0)	5.7164 (0)	6.3828 (0)
2.1	8.909 (−1)	2.2155 (0)	3.7310 (0)	5.1185 (0)	6.2099 (0)	6.9788 (0)
2.2	9.002 (−1)	2.3051 (0)	3.9571 (0)	5.5028 (0)	6.7408 (0)	7.6261 (0)
2.3	9.089 (−1)	2.3956 (0)	4.1921 (0)	5.9102 (0)	7.3113 (0)	8.3283 (0)
2.4	9.168 (−1)	2.4868 (0)	4.4362 (0)	6.3416 (0)	7.9237 (0)	9.0897 (0)
2.5	9.241 (−1)	2.5789 (0)	4.6895 (0)	6.7978 (0)	8.5804 (0)	9.9145 (0)
2.6	9.309 (−1)	2.6716 (0)	4.9520 (0)	7.2798 (0)	9.2841 (0)	1.0807 (+1)
2.7	9.370 (−1)	2.7650 (0)	5.2238 (0)	7.7885 (0)	1.0037 (+1)	1.1773 (+1)
2.8	9.427 (−1)	2.8590 (0)	5.5050 (0)	8.3249 (0)	1.0843 (+1)	1.2817 (+1)
2.9	9.478 (−1)	2.9536 (0)	5.7957 (0)	8.8898 (0)	1.1703 (+1)	1.3943 (+1)
3.0	9.526 (−1)	3.0486 (0)	6.0958 (0)	9.4843 (0)	1.2622 (+1)	1.5159 (+1)
3.1	9.569 (−1)	3.1441 (0)	6.4054 (0)	1.0109 (+1)	1.3601 (+1)	1.6470 (+1)
3.2	9.608 (−1)	3.2400 (0)	6.7246 (0)	1.0766 (+1)	1.4645 (+1)	1.7882 (+1)
3.3	9.644 (−1)	3.3363 (0)	7.0534 (0)	1.1455 (+1)	1.5755 (+1)	1.9401 (+1)
3.4	9.677 (−1)	3.4328 (0)	7.3918 (0)	1.2177 (+1)	1.6937 (+1)	2.1035 (+1)
3.5	9.707 (−1)	3.5298 (0)	7.7400 (0)	1.2933 (+1)	1.8192 (+1)	2.2791 (+1)
3.6	9.734 (−1)	3.6270 (0)	8.0978 (0)	1.3725 (+1)	1.9524 (+1)	2.4676 (+1)
3.7	9.759 (−1)	3.7244 (0)	8.4654 (0)	1.4553 (+1)	2.0938 (+1)	2.6698 (+1)
3.8	9.781 (−1)	3.8221 (0)	8.8427 (0)	1.5418 (+1)	2.2436 (+1)	2.8866 (+1)
3.9	9.802 (−1)	3.9200 (0)	9.2298 (0)	1.6322 (+1)	2.4023 (+1)	3.1188 (+1)
4.0	9.820 (−1)	4.0181 (0)	9.6267 (0)	1.7265 (+1)	2.5702 (+1)	3.3674 (+1)

Table B.1. (contd.)—Fermi–Dirac integrals of integer order for positive arguments

η	$\mathscr{F}_{-1}$	$\mathscr{F}_0$	$\mathscr{F}_1$	$\mathscr{F}_2$	$\mathscr{F}_3$	$\mathscr{F}_4$
4.0	9.820 (−1)	4.0181 (0)	9.6267 (0)	1.7265 (+1)	2.5702 (+1)	3.3674 (+1)
4.2	9.852 (−1)	4.2149 (0)	1.0450 (+1)	1.9272 (+1)	2.9353 (+1)	3.9173 (+1)
4.4	9.879 (−1)	4.4122 (0)	1.1313 (+1)	2.1447 (+1)	3.3422 (+1)	4.5443 (+1)
4.6	9.901 (−1)	4.6100 (0)	1.2215 (+1)	2.3799 (+1)	3.7944 (+1)	5.2572 (+1)
4.8	9.918 (−1)	4.8082 (0)	1.3157 (+1)	2.6336 (+1)	4.2954 (+1)	6.0653 (+1)
5.0	9.933 (−1)	5.0067 (0)	1.4138 (+1)	2.9065 (+1)	4.8491 (+1)	6.9788 (+1)
5.2	9.945 (−1)	5.2055 (0)	1.5159 (+1)	3.1994 (+1)	5.4593 (+1)	8.0087 (+1)
5.4	9.955 (−1)	5.4045 (0)	1.6220 (+1)	3.5131 (+1)	6.1302 (+1)	9.1666 (+1)
5.6	9.963 (−1)	5.6037 (0)	1.7321 (+1)	3.8485 (+1)	6.8660 (+1)	1.0465 (+2)
5.8	9.970 (−1)	5.8030 (0)	1.8462 (+1)	4.2062 (+1)	7.6711 (+1)	1.1918 (+2)
6.0	9.975 (−1)	6.0025 (0)	1.9643 (+1)	4.5872 (+1)	8.5500 (+1)	1.3539 (+2)
6.2	9.980 (−1)	6.2020 (0)	2.0863 (+1)	4.9922 (+1)	9.5076 (+1)	1.5343 (+2)
6.4	9.983 (−1)	6.4017 (0)	2.2123 (+1)	5.4220 (+1)	1.0549 (+2)	1.7347 (+2)
6.6	9.986 (−1)	6.6014 (0)	2.3424 (+1)	5.8774 (+1)	1.1678 (+2)	1.9568 (+2)
6.8	9.989 (−1)	6.8011 (0)	2.4764 (+1)	6.3592 (+1)	1.2901 (+2)	2.2025 (+2)
7.0	9.991 (−1)	7.0009 (0)	2.6144 (+1)	6.8682 (+1)	1.4224 (+2)	2.4735 (+2)
7.2	9.993 (−1)	7.2008 (0)	2.7564 (+1)	7.4052 (+1)	1.5650 (+2)	2.7721 (+2)
7.4	9.994 (−1)	7.4006 (0)	2.9024 (+1)	7.9711 (+1)	1.7188 (+2)	3.1003 (+2)
7.6	9.995 (−1)	7.6005 (0)	3.0524 (+1)	8.5665 (+1)	1.8841 (+2)	3.4604 (+2)
7.8	9.996 (−1)	7.8004 (0)	3.2065 (+1)	9.1923 (+1)	2.0616 (+2)	3.8547 (+2)
8.0	9.997 (−1)	8.0003 (0)	3.3645 (+1)	9.8493 (+1)	2.2520 (+2)	4.2859 (+2)
8.2	9.997 (−1)	8.2003 (0)	3.5265 (+1)	1.0538 (+2)	2.4558 (+2)	4.7564 (+2)
8.4	9.998 (−1)	8.4002 (0)	3.6925 (+1)	1.1260 (+2)	2.6737 (+2)	5.2691 (+2)
8.6	9.998 (−1)	8.6002 (0)	3.8625 (+1)	1.2016 (+2)	2.9064 (+2)	5.8269 (+2)
8.8	9.999 (−1)	8.8002 (0)	4.0365 (+1)	1.2805 (+2)	3.1546 (+2)	6.4327 (+2)
9.0	9.999 (−1)	9.0001 (0)	4.2145 (+1)	1.3631 (+2)	3.4189 (+2)	7.0898 (+2)
9.2	9.999 (−1)	9.2001 (0)	4.3965 (+1)	1.4492 (+2)	3.7001 (+2)	7.8014 (+2)
9.4	9.999 (−1)	9.4001 (0)	4.5825 (+1)	1.5389 (+2)	3.9988 (+2)	8.5710 (+2)
9.6	9.999 (−1)	9.6001 (0)	4.7725 (+1)	1.6325 (+2)	4.3159 (+2)	9.4022 (+2)
9.8	9.999 (−1)	9.8001 (0)	4.9665 (+1)	1.7299 (+2)	4.6520 (+2)	1.0299 (+3)
10.0	9.999 (−1)	1.0000 (+1)	5.1645 (+1)	1.8312 (+2)	5.0081 (+2)	1.1264 (+3)

Table B.2.—Fermi–Dirac integrals of half-integer orders for negative arguments

η	$\mathscr{F}_{-3/2}$	$\mathscr{F}_{-1/2}$	$\mathscr{F}_{1/2}$	$\mathscr{F}_{3/2}$	$\mathscr{F}_{5/2}$	$\mathscr{F}_{7/2}$
−4.0	1.78 (−2)	1.808 (−2)	1.8199 (−2)	1.8256 (−2)	1.8287 (−2)	1.8301 (−2)
−3.9	1.96 (−2)	1.995 (−2)	2.0099 (−2)	2.0170 (−2)	2.0206 (−2)	2.0224 (−2)
−3.8	2.17 (−2)	2.203 (−2)	2.2195 (−2)	2.2283 (−2)	2.2327 (−2)	2.2349 (−2)
−3.7	2.38 (−2)	2.429 (−2)	2.4510 (−2)	2.4617 (−2)	2.4670 (−2)	2.4697 (−2)
−3.6	2.63 (−2)	2.681 (−2)	2.7063 (−2)	2.7193 (−2)	2.7259 (−2)	2.7291 (−2)
−3.5	2.89 (−2)	2.956 (−2)	2.9880 (−2)	3.0037 (−2)	3.0118 (−2)	3.0158 (−2)
−3.4	3.18 (−2)	3.260 (−2)	3.2986 (−2)	3.3179 (−2)	3.3276 (−2)	3.3325 (−2)
−3.3	3.50 (−2)	3.595 (−2)	3.6412 (−2)	3.6645 (−2)	3.6764 (−2)	3.6824 (−2)
−3.2	3.85 (−2)	3.962 (−2)	4.0187 (−2)	4.0473 (−2)	4.0617 (−2)	4.0690 (−2)
−3.1	4.23 (−2)	4.367 (−2)	4.4349 (−2)	4.4696 (−2)	4.4872 (−2)	4.4961 (−2)
−3.0	4.65 (−2)	4.810 (−2)	4.8933 (−2)	4.9356 (−2)	4.9571 (−2)	4.9679 (−2)
−2.9	5.10 (−2)	5.298 (−2)	5.3984 (−2)	5.4498 (−2)	5.4759 (−2)	5.4891 (−2)
−2.8	5.60 (−2)	5.831 (−2)	5.9545 (−2)	6.0170 (−2)	6.0488 (−2)	6.0649 (−2)
−2.7	6.13 (−2)	6.417 (−2)	6.5665 (−2)	6.6425 (−2)	6.6813 (−2)	6.7009 (−2)
−2.6	6.71 (−2)	7.059 (−2)	7.2398 (−2)	7.3323 (−2)	7.3795 (−2)	7.4033 (−2)
−2.5	7.35 (−2)	7.762 (−2)	7.9804 (−2)	8.0927 (−2)	8.1501 (−2)	8.1791 (−2)
−2.4	8.02 (−2)	8.529 (−2)	8.7944 (−2)	8.9309 (−2)	9.0006 (−2)	9.0360 (−2)
−2.3	8.76 (−2)	9.369 (−2)	9.6887 (−2)	9.8544 (−2)	9.9391 (−2)	9.9822 (−2)
−2.2	9.55 (−2)	1.0284 (−1)	1.0671 (−1)	1.0872 (−1)	1.0975 (−1)	1.1027 (−1)
−2.1	1.040 (−1)	1.1280 (−1)	1.1748 (−1)	1.1992 (−1)	1.2117 (−1)	1.2181 (−1)
−2.0	1.132 (−1)	1.2366 (−1)	1.2930 (−1)	1.3225 (−1)	1.3377 (−1)	1.3454 (−1)
−1.9	1.229 (−1)	1.3546 (−1)	1.4225 (−1)	1.4581 (−1)	1.4766 (−1)	1.4860 (−1)
−1.8	1.331 (−1)	1.4826 (−1)	1.5642 (−1)	1.6074 (−1)	1.6297 (−1)	1.6412 (−1)
−1.7	1.442 (−1)	1.6213 (−1)	1.7193 (−1)	1.7714 (−1)	1.7986 (−1)	1.8125 (−1)
−1.6	1.558 (−1)	1.7712 (−1)	1.8889 (−1)	1.9517 (−1)	1.9846 (−1)	2.0015 (−1)
−1.5	1.680 (−1)	1.9330 (−1)	2.0740 (−1)	2.1497 (−1)	2.1895 (−1)	2.2099 (−1)
−1.4	1.808 (−1)	2.1074 (−1)	2.2759 (−1)	2.3671 (−1)	2.4152 (−1)	2.4401 (−1)
−1.3	1.941 (−1)	2.2948 (−1)	2.4959 (−1)	2.6055 (−1)	2.6636 (−1)	2.6938 (−1)
−1.2	2.080 (−1)	2.4958 (−1)	2.7353 (−1)	2.8669 (−1)	2.9370 (−1)	2.9736 (−1)
−1.1	2.222 (−1)	2.7108 (−1)	2.9955 (−1)	3.1533 (−1)	3.2378 (−1)	3.2822 (−1)
−1.0	2.367 (−1)	2.9402 (−1)	3.2780 (−1)	3.4667 (−1)	3.5686 (−1)	3.6222 (−1)
−0.9	2.517 (−1)	3.1845 (−1)	3.5841 (−1)	3.8096 (−1)	3.9321 (−1)	3.9970 (−1)
−0.8	2.667 (−1)	3.4438 (−1)	3.9154 (−1)	4.1844 (−1)	4.3316 (−1)	4.4098 (−1)
−0.7	2.820 (−1)	3.7181 (−1)	4.2733 (−1)	4.5936 (−1)	4.7702 (−1)	4.8646 (−1)
−0.6	2.971 (−1)	4.0077 (−1)	4.6595 (−1)	5.0400 (−1)	5.2515 (−1)	5.3653 (−1)
−0.5	3.121 (−1)	4.3123 (−1)	5.0754 (−1)	5.5265 (−1)	5.7795 (−1)	5.9164 (−1)
−0.4	3.268 (−1)	4.6318 (−1)	5.5224 (−1)	6.0561 (−1)	6.3583 (−1)	6.5229 (−1)
−0.3	3.410 −1)	4.9657 (−1)	6.0022 (−1)	6.6321 (−1)	6.9923 (−1)	7.1899 (−1)
−0.2	3.548 (−1)	5.3137 (−1)	6.5161 (−1)	7.2577 (−1)	7.6863 (−1)	7.9234 (−1)
−0.1	3.677 (−1)	5.6750 (−1)	7.0654 (−1)	7.9365 (−1)	8.4455 (−1)	8.7294 (−1)
0.0	3.800 (−1)	6.0490 (−1)	7.6515 (−1)	8.6720 (−1)	9.2755 (−1)	9.6148 (−1)

Table B.2.—(contd.). Fermi–Dirac integrals of half-integer orders for small positive arguments

η	$\mathcal{F}_{-3/2}$	$\mathcal{F}_{-1/2}$	$\mathcal{F}_{1/2}$	$\mathcal{F}_{3/2}$	$\mathcal{F}_{5/2}$	$\mathcal{F}_{7/2}$
0.0	3.800 (−1)	6.0490 (−1)	7.6515 (−1)	8.6720 (−1)	9.2755 (−1)	9.6148 (−1)
0.1	3.915 (−1)	6.4348 (−1)	8.2756 (−1)	9.4680 (−1)	1.0182 (0)	1.0587 (0)
0.2	4.019 (−1)	6.8317 (−1)	8.9388 (−1)	1.0328 (0)	1.1171 (0)	1.1654 (0)
0.3	4.114 (−1)	7.2384 (−1)	9.6422 (−1)	1.1257 (0)	1.2250 (0)	1.2824 (0)
0.4	4.196 (−1)	7.6540 (−1)	1.0387 (0)	1.2258 (0)	1.3425 (0)	1.4107 (0)
0.5	4.269 (−1)	8.0774 (−1)	1.1173 (0)	1.3336 (0)	1.4704 (0)	1.5513 (0)
0.6	4.328 (−1)	8.5074 (−1)	1.2003 (0)	1.4494 (0)	1.6095 (0)	1.7052 (0)
0.7	4.378 (−1)	8.9429 (−1)	1.2875 (0)	1.5738 (0)	1.7606 (0)	1.8736 (0)
0.8	4.415 (−1)	9.3826 (−1)	1.3791 (0)	1.7071 (0)	1.9246 (0)	2.0577 (0)
0.9	4.441 (−1)	9.8255 (−1)	1.4752 (0)	1.8497 (0)	2.1023 (0)	2.2589 (0)
1.0	4.457 (−1)	1.0271 (0)	1.5756 (0)	2.0023 (0)	2.2948 (0)	2.4787 (0)
1.1	4.463 (−1)	1.0717 (0)	1.6806 (0)	2.1650 (0)	2.5031 (0)	2.7184 (0)
1.2	4.459 (−1)	1.1163 (0)	1.7900 (0)	2.3385 (0)	2.7282 (0)	2.9799 (0)
1.3	4.447 (−1)	1.1608 (0)	1.9038 (0)	2.5232 (0)	2.9712 (0)	3.2647 (0)
1.4	4.427 (−1)	1.2052 (0)	2.0221 (0)	2.7194 (0)	3.2332 (0)	3.5747 (0)
1.5	4.398 (−1)	1.2493 (0)	2.1449 (0)	2.9278 (0)	3.5155 (0)	3.9120 (0)
1.6	4.365 (−1)	1.2931 (0)	2.2720 (0)	3.1486 (0)	3.8192 (0)	4.2786 (0)
1.7	4.325 (−1)	1.3366 (0)	2.4035 (0)	3.3823 (0)	4.1456 (0)	4.6766 (0)
1.8	4.281 (−1)	1.3796 (0)	2.5393 (0)	3.6294 (0)	4.4961 (0)	5.1085 (0)
1.9	4.233 (−1)	1.4222 (0)	2.6794 (0)	3.8903 (0)	4.8719 (0)	5.5767 (0)
2.0	4.182 (−1)	1.4643 (0)	2.8237 (0)	4.1654 (0)	5.2746 (0)	6.0838 (0)
2.1	4.126 (−1)	1.5058 (0)	2.9722 (0)	4.4552 (0)	5.7055 (0)	6.6325 (0)
2.2	4.070 (−1)	1.5468 (0)	3.1249 (0)	4.7600 (0)	6.1662 (0)	7.2258 (0)
2.3	4.013 (−1)	1.5872 (0)	3.2816 (0)	5.0803 (0)	6.6580 (0)	7.8668 (0)
2.4	3.954 (−1)	1.6271 (0)	3.4423 (0)	5.4164 (0)	7.1827 (0)	8.5585 (0)
2.5	3.893 (−1)	1.6663 (0)	3.6070 (0)	5.7689 (0)	7.7419 (0)	9.3044 (0)
2.6	3.833 (−1)	1.7049 (0)	3.7755 (0)	6.1380 (0)	8.3371 (0)	1.0108 (+1)
2.7	3.772 (−1)	1.7430 (0)	3.9480 (0)	6.5241 (0)	8.9700 (0)	1.0973 (+1)
2.8	3.712 (−1)	1.7804 (0)	4.1241 (0)	6.9277 (0)	9.6425 (0)	1.1903 (+1)
2.9	3.654 (−1)	1.8172 (0)	4.3040 (0)	7.3491 (0)	1.0356 (+1)	1.2903 (+1)
3.0	3.595 (−1)	1.8535 (0)	4.4876 (0)	7.7886 (0)	1.1113 (+1)	1.3976 (+1)
3.1	3.537 (−1)	1.8891 (0)	4.6747 (0)	8.2467 (0)	1.1915 (+1)	1.5127 (+1)
3.2	3.481 (−1)	1.9242 (0)	4.8653 (0)	8.7237 (0)	1.2763 (+1)	1.6360 (+1)
3.3	3.425 (−1)	1.9588 (0)	5.0595 (0)	9.2199 (0)	1.3660 (+1)	1.7681 (+1)
3.4	3.370 (−1)	1.9927 (0)	5.2571 (0)	9.7357 (0)	1.4608 (+1)	1.9094 (+1)
3.5	3.319 (−1)	2.0262 (0)	5.4580 (0)	1.0271 (+1)	1.5608 (+1)	2.0605 (+1)
3.6	3.267 (−1)	2.0591 (0)	5.6623 (0)	1.0827 (+1)	1.6662 (+1)	2.2218 (+1)
3.7	3.216 (−1)	2.0915 (0)	5.8699 (0)	1.1404 (+1)	1.7774 (+1)	2.3939 (+1)
3.8	3.167 (−1)	2.1235 (0)	6.0806 (0)	1.2001 (+1)	1.8944 (+1)	2.5774 (+1)
3.9	3.120 (−1)	2.1549 (0)	6.2945 (0)	1.2620 (+1)	2.0175 (+1)	2.7730 (+1)
4.0	3.075 (−1)	2.1859 (0)	6.5115 (0)	1.3260 (+1)	2.1469 (+1)	2.9812 (+1)

Table B.2.—(contd.). Fermi–Dirac integrals of half-integer orders and positive arguments

η	$\mathcal{F}_{-3/2}$	$\mathcal{F}_{-1/2}$	$\mathcal{F}_{1/2}$	$\mathcal{F}_{3/2}$	$\mathcal{F}_{5/2}$	$\mathcal{F}_{7/2}$
4.0	3.08 (−1)	2.1859 (0)	6.5115 (0)	1.3260 (+1)	2.1469 (+1)	2.9812 (+1)
4.2	2.99 (−1)	2.2465 (0)	6.9548 (0)	1.4607 (+1)	2.4254 (+1)	3.4379 (+1)
4.4	2.90 (−1)	2.3054 (0)	7.4100 (0)	1.6043 (+1)	2.7317 (+1)	3.9532 (+1)
4.6	2.82 (−1)	2.3627 (0)	7.8769 (0)	1.7572 (+1)	3.0677 (+1)	4.5326 (+1)
4.8	2.75 (−1)	2.4186 (0)	8.3550 (0)	1.9195 (+1)	3.4352 (+1)	5.1824 (+1)
5.0	2.69 (−1)	2.4730 (0)	8.8442 (0)	2.0914 (+1)	3.8361 (+1)	5.9089 (+1)
5.2	2.62 (−1)	2.5261 (0)	9.3441 (0)	2.2733 (+1)	4.2725 (+1)	6.7192 (+1)
5.4	2.56 (−1)	2.5780 (0)	9.8546 (0)	2.4653 (+1)	4.7462 (+1)	7.6204 (+1)
5.6	2.51 (−1)	2.6288 (0)	1.0375 (+1)	2.6676 (+1)	5.2593 (+1)	8.6203 (+1)
5.8	2.46 (−1)	2.6784 (0)	1.0906 (+1)	2.8804 (+1)	5.8139 (+1)	9.7268 (+1)
6.0	2.40 (−1)	2.7272 (0)	1.1447 (+1)	3.1039 (+1)	6.4121 (+1)	1.0949 (+2)
6.2	2.36 (−1)	2.7748 (0)	1.1997 (+1)	3.3383 (+1)	7.0561 (+1)	1.2295 (+2)
6.4	2.31 (−1)	2.8216 (0)	1.2556 (+1)	3.5838 (+1)	7.7482 (+1)	1.3774 (+2)
6.6	2.27 (−1)	2.8677 (0)	1.3125 (+1)	3.8406 (+1)	8.4904 (+1)	1.5397 (+2)
6.8	2.23 (−1)	2.9128 (0)	1.3703 (+1)	4.1089 (+1)	9.2852 (+1)	1.7174 (+2)
7.0	2.20 (−1)	2.9573 (0)	1.4290 (+1)	4.3888 (+1)	1.0135 (+2)	1.9115 (+2)
7.2	2.16 (−1)	3.0009 (0)	1.4886 (+1)	4.6806 (+1)	1.1041 (+2)	2.1232 (+2)
7.4	2.13 (−1)	3.0439 (0)	1.5491 (+1)	4.9843 (+1)	1.2008 (+2)	2.3536 (+2)
7.6	2.10 (−1)	3.0862 (0)	1.6104 (+1)	5.3003 (+1)	1.3036 (+2)	2.6039 (+2)
7.8	2.07 (−1)	3.1280 (0)	1.6725 (+1)	5.6286 (+1)	1.4129 (+2)	2.8754 (+2)
8.0	2.04 (−1)	3.1691 (0)	1.7355 (+1)	5.9693 (+1)	1.5288 (+2)	3.1695 (+2)
8.2	2.01 (−1)	3.2097 (0)	1.7993 (+1)	6.3228 (+1)	1.6517 (+2)	3.4874 (+2)
8.4	1.99 (−1)	3.2497 (0)	1.8639 (+1)	6.6891 (+1)	1.7818 (+2)	3.8307 (+2)
8.6	1.96 (−1)	3.2892 (0)	1.9293 (+1)	7.0684 (+1)	1.9194 (+2)	4.2007 (+2)
8.8	1.94 (−1)	3.3282 (0)	1.9954 (+1)	7.4609 (+1)	2.0646 (+2)	4.5989 (+2)
9.0	1.91 (−1)	3.3667 (0)	2.0624 (+1)	7.8666 (+1)	2.2179 (+2)	5.0271 (+2)
9.2	1.89 (−1)	3.4048 (0)	2.1301 (+1)	8.2859 (+1)	2.3794 (+2)	5.4867 (+2)
9.4	1.87 (−1)	3.4425 (0)	2.1986 (+1)	8.7187 (+1)	2.5494 (+2)	5.9794 (+2)
9.6	1.85 (−1)	3.4796 (0)	2.2678 (+1)	9.1654 (+1)	2.7282 (+2)	6.5070 (+2)
9.8	1.83 (−1)	3.5164 (0)	2.3378 (+1)	9.6259 (+1)	2.9161 (+2)	7.0713 (+2)
10.0	1.81 (−1)	3.5528 (0)	2.4085 (+1)	1.0101 (+2)	3.1134 (+2)	7.6741 (+2)

Appendix C

SOME APPLICATIONS AND PROPERTIES OF THE FERMI-DIRAC INTEGRALS §

In this appendix we give a brief indication of how the Fermi–Dirac integrals of various orders can become important. The widest range of orders is encountered in discussions of transport phenomena, but orders other than $\frac{1}{2}$ are required for an understanding of carrier statistics in bands of non-standard form.

The asymptotic forms taken by the various functions for non-degenerate and highly degenerate cases are reviewed, and some simple approximate expressions attempted, particularly for $\mathscr{F}_{1/2}(\eta)$.

C.1 Fermi–Dirac Integrals and Transport Properties

When the Boltzmann transport equation is solved on the assumption that a scattering time exists, the result for the current density is the sum of terms which depend on applied electric, magnetic and thermal fields, and their gradients, in various fashions. Each of these terms can be associated with a macroscopic effect, such as conductivity, Hall effect, magnetoconductivity, Nernst effect, etc. Many of these terms involve one or more of the integrals

$$I_m = -\int_{E_c}^{\infty} (E-E_c)^m \lambda(E) \frac{\partial f(E)}{\partial E} \, . \, \mathrm{d}E \tag{C1.1}$$

where λ is the mean free path for an electron of energy $E, f(E)$ is the Fermi probability factor of Eq. (122.4), and m is an integer. Electrical conductivity, for example, depends on I_1 for bands of standard form; while the thermoelectric power is controlled by I_2 and I_1, and the electronic thermal conductivity is determined by the values of I_1, I_2 and I_3.

Now for many kinds of scattering, the mean free path can be expressed as $\lambda = \lambda_0(E-E_c)^r$ over the limited range of energies which decides the fate of conduction phenomena. In this, λ_0 may be a function of temperature but not of energy (1951:**4**). When the mean free path can legitimately be expressed in this way, then

$$I_m/\lambda_0(kT)^{m+r} = -\int_0^\infty \epsilon^{m+r} \cdot \frac{\partial f(\epsilon)}{\partial \epsilon} \cdot d\epsilon \tag{C1.2}$$

Integrating by parts,

$$I_m/\lambda_0(kT)^{m+r} = \Big[\epsilon^{m+r} \cdot f(\epsilon)\Big]_\infty^0 + (m+r) \cdot \int_0^\infty \epsilon^{m+r-1} \cdot f(\epsilon) \cdot d\epsilon$$

$$= 0 + \Gamma(m+r+1) \cdot \mathscr{F}_{m+r-1}(\eta) \tag{C1.3}$$

This permits the expression of any transport quantity which involves an integral I_m in terms of a Fermi–Dirac integral $\mathscr{F}_j$ with order

$$j = (m+r-1)$$

Transport effects associated with magnetic fields involve one or more integrals of the series

$$J_n = -\int_0^\infty (E-E_c)^{n+1/2}\lambda^2 \cdot \frac{\partial f(E)}{\partial E} \cdot dE \tag{C1.4}$$

It will readily be seen by the same approach that each J_n can be associated with a Fermi–Dirac integral $\mathscr{F}_j$ of order $j = (n+2r-\frac{1}{2})$.

The widespread interest in transport effects of semiconductors provides ample justification for providing data of Fermi–Dirac integrals of orders other than $\frac{1}{2}$ in Tables B.1 and B.2. There is in fact a further justification even in the more limited sphere of carrier statistics, as noted in the next section.

C.2 Fermi–Dirac Integrals for Non-standard Bands

In the preceding discussion it has been seen that the number of charge carriers in a band of standard form is related to the Fermi level by the Fermi–Dirac integral $\mathscr{F}_{1/2}(\eta)$. This ceases to be rigorously true if the band is non-standard, i.e. if energy does not increase as the square of wave-vector. A simple hypothetical example will serve to demonstrate the point.

Suppose a conduction band for which the behavior near the extremum may be described by

$$E = E_c + \frac{\hbar^2 k^2}{2m^*}[1-\alpha k^2], \qquad (E-E_c) \ll \hbar^2/\alpha m^* \tag{C2.1}$$

This is not unlike the manner in which the conduction band develops for InSb. The effective mass at the very bottom of the band is quite small, but since energy increases less rapidly than the square of wave-vector, higher energy states must be described in terms of a larger effective mass.

Eq. (C2.1) is a quadratic in k^2. The standard form of solution then gives

$$2\alpha k^2 = 1-[1-8\alpha m^*(E-E_c)/\hbar^2]^{1/2} \tag{C2.2}$$

From this we can write approximately that

$$k \approx \frac{(2m)^{1/2}(E-E_c)^{1/2}}{\hbar}[1-2\alpha m^*(E-E_c)/\hbar^2+...]^{1/2}, \qquad k \ll \alpha^{-1/2} \tag{C2.3}$$

for states close to the bottom of the band. From Eqs. (C2.1) and (C2.2) it is evident that

$$\frac{\mathrm{d}E}{\mathrm{d}k} = \frac{\hbar^2 k}{m^*}[1-2\alpha k^2] = \frac{\hbar^2 k}{m^*}[1-8\alpha m^*(E-E_c)/\hbar^2]^{1/2} \tag{C2.4}$$

This result and (C2.3) can be applied to the basic expression for the density of states

$$g(E) = (k/\pi)^2(\mathrm{d}k/\mathrm{d}E) \tag{C2.5}$$

to yield

$$g(E) = 4\pi(2m^*/h^2)^{3/2}(E-E_c)^{1/2} \cdot \left[\frac{1-2\alpha m^*(E-E_c)/\hbar^2}{1-8\alpha m^*(E-E_c)/\hbar^2}\right]^{1/2} \tag{C2.6}$$

Since we are considering only energies quite near to the base of the band, this can be approximated by

$$g(E) \approx 4\pi(2m^*/h^2)^{3/2}(E-E_c)^{1/2}[1+3\alpha m^*(E-E_c)/\hbar^2], \qquad (E-E_c) \ll \hbar^2/\alpha m^* \tag{C2.7}$$

When the number of occupied states in such a band is to be related to the Fermi level by application of

$$n_0 = \int_{E_c}^{\infty} f(E)g(E) \,.\, \mathrm{d}E \tag{C2.8}$$

it is obvious that the result will involve terms in *both* $\mathscr{F}_{1/2}(\eta)$ and $\mathscr{F}_{3/2}(\eta)$. Other forms of departure from standard form in a band can similarly lead to the use of $\mathscr{F}_j(\eta)$ with orders other than $\frac{1}{2}$ in the description of carrier density $\leftrightarrow$ Fermi level equilibrium.

C.3 Analytic Properties of the Fermi Integrals, and Asymptotic Expansions for Non-degenerate and Degenerate Cases

Physicists first became aware of the integrals we now know as the Fermi–Dirac integrals through the work of Sommerfeld (1928:**1**) on the free electron theory. At that time Sommerfeld discussed asymptotic series for the set of integrals, which are still of value today. McDougall and Stoner (1938:**2**) in addition to tabulations, explored a number of analytic aspects of the functions and appear to have been the first to make the observation previously quoted as Eq. (B.3), that

$$\mathscr{F}_j'(\eta) = \frac{\mathrm{d}}{\mathrm{d}\eta}\mathscr{F}_j(\eta) = \mathscr{F}_{j-1}(\eta) \tag{C3.1}$$

This differentiation formula is a valuable tool in obtaining one order from another. Thus Beer *et al.* (1955:**4**) used the inverse process of integration to calculate and tabulate $\mathscr{F}_{5/2}$, $\mathscr{F}_{7/2}$, $\mathscr{F}_{9/2}$ and $\mathscr{F}_{11/2}$ from McDougall and Stoner's values of $\mathscr{F}_{1/2}$ and $\mathscr{F}_{3/2}$. In the same connection we should note that each entry in Table B.1 or Table B.2 is the first derivative of the next entry to the right (i.e. the entry for the same η and for j larger by unity).

The expansion for $\mathscr{F}_j(\eta)$ when η is negative or zero is

$$\mathscr{F}_j(\eta) = \sum_{r=1}^{\infty} \frac{(-1)^{r+1}\exp(r\eta)}{r^{j+1}}, \qquad \eta \leqslant 0 \tag{C3.2}$$

The so-called "classical" or completely non-degenerate approximation is that $\mathscr{F}_j(\eta) \approx \exp(\eta)$; which we can see from Eq. (C3.2) will be correct when η is sufficiently large and negative. This approximation will be adequate for many situations, but is admittedly of limited accuracy when $-\eta$ is rather small. (As an example, note that $\exp(\eta)$ is 1% larger than $\mathscr{F}_{1/2}(\eta)$ for $\eta = -3{\cdot}5$, 5% high at $\eta = -2$ and 30% high at $\eta = 0$.) The error can be reduced by using additional terms of Eq. (C3.2), but this series is not very strongly convergent for small negative η and small j.

McDougall and Stoner noted that the integrals for $\eta = 0$ may be expressed in terms of the ordinary Riemann zeta function,

$$\mathscr{F}_j(0) = \sum_{r=1}^{\infty} \frac{(-1)^{r+1}}{r^{j+1}} = [1-2^{-j}]\zeta(j+1) \tag{C3.3}$$

A Taylor series expansion for $\mathscr{F}_j(\eta)$ when $|\eta|$ is small has been derived by Dingle (1956:**2**) on the basis of Eqs. (C3.1) and (C3.3). Such an expansion is useful for highly precise calculations, but is unnecessarily cumbersome when computations of moderate accuracy are to be made. Fortunately, simpler expressions of tolerable validity can be contrived.

Let us concentrate on expressions for $\mathscr{F}_{1/2}(\eta)$, since this is the important member for carrier statistics with bands of normal form. The correct expansion for this quantity is

$$\mathscr{F}_{1/2}(\eta) = \exp(\eta) - 2^{-3/2}\exp(2\eta) + 3^{-3/2}\exp(3\eta)\ldots, \qquad \eta \leqslant 0 \tag{C3.4}$$

Instead of taking the first few terms of this expansion as they stand, it is preferable to modify the coefficients of higher order terms. In this manner it is possible to minimize the error over a desired range of η. Thus the simple expression

$$\exp(\eta) - 0{\cdot}25\exp(2\eta) \tag{C3.5}$$

does not depart from $\mathscr{F}_{1/2}(\eta)$ by more than $\pm 2\%$ for any negative value of η, as may be seen from Fig. C.1. This figure shows that a better approximation still is

$$\exp(\eta) - 0{\cdot}3\exp(2\eta) + 0{\cdot}06\exp(3\eta) \tag{C3.6}$$

which has an error of less than $\pm 0{\cdot}75\%$ for negative η and is acceptable up to $\eta = +0{\cdot}9$.

There are some occasions when the expressions (C3.5) and (C3.6) prove useful, but solutions of this form are decidedly inconvenient for many types of problem. For in solving the equations which relate the numbers of carriers in impurity levels and electron bands to the Fermi energy, it is necessary to solve a cubic equation for $\exp(\eta)$ when (C3.5)

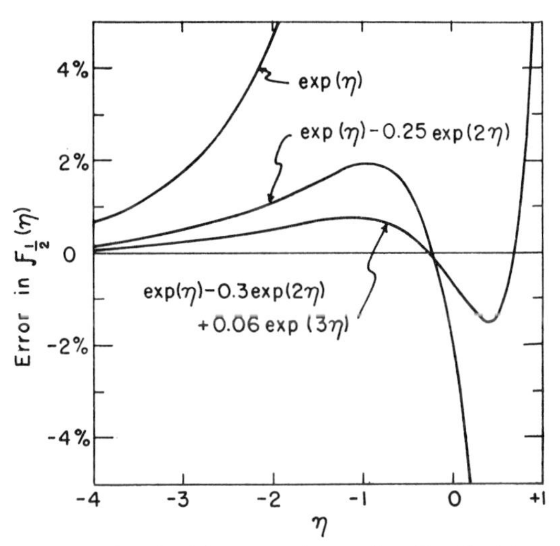

FIG. C.1. Error involved in attempting to describe $\mathcal{F}_{1/2}(\eta)$ as $\exp(\eta)$ or by the expressions of Eqs. (C3.5) and (C3.6), when η is negative or only very slightly positive.

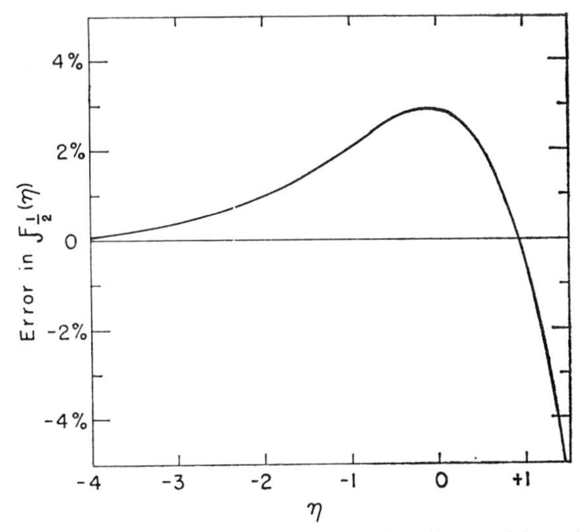

FIG. C.2. Error involved in attempting to describe $\mathcal{F}_{1/2}(\eta)$ as the expression in Eq. (C3.8) when η is negative or slightly positive.

is used, and a quartic when (C3.6) is employed. It is of course much more desirable to deal with a quadratic equation, and this can be done if an expression of the form

$$\mathscr{F}_{1/2}(\eta) \approx \frac{\exp(\eta)}{1+C\exp(\eta)} \tag{C3.7}$$

is used, as suggested by Ehrenberg (1950:**4**). Landsberg *et al.* (1951:**5**) remarked that differing values of C optimize the fit for various ranges of η; but for the whole range from classical conditions up to a small positive value of η probably the best compromise is effected with the value $C = 0{\cdot}27$ proposed by the present author (1952:**2**). As shown by the curve of Fig. C.2, the quantity

$$\frac{\exp(\eta)}{1+0{\cdot}27\exp(\eta)} \tag{C3.8}$$

lies within $\pm 3\%$ of $\mathscr{F}_{1/2}(\eta)$ for $\eta < +1{\cdot}3$, and an error no greater than this can almost always be tolerated in carrier density discussions.

Having noted these attempts to make the non-degenerate form of expression more palatable in semi-degenerate situations, we must now turn to the asymptotic forms which are specific for degenerate systems. Eventually we shall again wish to concentrate on $\mathscr{F}_{1/2}(\eta)$, but it is informative to review a broader field at first.

Sommerfeld (1928:**1**) found that the various $\mathscr{F}_j(\eta)$ could be expressed in the form

$$\mathscr{F}_j(\eta) \approx \frac{\eta^{j+1}}{\Gamma(j+2)}[1+R_j(\eta)], \quad \eta \gg 0 \tag{C3.9}$$

where $R_j(\eta)$ is a series in negative powers of η. Rhodes (1950:**3**) noted that when j is an integer, the expression (C3.9) omits a term which can not be described in powers of η, and showed that this term was $(-1)^j\mathscr{F}_j(-\eta)$. This analysis was extended by Dingle (1956:**2**) to arbitrary j; he found the residue to be $\cos(j\pi)\cdot\mathscr{F}_j(-\eta)$ (which includes Rhodes' result as a special case for integral j). Thus in general we have that

$$\mathscr{F}_j(\eta) = \cos(j\pi)\cdot\mathscr{F}_j(-\eta) + \frac{\eta^{j+1}}{\Gamma(j+2)}[1+R_j(\eta)], \quad \eta > 0 \tag{C3.10}$$

Sommerfeld's expansion for $R_j(\eta)$ is

$$R_j(\eta) = \sum_{r=1}^{\infty} \frac{\alpha_r}{\eta^{2r}} \cdot \frac{\Gamma(j+2)}{\Gamma(j+2-2r)} \tag{C3.11}$$

Each of the quantities α_r can itself be expressed as an infinite series, whose sum is related to a Bernoulli number of order r or to an ordinary zeta function of order $2r$:

$$\alpha_r = \sum_{\mu=1}^{\infty} 2(-1)^{\mu+1} \,.\, \mu^{-2r} = \frac{(2\pi)^{2r}[1-2^{1-2r}]B_r}{\Gamma(2r+1)}$$
$$= 2[1-2^{1-2r}]\zeta(2r) \qquad \text{(C3.12)}$$

The first four members† of this set are given in Table C.1.

Table C.1

r	B_r	$\zeta\ (2r)$	α_r
1	1/6	$\pi^2/6$	$\pi^2/6$
2	1/30	$\pi^4/90$	$7\pi^4/360$
3	1/42	$\pi^6/945$	$31\pi^6/15{,}120$
4	1/30	$\pi^8/9450$	$127\pi^8/604{,}800$

Table C.2

j	$\mathscr{F}_j(\eta)$ for integral j
−1	$[1+\exp(-\eta)]^{-1}$
0	$\ln[1+\exp(\eta)]$
1	$-\mathscr{F}_1(-\eta)+(\eta^2/2)+(\pi^2/6)$
2	$+\mathscr{F}_2(-\eta)+(\eta^3/6)+(\pi^2\eta/6)$
3	$-\mathscr{F}_3(-\eta)+(\eta^4/24)+(\pi^2\eta^2/12)+(7\pi^4/360)$
4	$+\mathscr{F}_4(-\eta)+(\eta^5/120)+(\pi^2\eta^3/36)+(7\pi^4\eta/360)$
5	$-\mathscr{F}_5(-\eta)+(\eta^6/720)+(\pi^2\eta^4/144)+(7\pi^4\eta^2/720)+(31\pi^6/15{,}120)$

When j is an integer, $R_j(\eta)$ is a polynomial rather than an asymptotic expansion, and the relation between $\mathscr{F}_j(\eta)$ and $\mathscr{F}_j(-\eta)$ can be expressed *exactly*. For $j = 1$ or $j = 2$, $R_j(\eta)$ has but a single term involving α_1. The polynomial has two terms for $j = 3$ or 4, three terms for $j = 5$ or 6, and so on. Expressions for $\mathscr{F}_j(\eta)$ when j is a small integer are

† α_0, which is unity, is not properly a member of the set. All members beyond α_4 are very close to the value 2·000.

summarized in Table C.2. It will be noted that these entries are consistent with the differentiation formula Eq. (C3.1).

When j is not an integer, the series (C3.11) does not terminate, and is at best an asymptotic approximation. Gamma functions of negative quantities can be avoided by using the property

$$\frac{1}{\Gamma(z)} = \frac{\sin(\pi z)}{\pi} \, . \, \Gamma(1-z) \tag{C3.13}$$

[e.g. Whittaker and Watson (1927:**2**)] and writing (C3.11) as two summations,

$$R_j(\eta) = \sum_{r=1}^{[\frac{1}{2}(j+1)]} \frac{\alpha_r \Gamma(j+2)}{\eta^{2r}\Gamma(j+2-2r)} + \\ + \sum_{[\frac{1}{2}(j+3)]}^{\infty} \frac{\sin(j\pi)}{\pi} \cdot \frac{\alpha_r \, . \, \Gamma(j+2)\Gamma(2r-j-1)}{\eta^{2r}} \tag{C3.14}$$

The notation here indicates that $[\frac{1}{2}(j+1)]$ is the largest integer contained within $\frac{1}{2}(j+1)$.

A highly unsatisfactory feature of Eq. (C3.14) is that the terms of the second summation begin to increase when r is larger than $\sim\frac{1}{2}(j+\eta)$. Dingle (1956:**2**) shows that when a finite number of terms in this summation are included, the remainder of $R_j(\eta)$ *can* be expressed in convergent form, but the necessary series are far from simple. When η is sufficiently large, there is little problem; the difficulty is as usual in expressing $\mathscr{F}_j(\eta)$ for *small* positive η.

Having said this much on the general case, we now focus our attention on the particular function $\mathscr{F}_{1/2}(\eta)$. One useful simplification which occurs whenever $j = \frac{1}{2}$ plus integer is that the term $\cos(j\pi) \cdot \mathscr{F}_j(-\eta)$ in Eq. (C3.10) vanishes. Thus

$$\mathscr{F}_{1/2}(\eta) = (4\eta^{3/2}/3\pi^{1/2})[1+R_{1/2}(\eta)], \qquad \eta \geqslant 0 \tag{C3.15}$$

where

$$R_{1/2}(\eta) \approx (\pi^2/8\eta^2) - (7\pi^4/640\eta^4) + (31\pi^6/3072\eta^6)\ldots \tag{C3.16}$$

according to Eq. (C3.14).

We know that in attempting to describe $\mathscr{F}_{1/2}(\eta)$ for small positive η, it will not profit us to retain many terms of the series (C3.16); indeed for the region $\eta < 3$, every term beyond the *first* is a distinct liability.

Rather surprisingly, the simple expression

$$(4\eta^{3/2}/3\pi^{1/2})[1+\pi^2/8\eta^2] \tag{C3.17}$$

provides a reasonable approximation to the behavior of $\mathscr{F}_{1/2}(\eta)$ for $\eta > 1{\cdot}25$. The percentage error involved is indicated in Fig. C.3.

It may be queried at this point whether the range can be usefully extended to smaller values of η by replacing the coefficient $(\pi^2/8)$ in

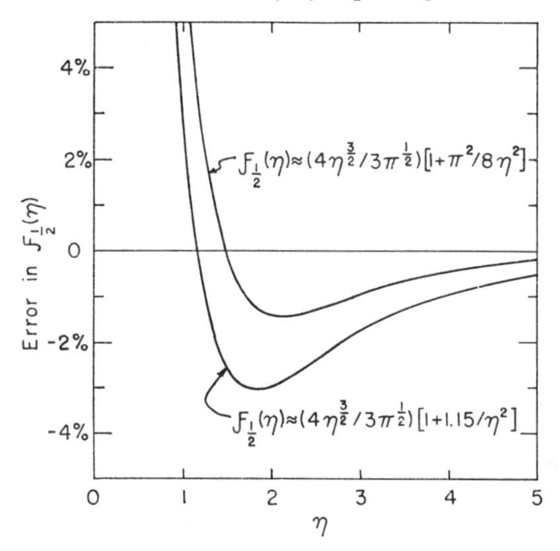

FIG. C.3. The error involved in attempting to express $\mathscr{F}_{1/2}(\eta)$ by approximate expressions of the forms of Eqs. (C3.17) or (C3.18), when η is positive and rather small.

Eq. (C3.17) with a slightly smaller number. If it is desired that an error of not more than $\pm 3\%$ in $\mathscr{F}_{1/2}(\eta)$ should be incurred through the range of η, then the smallest permissible value for this coefficient is 1.15. As the appropriate curve of Fig. C.3. shows,

$$(4\eta^{3/2}/3\pi^{1/2}) \,.\, [1+1{\cdot}15/\eta^2] \tag{C3.18}$$

lies within about $\pm 3\%$ of $\mathscr{F}_{1/2}(\eta)$ for $\eta \geqslant 1{\cdot}0$.

An alternative procedure for extending the range to smaller values of η is based on the observation† that the first two terms of Eqs. (C3.15)

† This observation was made by Mr. L. Lewin and was used by the present author in an earlier discussion of this topic (1952:3).

and (C3.16) are identical with the first two terms of

$$(4/3\pi^{1/2}) \,.\, [\eta^2 + \pi^2/6]^{3/4} \tag{C3.19}$$

yet the succeeding terms of Eq. (C3.19) are considerably smaller than their counterparts in the other series. Numerical investigation confirms that Eq. (C3.19) satisfactorily describes the behavior of $\mathscr{F}_{1/2}(\eta)$ for $\eta \geqslant 0{\cdot}7$, as shown by the appropriate error curve in Fig. C.4. The

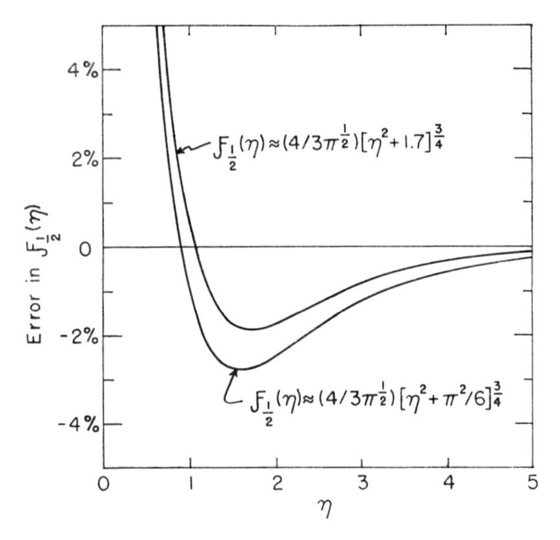

FIG. C.4. The error involved in attempting to express $\mathscr{F}_{1/2}(\eta)$ by an approximate expression having the form of Eq. (C3.19) or (C3.20), when η is positive and rather small.

maximum negative error can be reduced by replacing $\pi^2/6$ with a slightly larger number, but this of course automatically restricts the range of η. Thus

$$(4/3\pi^{1/2})[\eta^2 + 1{\cdot}7]^{3/4} \tag{C3.20}$$

is never more than 2% smaller than $\mathscr{F}_{1/2}(\eta)$, but becomes unacceptably large when $\eta < 0{\cdot}9$.

It will depend on the form of the problem to be solved whether it is preferable to express $\mathscr{F}_{1/2}(\eta)$ in weakly degenerate systems by Eq.

(C3.18), or by one of the expressions (C3.19), (C3.20). Certainly any of these three will permit calculation of free carrier densities or Fermi level with reasonable accuracy whenever $\eta \geqslant 1$. Since Eq. (C3.8) can be used for any smaller value of η, the entire range from complete *degeneracy* to complete *non-degeneracy* is covered.

REFERENCES

1853:**1** WIEDEMANN and FRANZ, *Ann. Physik* **89**, 497.
1904:**1** DRUDE, *Ann. Physik* **1**, 566.
1909:**1** LORENTZ, *The Theory of Electrons.* Teubner, Leipzig.
1917:**1** EINSTEIN, *Z. Physik* **18**, 121.
1926:**1** FRENKEL, *Z. Physik* **35**, 652.
1926:**2** BORN, *Z. Physik* **38**, 803.
1927:**1** PAULI, *Z. Physik* **41**, 8.
1927:**2** WHITTAKER and WATSON, *Modern Analysis.* Cambridge University Press.
1927:**3** HEITLER and LONDON, *Z. Physik* **44**, 455.
1928:**1** SOMMERFELD, *Z. Physik* **47**, 1.
1928:**2** HARTREE, *Proc. Cambridge Phil. Soc.* **24**, 89.
1928:**3** BLOCH, *Z. Physik* **52**, 555.
1930:**1** FOCK, *Z. Physik* **61**, 126.
1930:**2** KRONIG and PENNEY, *Proc. Roy. Soc. London* A **130**, 499.
1930:**3** LANDAU, *Z. Physik* **64**, 629.
1930:**4** DE HAAS and VAN ALPHEN, *Leiden Comm.* 208d, 212a.
1931:**1** WILSON, *Proc. Roy. Soc. London* A **133**, 458.
1931:**2** WILSON, *Proc. Roy. Soc. London* A **134**, 277.
1931:**3** FRENKEL, *Phys. Rev.* **37**, 17, 1276.
1931:**4** HEISENBERG, *Ann. Physik* **10**, 888.
1931:**5** WAGNER and SCHOTTKY, *Z. Phys. Chem. Leipzig* B **11**, 163.
1932:**1** TAMM, *Z. Physik* **76**, 849.
1933:**1** LANDAU, *J. Exptl. Theoret. Phys. U.S.S.R.* **3**, 664.
1933:**2** PEIERLS, *Z. Physik* **80**, 763.
1933:**3** BETHE, *Handbuch der Physik* vol. 24.1. Springer, Berlin.
1934:**1** BAUMBACH and WAGNER, *Z. Phys. Chem.* B **24**, 59.
1934:**2** ZENER, *Proc. Roy. Soc. London* A **145**, 523.
1935:**1** DE BOER and VAN GEEL, *Physica* **2**, 286.
1936:**1** MOTT and JONES, *Theory of the Properties of Metals and Alloys.* Oxford University Press.
1936:**2** VON HIPPEL, *Z. Physik* **101**, 680.
1937:**1** WANNIER, *Phys. Rev.* **52**, 191.
1937:**2** DE BOER and VERWEY, *Proc. Phys. Soc. London* **49** (extra part), 59.
1937:**3** GURNEY and MOTT, *Proc. Phys. Soc. London* **49** (extra part), 32.
1938:**1** MOTT, *Proc. Roy. Soc. London* A **167**, 384.
1938:**2** MCDOUGALL and STONER, *Phil. Trans. Roy. Soc. London* A **237**, 67.
1939:**1** NIJBOER, *Proc. Phys. Soc. London* **51**, 575.

1939:**2** RIEHL and SCHÖN, *Z. Physik* **114**, 682.
1940:**1** SEITZ, *Modern Theory of Solids*. McGraw-Hill, New York.
1940:**2** KRÖGER, *Physica* **7**, 1.
1941:**1** VERWEY and HAAYMAN, *Physica* **8**, 979.
1942:**1** BORN, *Proc. Phys. Soc. London* **54**, 362.
1944:**1** SHIFRIN, *J. Phys. U.S.S.R.* **8**, 242.
1946:**1** BRILLOUIN, *Wave Propagation in Periodic Structures*. McGraw-Hill, New York.
1946:**2** PEKAR, *J. Exptl. Theoret. Phys. U.S.S.R.* **16**, 341.
1947:**1** VERWEY and HEILMANN, *J. Chem. Phys.* **15**, 174.
1947:**2** GOODMAN, LAWSON and SCHIFF, *Phys. Rev.* **71**, 191.
1947:**3** BARDEEN, *Phys. Rev.* **71**, 717.
1947:**4** CARSLAW and JAEGER, *Conduction of Heat in Solids*. Clarendon Press, Oxford.
1948:**1** VONSOVSKY, *Izvest. Akad. Nauk. SSSR* **12**, 337.
1948:**2** MOTT and GURNEY, *Electronic Processes in Ionic Crystals*, 2nd Ed. Clarendon Press, Oxford.
1948:**3** VERWEY, HAAYMAN and ROMEYN, *Chem. Weekblad* **44**, 705.
1949:**1** SHOCKLEY and BARDEEN, *Phys. Rev.* **77**, 407.
1949:**2** BOGOLYUBOV and TYABLIKOV, *J. Exptl. Theoret. Phys. U.S.S.R.* **19**, 251.
1949:**3** PEKAR, *J. Exptl. Theoret. Phys. U.S.S.R.* **19**, 796.
1949:**4** PEARSON and BARDEEN, *Phys. Rev.* **75**, 865.
1949:**5** SHOCKLEY, *Bell System Tech. J.* **28**, 435.
1949:**6** MOTT, *Proc. Phys. Soc. London* A **62**, 416.
1949:**7** WRIGHT and ANDREWS, *Proc. Phys. Soc. London* A **62**, 446.
1949:**8** MOTT and MASSEY, *Theory of Atomic Collisions*, 2nd Ed. Clarendon Press, Oxford.
1949:**9** SCHIFF, *Quantum Mechanics*. McGraw-Hill, New York.
1950:**1** SHOCKLEY, *Electrons and Holes in Semiconductors*. D. Van Nostrand, New York.
1950:**2** FRÖHLICH, PELZER and ZIENAU, *Phil. Mag.* **41**, 221.
1950:**3** RHODES, *Proc. Roy. Soc. London* A **204**, 396.
1950:**4** EHRENBERG, *Proc. Phys. Soc. London* A **63**, 75.
1950:**5** HUTNER, RITTNER and DUPRÉ, *Philips Research Repts.* **5**, 188.
1950:**6** VERWEY, HAAIJMAN, ROMEIJN and VAN OOSTERHOUT, *Philips Research Repts.* **5**, 173.
1950:**7** BARDEEN and SHOCKLEY, *Phys. Rev.* **77**, 407.
1950:**8** ERGINSOY, *Phys. Rev.* **80**, 1104.
1950:**9** FRÖHLICH and O'DWYER, *Proc. Phys. Soc. London* A **63**, 81.
1951:**1** ANSEL'M, *J. Tech. Phys. U.S.S.R.* **21**, 489.
1951:**2** VOL'KENSHTEYN, *J. Tech. Phys. U.S.S.R.* **21**, 1544.
1951:**3** WRIGHT, *Proc. Phys. Soc. London* A **64**, 350.
1951:**4** WRIGHT, *Proc. Phys. Soc. London* A **64**, 984.
1951:**5** LANDSBERG, MACKAY and MCRONALD, *Proc. Phys. Soc. London* A **64**, 476.
1951:**6** CASTELLAN and SEITZ, *Semiconducting Materials* (Edited by H. K. Henisch). Butterworths, London.
1951:**7** PINCHERLE, *Proc. Phys. Soc. London* A **64**, 663.
1951:**8** PUTLEY, *Proc. Phys. Soc. London* B **65**, 736, 992.
1951:**9** LUTTINGER, *Phys. Rev.* **84**, 814.
1951:**10** COESTER, *Phys. Rev.* **84**, 1259
1951:**11** SLATER, *Phys. Rev.* **82**, 538.

1951:**12** Hogarth, *Proc. Phys. Soc. London* B **64**, 691
1951:**13** Lark-Horovitz, *Semiconducting Materials*. Butterworths, London.
1951:**14** James and Lehman, *Semiconducting Materials*. Butterworths, London.
1951:**15** Lehovec and Kedesdy, *J. Appl. Phys.* **22**, 65.
1951:**16** McAfee, Ryder, Shockley and Sparks, *Phys. Rev.* **83**, 650.
1951:**17** Rose, *R.C.A. Rev.* **12**, 362.
1951:**18** Hall, *Phys. Rev.* **83**, 228.
1951:**19** Plessner, *Proc. Phys. Soc. London* B **64,** 671.
1952:**1** Raynor, *Repts. Progr. Phys.* **15**, 173.
1952:**2** Blakemore, *Proc. Phys. Soc. London* A **65**, 460.
1952:**3** Blakemore, *Elec. Commun.* **29**, 131.
1952:**4** Landsberg, *Proc. Phys. Soc. London* A **65**, 604.
1952:**5** Fuller and Struthers, *Phys. Rev.* **87**, 526.
1952:**6** Fuller, Theurer and van Roosbroeck, *Phys. Rev.* **85**, 678.
1952:**7** Shockley and Read, *Phys. Rev.* **87**, 835.
1952:**8** Hall, *Phys. Rev.* **87**, 387.
1952:**9** Dunlap, *Phys. Rev.* **85**, 945.
1952:**10** Katz, *Phys. Rev.* **85**, 495.
1952:**11** Kubo, *Phys. Rev.* **86**, 929.
1953:**1** Bohm and Pines, *Phys. Rev.* **92**, 609.
1953:**2** Kittel, *Introduction to Solid State Physics*. John Wiley, New York.
1953:**3** Johnson and Shipley, *Phys. Rev.* **90**, 523.
1953:**4** Wilson, *The Theory of Metals*, 2nd ed. Cambridge University Press.
1953:**5** Landsberg, *Proc. Phys. Soc. London* A **66**, 662.
1953:**6** Guggenheim, *Proc. Phys. Soc. London* A **66**, 121.
1953:**7** Scanlon, *Phys. Rev.* **92**, 1573.
1953:**8** Blakemore, DeBarr and Gunn, *Repts. Progr. Phys.* **15**, 160.
1953:**9** Pekar, *Uspekhi Fiz. Nauk.* **50**, 197.
1953:**10** Tanenbaum and Briggs, *Phys. Rev.* **91**, 1561.
1953:**11** Logan, *Phys. Rev.* **91**, 757.
1953:**12** Mayburg and Rotondi, *Phys. Rev.* **91**, 1015.
1953:**13** Moss, *Proc. Phys. Soc. London* B **66**, 993.
1953:**14** Isay, *Ann. Physik* **13**, 327.
1953:**15** Morse and Feshbach, *Methods of Theoretical Physics*. McGraw-Hill, New York.
1953:**16** Fan, *Phys. Rev.* **92**, 1424.
1953:**17** Cottrell, *Dislocations and Plastic Flow in Crystals*. Clarendon Press, Oxford
1954:**1** Herman, *Phys. Rev.* **93**, 1214; **95**, 847.
1954:**2** Debye and Conwell, *Phys. Rev.* **93**, 693.
1954:**3** Morin and Maita, *Phys. Rev.* **94**, 1525.
1954:**4** Morin and Maita, *Phys. Rev.* **96**, 28.
1954:**5** Elliott, *Phys. Rev.* **96**, 266, 280.
1954:**6** Pearson and Herring, *Physica* **20**, 975.
1954:**7** Smith, *Phys. Rev.* **94**, 42.
1954:**8** Smith, *Physica* **20**, 910.
1954:**9** Austin and McClymont, *Physica* **20**, 1077.
1954:**10** Burstein, *Phys. Rev.* **93**, 632.
1954:**11** Moss, *Proc. Phys. Soc.* B **67**, 775.

1954:**12** Gibson, *Physica* **20**, 1058.
1954:**13** Kittel and Mitchell, *Phys. Rev.* **96**, 1488.
1954:**14** Nussbaum, *Phys. Rev.* **94**, 337.
1954:**15** van Roosbroeck and Shockley, *Phys. Rev.* **94**, 1558.
1954:**16** Newman and Tyler, *Phys. Rev.* **96**, 882.
1954:**17** Burstein, Davisson, Bell, Turner and Lipson, *Phys. Rev.* **93**, 65.
1954:**18** Toyazawa, *Progr. Theoret. Phys. Kyoto* **12**, 421.
1954:**19** Haken, *Physica*, **20**, 1013.
1954:**20** Stevenson and Keyes, *Physica* **20**, 1041.
1954:**21** Visvanathan and Battey, *J. Appl. Phys.* **25**, 99.
1954:**22** Read, *Phil. Mag.* **45**, 775, 1119.
1955:**1** Pines, *Revs. Modern Phys.* **28**, 184.
1955:**2** Hubbard, *Proc. Phys. Soc. London* A **68**, 441.
1955:**3** Löwdin, *Phys. Rev.* **97**, 1474
1955:**4** Beer, Chase and Choquard, *Helv. Phys. Acta* **28**, 529.
1955:**5** Brooks, *Advances in Electronics and Electron Physics*. Academic Press, New York.
1955:**6** Hrostowski, Morin, Geballe and Wheatley, *Phys. Rev.* **100**, 1672.
1955:**7** Herman, *Proc. I.R.E.* **43**, 1703.
1955:**8** Dresselhaus, Kip and Kittel, *Phys. Rev.* **98**, 368.
1955:**9** Lax and Mavroides, *Phys. Rev.* **100**, 1650.
1955:**10** Dash and Newman, *Phys. Rev.* **99**, 1151.
1955:**11** Kahn, *Phys. Rev.* **97**, 1647.
1955:**12** Dresselhaus, Kip, Kittel and Wagoner, *Phys. Rev.* **98**, 556.
1955:**13** Roberts and Quarrington, *J. Electronics* **1**, 152.
1955:**14** Nikolskya and Regel, *J. Tech. Phys. U.S.S.R.* **25**, 1352.
1955:**15** Rose, *Proc. I.R.E.* **43**, 1850.
1955:**16** Rose, *Phys. Rev.* **97**, 322.
1955:**17** Luttinger and Kohn, *Phys. Rev.* **97**, 869.
1955:**18** Macfarlane and Roberts, *Phys. Rev.* **97**, 1714.
1955:**19** Low, *Proc. Phys. Soc.* B **68**, 310.
1955:**20** Conwell, *Phys. Rev.* **99**, 1195.
1955:**21** Nishizawa and Watanabe, *Repts. Sci. Inst. Elect. Comm., Tohoku*, **7**, 149.
1955:**22** Kohn and Luttinger, *Phys. Rev.* **97**, 1721; **98**, 915.
1955:**23** Kohn and Schechter, *Phys. Rev.* **99**, 1903.
1955:**24** Heikes, *Phys. Rev.* **99**, 1232.
1955:**25** Woodbury and Tyler, *Phys. Rev.* **100**, 659.
1955:**26** Tyler, Newman and Woodbury, *Phys. Rev.* **97**, 669.
1955:**27** Tyler, Newman and Woodbury, *Phys. Rev.* **98**, 461.
1955:**28** Bowers and Melamed, *Phys. Rev.* **99**, 1781.
1955:**29** Fritzsche, *Phys. Rev.* **99**, 406.
1955:**30** Sclar and Burstein, *Phys. Rev.* **98**, 1757.
1955:**31** Pincherle, *Proc. Phys. Soc. London* B **68**, 319.
1955:**32** Knott, Colson and Young, *Proc. Phys. Soc. London* B **68**, 182.
1955:**33** Miller, *Phys. Rev.* **99**, 1234.
1955:**34** Gummel and Lax, *Phys. Rev.* **97**, 1469
1955:**35** Peierls, *Quantum Theory of Solids*. Clarendon Press, Oxford.
1955:**36** Hornbeck and Haynes, *Phys. Rev.* **97**, 311.
1955:**37** Haynes and Hornbeck, *Phys. Rev.* **100**, 606.

1955:**38** Newman, *Phys. Rev.* **99**, 465.
1955:**39** Stevenson and Keyes, *J. Appl. Phys.* **26**, 190.
1956:**1** Schultz, Solid State Group Tech. Report No. 9 (M.I.T.) (unpublished).
1956:**2** Dingle, *J. Appl. Res.* B **6**, 225.
1956:**3** Mott, *Can. J. Phys.* **34**, 1356.
1956:**4** Kane, *J. Phys. Chem. Solids* **1**, 82.
1956:**5** Dexter, Zeiger and Lax, *Phys. Rev.* **104**, 637.
1956:**6** Potter, *Phys. Rev.* **103**, 861.
1956:**7** Ewald and Kohnke, *Phys. Rev.* **102**, 1481.
1956:**8** Champness, *Proc. Phys. Soc. London* B **69**, 1335.
1956:**9** Meyer, *Physica* **22**, 109.
1956:**10** Burgess, *Electrochem. Soc. Meeting, San Francisco*, May 1956.
1956:**11** Dresselhaus, *J. Phys. Chem. Solids* **1**, 15.
1956:**12** Bardeen, Blatt and Hall, *Photoconductivity Conference*. John Wiley, New York.
1956:**13** Rittner, *Photoconductivity Conference*. John Wiley, New York.
1956:**14** Landsberg, *Proc. Phys. Soc. London* B **69**, 1056.
1956:**15** Blakemore, *Can. J. Phys.* **34**, 938.
1956:**16** Adirovich and Goureau, *Soviet Physics: Doklady* **1**, 306.
1956:**17** Burstein, Picus, Henvis and Wallis, *J. Phys. Chem. Solids* **1**, 65.
1956:**18** Picus, Burstein and Henvis, *J. Phys. Chem. Solids* **1**, 75.
1956:**19** Newman, *Phys. Rev.* **103**, 103.
1956:**20** Schechter, Thesis, Carnegie Institute of Technology.
1956:**21** Price, *Phys. Rev.* **104,** 1223.
1956:**22** Yafet, Keyes and Adams, *J. Phys. Chem. Solids* **1**, 137.
1956:**23** Keyes and Sladek, *J. Phys. Chem. Solids* **1**, 143.
1956:**24** Tyler and Woodbury, *Phys. Rev.* **102**, 647.
1956:**25** Morton, Hahn and Schultz, *Photoconductivity Conference*. John Wiley, New York.
1956:**26** Scanlon, Brebrick and Petritz, *Photoconductivity Conference*. John Wiley, New York.
1956:**27** Kröger and Vink, *Solid State Physics*, vol. 2. Academic Press, New York.
1956:**28** Koshino, *J. Phys. Soc. Japan* **11**, 608.
1956:**29** Conwell, *Phys. Rev.* **103**, 51.
1956:**30** Kamke, *Differentialgleichungen Lösungsmethoden und Lösungen*. Akad. Verlogs. Geest und Portig, Leipzig.
1956:**31** Haynes and Westphal, *Phys. Rev.* **101**, 1676.
1956:**32** deVore, *Phys. Rev.* **102**, 86.
1956:**33** Stöckmann, *Photoconductivity Conference*. John Wiley, New York.
1956:**34** Kalashnikov, *J. Tech. Phys. U.S.S.R.* **26**, 241.
1956:**35** Morrison, *Phys. Rev.* **104,** 619.
1957:**1** Born, *Atomic Physics*, 5th ed. Blackie, Glasgow.
1957:**2** Kohn, *Phys. Rev.* **105**, 509.
1957:**3** Dekker, *Solid State Physics*. Prentice-Hall, Englewood Cliffs, N.J.
1957:**4** Gold, *J. Electronics and Control* **2**, 323.
1957:**5** Kane, *J. Phys. Chem. Solids* **1**, 249.
1957:**6** Herman, Report of Second Symposium on Physics of Semiconductors. *J. Phys. Chem. Solids* **2,** 72.

1957:**7** Macfarlane, McLean, Quarrington and Roberts, *Phys. Rev.* **108**, 1377.
1957:**8** Zwerdling and Lax, *Phys. Rev.* **106**, 51.
1957:**9** Dumke, *Phys. Rev.* **108**, 1419.
1957:**10** Kohn, *Solid State Physics*, vol. 5. Academic Press, New York.
1957:**11** Herman, Glicksman and Parmenter, *Progress in Semiconductors*, vol. 2. Heywood, London.
1957:**12** Chynoweth and McKay, *Phys. Rev.* **106**, 418.
1957:**13** Burstein and Picus, *Phys. Rev.* **105**, 1123.
1957:**14** Heine, *Proc. Roy. Soc. London* A **240**, 340.
1957:**15** Dumke, *Phys. Rev.* **105**, 139.
1957:**16** Elcock and Landsberg, *Proc. Phys. Soc. London* B **70**, 161.
1957:**17** Bess, *Phys. Rev.* **105**, 1469.
1957:**18** Sandiford, *Phys. Rev.* **105**, 524.
1957:**19** Goureau, *J. Exptl. Theoret. Phys. U.S.S.R.* **33**, 158.
1957:**20** Rose, *Progress in Semiconductors*, vol. 2. John Wiley, New York.
1957:**21** Shockley and Last, *Phys. Rev.* **107**, 392.
1957:**22** Landsberg, *Proc. Phys. Soc. London* B **70**, 282.
1957:**23** Okada, *J. Phys. Soc. Japan* **12**, 1338.
1957:**24** Clarke, *J. Electronics and Control* **3**, 375.
1957:**25** Ridout, *Report of the Meeting on Semiconductors*. Physical Society, London.
1957:**26** Blakemore, *Bull. Amer. Phys. Soc.* **2,** 153.
1957:**27** Crawford and Cleland, *Progress in Semiconductors*, vol. 2. Heywood, London.
1957:**28** Dunlap, *Progress in Semiconductors*, vol. 2. Heywood, London.
1957:**29** Price, *J. Phys. Chem. Solids* **2**, 282.
1957:**30** Koenig and Gunther-Mohr, *J. Phys. Chem. Solids* **2**, 268.
1957:**31** Bube, *J. Phys. Chem. Solids* **1**, 234.
1957:**32** Henisch, *Rectifying Semiconductor Contacts*. Oxford University Press.
1957:**33** Kingston (Ed.), *Semiconductor Surface Physics*. Pennsylvania University Press, Philadelphia.
1957:**34** Middlebrook, *An Introduction to Junction Transistor Theory*. John Wiley, New York.
1957:**35** McKelvey, *Phys. Rev.* **106**, 910.
1957:**36** Scanlon, *Phys. Rev.* **106**, 718.
1957:**37** Bell and Hogarth, *J. Electronics and Control* **3**, 455.
1957:**38** Shaw, Hudson and Danielson, *Phys. Rev.* **107,** 419.
1958:**1** Herman, *Revs. Modern Phys.* **30**, 102.
1958:**2** Lax, *Revs. Modern Phys.* **30**, 122.
1958:**3** MacFarlane, McLean, Quarrington and Roberts, *Phys. Rev.* **111**, 1245.
1958:**4** MacFarlane, McLean, Quarrington and Roberts, *Proc. Phys. Soc. London* B **71**, 863.
1958:**5** Esaki, *Phys. Rev.* **109**, 603.
1958:**6** Blakemore, *Proc. Phys. Soc. London* **71**, 692.
1958:**7** Ter Haar, *Introduction to the Physics of Many-Body Problems*. Interscience, New York.
1958:**8** Kittel, *Elementary Statistical Physics*. John Wiley, New York.
1958:**9** Ehrenberg, *Electric Conduction in Metals and Semiconductors*. Clarendon Press, Oxford.

1958:**10** LANDSBERG, *Semiconductors and Phosphors*. Interscience, New York.
1958:**11** SAH and SHOCKLEY, *Phys. Rev.* **109**, 1103.
1958:**12** RIDLEY, *J. Electronics and Control* **5**, 549.
1958:**13** NOMURA and BLAKEMORE, *Phys. Rev.* **112**, 1607.
1958:**14** WERTHEIM, *Phys. Rev.* **109**, 1086.
1958:**15** BEMSKI, *Proc. I.R.E.* **46**, 990.
1958:**16** SHOCKLEY, *Proc. I.R.E.* **46**, 973.
1958:**17** BLAKEMORE, *Phys. Rev.* **110**, 1301.
1958:**18** MCKELVEY, *I.R.E. Trans. on Electron Devices* **ED-5**, 260.
1958:**19** YAMASHITA and KUROSAWA, *J. Phys. Chem. Solids* **5**, 34.
1958:**20** HROSTOWSKI and KAISER, *J. Phys. Chem. Solids* **4**, 148.
1958:**21** PRICE, *I.B.M. Journal*, **2**, 123.
1958:**22** KASUYA and KOIDE, *J. Phys. Soc. Japan* **13**, 1287.
1958:**23** KLASENS, *J. Phys. Chem. Solids* **7**, 175.
1958:**24** SIM, *J. Electronics and Control* **5**, 251.
1959:**1** SLATER, *J. Phys. Chem. Solids* **8**, 21.
1959:**2** LUTTINGER, *J. Phys. Chem. Solids* **8**, 123.
1959:**3** KOHN, *J. Phys. Chem. Solids* **8**, 45.
1959:**4** SMITH, *Semiconductors*. Cambridge University Press.
1959:**5** WELKER, *J. Phys. Chem. Solids* **8**, 14.
1959:**6** BLAKEMORE, *Phil. Mag.* Ser. 8, **4**, 560.
1959:**7** KAHN and FREDERIKSE, *Solid State Physics*, vol. 9. Academic Press, New York.
1959:**8** LAX, ROTH and ZWERDLING, *J. Phys. Chem. Solids* **8**, 311.
1959:**9** BURSTEIN, PICUS, WALLIS and BLATT, *Phys. Rev.* **113**, 15.
1959:**10** MOSS, SMITH and TAYLOR, *J. Phys. Chem. Solids* **8**, 323.
1959:**11** LAX, *J. Phys. Chem. Solids* **8**, 66.
1959:**12** TWOSE, Thesis, Cambridge University.
1959:**13** LONG and MYERS, *Phys. Rev.* **115**, 1119.
1959:**14** FRITZCHE, *J. Phys. Chem. Solids* **8**, 257.
1959:**15** LANDSBERG and BEATTIE, *J. Phys. Chem. Solids* **8**, 73.
1959:**16** BEATTIE and LANDSBERG, *Proc. Roy. Soc. London* A **249**, 16.
1959:**17** SIM, *Proc. I.E.E.* B **106**, Supplement 15, 308.
1959:**18** MOSS, *Optical Properties of Semiconductors*. Butterworths, London.
1960:**1** LANDSBERG, *Solid State Physics in Electronics and Telecommunications*. Academic Press, New York, Vol. 1, p. 436.
1960:**2** SCHOENBERG, *Phil. Mag.* Ser. 8, **5**, 105.
1960:**3** HARMAN, *Bull. Am. Phys. Soc.* Ser. II, **5**, 152.
1960:**4** BLAKEMORE and NOMURA, *J. Appl. Phys.* **31**, 753.
1960:**5** KENNEDY, *J. Appl. Phys.* **31**, 954.
1960:**6** FRITZSCHE, *Phys. Rev.* **120,** 1120.
1960:**7** KOENIG and BROWN, *Phys. Rev. Letters*, **4**, 170.
1960:**8** GUBANOV, KRIVKO and REINOV, *J. Exptl. Theoret. Phys.* **38**, 341.
1960:**9** ATKINS, DONOVAN and WALMSLEY, *Phys. Rev.* **118**, 411.
1960:**10** BUBE, *Photoconductivity of Solids*. John Wiley, New York.
1960:**11** BLAKEMORE, *International Semiconductor Conference, Prague*, p. 981.
1960:**12** BEATTIE and LANDSBERG, *Proc. Roy. Soc. London* A **258**, 486.
1960:**13** ASCARELLI and BROWN, *Phys. Rev.* **120,** 1615.
1960:**14** VAN ROOSBROECK, *Phys. Rev.* **119**, 636.

1960:**15** LAX, *Phys. Rev.* **119**, 1502.
1960:**16** KALASHNIKOV, *International Semiconductor Conference, Prague*, p. 241.
1960:**17** JONSCHER, *Principles of Semiconductor Device Operation*. Bell, London.
1960:**18** ZEMEL (Editor), Proceedings of the Second Conference on Semiconductor Surfaces. *J. Phys. Chem Solids* **14.**
1960:**19** ZIMAN, *Electrons and Phonons*. Clarendon Press, Oxford.
1960:**20** BLAKEMORE, SCHULTZ and NOMURA, *J. Appl. Phys.* **31**, 1901.
1960:**21** BROUDY and MCCLURE, *J. Appl. Phys.* **31,** 1511.
1960:**22** JOFFÉ and REGEL, *Progress in Semiconductors*, vol. 4. Heywood, London.
1960:**23** MILLER and ABRAHAMS, *Phys. Rev.* **120,** 745.
1961:**1** NOMURA and BLAKEMORE, *Phys. Rev.* **121,** 734.
1961:**2** FRITZSCHE, *Bull. Am. Phys. Soc.* **6,** 136.
1961:**3** BREBRICK, *J. Phys. Chem. Solids* **18,** 116.
1961:**4** FALICOV and HEINE, *Advances in Physics* **10,** 57.
1961:**5** LANDSBERG, *Thermodynamics*. Interscience, New York.
1961:**6** POKROVSKY and SVISTUNOVA, *International Photoconductivity Conference, Ithaca.*

INDEX

A CATALOG OF SELECTED

DOVER BOOKS

IN SCIENCE AND MATHEMATICS

A CATALOG OF SELECTED
DOVER BOOKS
IN SCIENCE AND MATHEMATICS

QUALITATIVE THEORY OF DIFFERENTIAL EQUATIONS, V.V. Nemytskii and V.V. Stepanov. Classic graduate-level text by two prominent Soviet mathematicians covers classical differential equations as well as topological dynamics and ergodic theory. Bibliographies. 523pp. 5⅜ × 8½. 65954-2 Pa. $10.95

MATRICES AND LINEAR ALGEBRA, Hans Schneider and George Phillip Barker. Basic textbook covers theory of matrices and its applications to systems of linear equations and related topics such as determinants, eigenvalues and differential equations. Numerous exercises. 432pp. 5⅜ × 8½. 66014-1 Pa. $9.95

QUANTUM THEORY, David Bohm. This advanced undergraduate-level text presents the quantum theory in terms of qualitative and imaginative concepts, followed by specific applications worked out in mathematical detail. Preface. Index. 655pp. 5⅜ × 8½. 65969-0 Pa. $13.95

ATOMIC PHYSICS (8th edition), Max Born. Nobel laureate's lucid treatment of kinetic theory of gases, elementary particles, nuclear atom, wave-corpuscles, atomic structure and spectral lines, much more. Over 40 appendices, bibliography. 495pp. 5⅜ × 8½. 65984-4 Pa. $11.95

ELECTRONIC STRUCTURE AND THE PROPERTIES OF SOLIDS: The Physics of the Chemical Bond, Walter A. Harrison. Innovative text offers basic understanding of the electronic structure of covalent and ionic solids, simple metals, transition metals and their compounds. Problems. 1980 edition. 582pp. 6⅛ × 9¼. 66021-4 Pa. $14.95

BOUNDARY VALUE PROBLEMS OF HEAT CONDUCTION, M. Necati Özisik. Systematic, comprehensive treatment of modern mathematical methods of solving problems in heat conduction and diffusion. Numerous examples and problems. Selected references. Appendices. 505pp. 5⅜ × 8½. 65990-9 Pa. $11.95

A SHORT HISTORY OF CHEMISTRY (3rd edition), J.R. Partington. Classic exposition explores origins of chemistry, alchemy, early medical chemistry, nature of atmosphere, theory of valency, laws and structure of atomic theory, much more. 428pp. 5⅜ × 8½. (Available in U.S. only) 65977-1 Pa. $10.95

A HISTORY OF ASTRONOMY, A. Pannekoek. Well-balanced, carefully reasoned study covers such topics as Ptolemaic theory, work of Copernicus, Kepler, Newton, Eddington's work on stars, much more. Illustrated. References. 521pp. 5⅜ × 8½. 65994-1 Pa. $11.95

PRINCIPLES OF METEOROLOGICAL ANALYSIS, Walter J. Saucier. Highly respected, abundantly illustrated classic reviews atmospheric variables, hydrostatics, static stability, various analyses (scalar, cross-section, isobaric, isentropic, more). For intermediate meteorology students. 454pp. 6⅛ × 9¼. 65979-8 Pa. $12.95

RELATIVITY, THERMODYNAMICS AND COSMOLOGY, Richard C. Tolman. Landmark study extends thermodynamics to special, general relativity; also applications of relativistic mechanics, thermodynamics to cosmological models. 501pp. 5⅜ × 8½. 65383-8 Pa. $12.95

APPLIED ANALYSIS, Cornelius Lanczos. Classic work on analysis and design of finite processes for approximating solution of analytical problems. Algebraic equations, matrices, harmonic analysis, quadrature methods, much more. 559pp. 5⅜ × 8½. 65656-X Pa. $12.95

SPECIAL RELATIVITY FOR PHYSICISTS, G. Stephenson and C.W. Kilmister. Concise elegant account for nonspecialists. Lorentz transformation, optical and dynamical applications, more. Bibliography. 108pp. 5⅜ × 8½. 65519-9 Pa. $4.95

INTRODUCTION TO ANALYSIS, Maxwell Rosenlicht. Unusually clear, accessible coverage of set theory, real number system, metric spaces, continuous functions, Riemann integration, multiple integrals, more. Wide range of problems. Undergraduate level. Bibliography. 254pp. 5⅜ × 8½. 65038-3 Pa. $7.95

INTRODUCTION TO QUANTUM MECHANICS With Applications to Chemistry, Linus Pauling & E. Bright Wilson, Jr. Classic undergraduate text by Nobel Prize winner applies quantum mechanics to chemical and physical problems. Numerous tables and figures enhance the text. Chapter bibliographies. Appendices. Index. 468pp. 5⅜ × 8½. 64871-0 Pa. $11.95

ASYMPTOTIC EXPANSIONS OF INTEGRALS, Norman Bleistein & Richard A. Handelsman. Best introduction to important field with applications in a variety of scientific disciplines. New preface. Problems. Diagrams. Tables. Bibliography. Index. 448pp. 5⅜ × 8½. 65082-0 Pa. $11.95

MATHEMATICS APPLIED TO CONTINUUM MECHANICS, Lee A. Segel. Analyzes models of fluid flow and solid deformation. For upper-level math, science and engineering students. 608pp. 5⅜ × 8½. 65369-2 Pa. $13.95

ELEMENTS OF REAL ANALYSIS, David A. Sprecher. Classic text covers fundamental concepts, real number system, point sets, functions of a real variable, Fourier series, much more. Over 500 exercises. 352pp. 5⅜ × 8½. 65385-4 Pa. $9.95

PHYSICAL PRINCIPLES OF THE QUANTUM THEORY, Werner Heisenberg. Nobel Laureate discusses quantum theory, uncertainty, wave mechanics, work of Dirac, Schroedinger, Compton, Wilson, Einstein, etc. 184pp. 5⅜ × 8½. 60113-7 Pa. $4.95

INTRODUCTORY REAL ANALYSIS, A.N. Kolmogorov, S.V. Fomin. Translated by Richard A. Silverman. Self-contained, evenly paced introduction to real and functional analysis. Some 350 problems. 403pp. 5⅜ × 8½. 61226-0 Pa. $9.95

PROBLEMS AND SOLUTIONS IN QUANTUM CHEMISTRY AND PHYSICS, Charles S. Johnson, Jr. and Lee G. Pedersen. Unusually varied problems, detailed solutions in coverage of quantum mechanics, wave mechanics, angular momentum, molecular spectroscopy, scattering theory, more. 280 problems plus 139 supplementary exercises. 430pp. 6½ × 9¼. 65236-X Pa. $11.95

ASYMPTOTIC METHODS IN ANALYSIS, N.G. de Bruijn. An inexpensive, comprehensive guide to asymptotic methods—the pioneering work that teaches by explaining worked examples in detail. Index. 224pp. 5⅜ × 8½. 64221-6 Pa. $6.95

OPTICAL RESONANCE AND TWO-LEVEL ATOMS, L. Allen and J.H. Eberly. Clear, comprehensive introduction to basic principles behind all quantum optical resonance phenomena. 53 illustrations. Preface. Index. 256pp. 5⅜ × 8½.
65533-4 Pa. $7.95

COMPLEX VARIABLES, Francis J. Flanigan. Unusual approach, delaying complex algebra till harmonic functions have been analyzed from real variable viewpoint. Includes problems with answers. 364pp. 5⅜ × 8½. 61388-7 Pa. $7.95

ATOMIC SPECTRA AND ATOMIC STRUCTURE, Gerhard Herzberg. One of best introductions; especially for specialist in other fields. Treatment is physical rather than mathematical. 80 illustrations. 257pp. 5⅜ × 8½. 60115-3 Pa. $5.95

APPLIED COMPLEX VARIABLES, John W. Dettman. Step-by-step coverage of fundamentals of analytic function theory—plus lucid exposition of five important applications: Potential Theory; Ordinary Differential Equations; Fourier Transforms; Laplace Transforms; Asymptotic Expansions. 66 figures. Exercises at chapter ends. 512pp. 5⅜ × 8½. 64670-X Pa. $10.95

ULTRASONIC ABSORPTION: An Introduction to the Theory of Sound Absorption and Dispersion in Gases, Liquids and Solids, A.B. Bhatia. Standard reference in the field provides a clear, systematically organized introductory review of fundamental concepts for advanced graduate students, research workers. Numerous diagrams. Bibliography. 440pp. 5⅜ × 8½. 64917-2 Pa. $11.95

UNBOUNDED LINEAR OPERATORS: Theory and Applications, Seymour Goldberg. Classic presents systematic treatment of the theory of unbounded linear operators in normed linear spaces with applications to differential equations. Bibliography. 199pp. 5⅜ × 8½. 64830-3 Pa. $7.95

LIGHT SCATTERING BY SMALL PARTICLES, H.C. van de Hulst. Comprehensive treatment including full range of useful approximation methods for researchers in chemistry, meteorology and astronomy. 44 illustrations. 470pp. 5⅜ × 8½. 64228-3 Pa. $10.95

CONFORMAL MAPPING ON RIEMANN SURFACES, Harvey Cohn. Lucid, insightful book presents ideal coverage of subject. 334 exercises make book perfect for self-study. 55 figures. 352pp. 5⅜ × 8¼. 64025-6 Pa. $8.95

OPTICKS, Sir Isaac Newton. Newton's own experiments with spectroscopy, colors, lenses, reflection, refraction, etc., in language the layman can follow. Foreword by Albert Einstein. 532pp. 5⅜ × 8½. 60205-2 Pa. $9.95

GENERALIZED INTEGRAL TRANSFORMATIONS, A.H. Zemanian. Graduate-level study of recent generalizations of the Laplace, Mellin, Hankel, K. Weierstrass, convolution and other simple transformations. Bibliography. 320pp. 5⅜ × 8½. 65375-7 Pa. $7.95

THE ELECTROMAGNETIC FIELD, Albert Shadowitz. Comprehensive undergraduate text covers basics of electric and magnetic fields, builds up to electromagnetic theory. Also related topics, including relativity. Over 900 problems. 768pp. 5⅜ × 8¼. 65660-8 Pa. $17.95

FOURIER SERIES, Georgi P. Tolstov. Translated by Richard A. Silverman. A valuable addition to the literature on the subject, moving clearly from subject to subject and theorem to theorem. 107 problems, answers. 336pp. 5⅜ × 8½. 63317-9 Pa. $7.95

THEORY OF ELECTROMAGNETIC WAVE PROPAGATION, Charles Herach Papas. Graduate-level study discusses the Maxwell field equations, radiation from wire antennas, the Doppler effect and more. xiii + 244pp. 5⅜ × 8½. 65678-0 Pa. $6.95

DISTRIBUTION THEORY AND TRANSFORM ANALYSIS: An Introduction to Generalized Functions, with Applications, A.H. Zemanian. Provides basics of distribution theory, describes generalized Fourier and Laplace transformations. Numerous problems. 384pp. 5⅜ × 8½. 65479-6 Pa. $9.95

THE PHYSICS OF WAVES, William C. Elmore and Mark A. Heald. Unique overview of classical wave theory. Acoustics, optics, electromagnetic radiation, more. Ideal as classroom text or for self-study. Problems. 477pp. 5⅜ × 8½. 64926-1 Pa. $11.95

CALCULUS OF VARIATIONS WITH APPLICATIONS, George M. Ewing. Applications-oriented introduction to variational theory develops insight and promotes understanding of specialized books, research papers. Suitable for advanced undergraduate/graduate students as primary, supplementary text. 352pp. 5⅜ × 8½. 64856-7 Pa. $8.95

A TREATISE ON ELECTRICITY AND MAGNETISM, James Clerk Maxwell. Important foundation work of modern physics. Brings to final form Maxwell's theory of electromagnetism and rigorously derives his general equations of field theory. 1,084pp. 5⅜ × 8½. 60636-8, 60637-6 Pa., Two-vol. set $19.90

AN INTRODUCTION TO THE CALCULUS OF VARIATIONS, Charles Fox. Graduate-level text covers variations of an integral, isoperimetrical problems, least action, special relativity, approximations, more. References. 279pp. 5⅜ × 8½. 65499-0 Pa. $7.95

HYDRODYNAMIC AND HYDROMAGNETIC STABILITY, S. Chandrasekhar. Lucid examination of the Rayleigh-Benard problem; clear coverage of the theory of instabilities causing convection. 704pp. 5⅜ × 8¼. 64071-X Pa. $14.95

CALCULUS OF VARIATIONS, Robert Weinstock. Basic introduction covering isoperimetric problems, theory of elasticity, quantum mechanics, electrostatics, etc. Exercises throughout. 326pp. 5⅜ × 8½. 63069-2 Pa. $7.95

DYNAMICS OF FLUIDS IN POROUS MEDIA, Jacob Bear. For advanced students of ground water hydrology, soil mechanics and physics, drainage and irrigation engineering and more. 335 illustrations. Exercises, with answers. 784pp. 6⅛ × 9¼. 65675-6 Pa. $19.95

NUMERICAL METHODS FOR SCIENTISTS AND ENGINEERS, Richard Hamming. Classic text stresses frequency approach in coverage of algorithms, polynomial approximation, Fourier approximation, exponential approximation, other topics. Revised and enlarged 2nd edition. 721pp. 5⅜ × 8½.
65241-6 Pa. $14.95

THEORETICAL SOLID STATE PHYSICS, Vol. I: Perfect Lattices in Equilibrium; Vol. II: Non-Equilibrium and Disorder, William Jones and Norman H. March. Monumental reference work covers fundamental theory of equilibrium properties of perfect crystalline solids, non-equilibrium properties, defects and disordered systems. Appendices. Problems. Preface. Diagrams. Index. Bibliography. Total of 1,301pp. 5⅜ × 8½. Two volumes. Vol. I 65015-4 Pa. $12.95
Vol. II 65016-2 Pa. $12.95

OPTIMIZATION THEORY WITH APPLICATIONS, Donald A. Pierre. Broad-spectrum approach to important topic. Classical theory of minima and maxima, calculus of variations, simplex technique and linear programming, more. Many problems, examples. 640pp. 5⅜ × 8½. 65205-X Pa. $13.95

THE MODERN THEORY OF SOLIDS, Frederick Seitz. First inexpensive edition of classic work on theory of ionic crystals, free-electron theory of metals and semiconductors, molecular binding, much more. 736pp. 5⅜ × 8½.
65482-6 Pa. $15.95

ESSAYS ON THE THEORY OF NUMBERS, Richard Dedekind. Two classic essays by great German mathematician: on the theory of irrational numbers; and on transfinite numbers and properties of natural numbers. 115pp. 5⅜ × 8½.
21010-3 Pa. $4.95

THE FUNCTIONS OF MATHEMATICAL PHYSICS, Harry Hochstadt. Comprehensive treatment of orthogonal polynomials, hypergeometric functions, Hill's equation, much more. Bibliography. Index. 322pp. 5⅜ × 8½. 65214-9 Pa. $9.95

NUMBER THEORY AND ITS HISTORY, Oystein Ore. Unusually clear, accessible introduction covers counting, properties of numbers, prime numbers, much more. Bibliography. 380pp. 5⅜ × 8½. 65620-9 Pa. $8.95

THE VARIATIONAL PRINCIPLES OF MECHANICS, Cornelius Lanczos. Graduate level coverage of calculus of variations, equations of motion, relativistic mechanics, more. First inexpensive paperbound edition of classic treatise. Index. Bibliography. 418pp. 5⅜ × 8½. 65067-7 Pa. $10.95

MATHEMATICAL TABLES AND FORMULAS, Robert D. Carmichael and Edwin R. Smith. Logarithms, sines, tangents, trig functions, powers, roots, reciprocals, exponential and hyperbolic functions, formulas and theorems. 269pp. 5⅜ × 8½. 60111-0 Pa. $5.95

THEORETICAL PHYSICS, Georg Joos, with Ira M. Freeman. Classic overview covers essential math, mechanics, electromagnetic theory, thermodynamics, quantum mechanics, nuclear physics, other topics. First paperback edition. xxiii + 885pp. 5⅜ × 8½. 65227-0 Pa. $18.95

SPECIAL FUNCTIONS, N.N. Lebedev. Translated by Richard Silverman. Famous Russian work treating more important special functions, with applications to specific problems of physics and engineering. 38 figures. 308pp. 5⅜ × 8½.
60624-4 Pa. $7.95

OBSERVATIONAL ASTRONOMY FOR AMATEURS, J.B. Sidgwick. Mine of useful data for observation of sun, moon, planets, asteroids, aurorae, meteors, comets, variables, binaries, etc. 39 illustrations. 384pp. 5⅜ × 8¼. (Available in U.S. only)
24033-9 Pa. $8.95

INTEGRAL EQUATIONS, F.G. Tricomi. Authoritative, well-written treatment of extremely useful mathematical tool with wide applications. Volterra Equations, Fredholm Equations, much more. Advanced undergraduate to graduate level. Exercises. Bibliography. 238pp. 5⅜ × 8½.
64828-1 Pa. $6.95

CELESTIAL OBJECTS FOR COMMON TELESCOPES, T.W. Webb. Inestimable aid for locating and identifying nearly 4,000 celestial objects. 77 illustrations. 645pp. 5⅜ × 8½.
20917-2, 20918-0 Pa., Two-vol. set $12.00

MODERN NONLINEAR EQUATIONS, Thomas L. Saaty. Emphasizes practical solution of problems; covers seven types of equations. ". . . a welcome contribution to the existing literature. . . ."—*Math Reviews*. 490pp. 5⅜ × 8½. 64232-1 Pa. $9.95

FUNDAMENTALS OF ASTRODYNAMICS, Roger Bate et al. Modern approach developed by U.S. Air Force Academy. Designed as a first course. Problems, exercises. Numerous illustrations. 455pp. 5⅜ × 8½.
60061-0 Pa. $8.95

INTRODUCTION TO LINEAR ALGEBRA AND DIFFERENTIAL EQUATIONS, John W. Dettman. Excellent text covers complex numbers, determinants, orthonormal bases, Laplace transforms, much more. Exercises with solutions. Undergraduate level. 416pp. 5⅜ × 8½.
65191-6 Pa. $9.95

INCOMPRESSIBLE AERODYNAMICS, edited by Bryan Thwaites. Covers theoretical and experimental treatment of the uniform flow of air and viscous fluids past two-dimensional aerofoils and three-dimensional wings; many other topics. 654pp. 5⅜ × 8½.
65465-6 Pa. $16.95

INTRODUCTION TO DIFFERENCE EQUATIONS, Samuel Goldberg. Exceptionally clear exposition of important discipline with applications to sociology, psychology, economics. Many illustrative examples; over 250 problems. 260pp. 5⅜ × 8½.
65084-7 Pa. $7.95

LAMINAR BOUNDARY LAYERS, edited by L. Rosenhead. Engineering classic covers steady boundary layers in two- and three-dimensional flow, unsteady boundary layers, stability, observational techniques, much more. 708pp. 5⅜ × 8½.
65646-2 Pa. $15.95

LECTURES ON CLASSICAL DIFFERENTIAL GEOMETRY, Second Edition, Dirk J. Struik. Excellent brief introduction covers curves, theory of surfaces, fundamental equations, geometry on a surface, conformal mapping, other topics. Problems. 240pp. 5⅜ × 8½.
65609-8 Pa. $6.95

GEOMETRY OF COMPLEX NUMBERS, Hans Schwerdtfeger. Illuminating, widely praised book on analytic geometry of circles, the Moebius transformation, and two-dimensional non-Euclidean geometries. 200pp. 5⅝ × 8¼.
63830-8 Pa. $6.95

MECHANICS, J.P. Den Hartog. A classic introductory text or refresher. Hundreds of applications and design problems illuminate fundamentals of trusses, loaded beams and cables, etc. 334 answered problems. 462pp. 5⅜ × 8½. 60754-2 Pa. $8.95

TOPOLOGY, John G. Hocking and Gail S. Young. Superb one-year course in classical topology. Topological spaces and functions, point-set topology, much more. Examples and problems. Bibliography. Index. 384pp. 5⅜ × 8¼.
65676-4 Pa. $8.95

STRENGTH OF MATERIALS, J.P. Den Hartog. Full, clear treatment of basic material (tension, torsion, bending, etc.) plus advanced material on engineering methods, applications. 350 answered problems. 323pp. 5⅜ × 8½. 60755-0 Pa. $7.50

ELEMENTARY CONCEPTS OF TOPOLOGY, Paul Alexandroff. Elegant, intuitive approach to topology from set-theoretic topology to Betti groups; how concepts of topology are useful in math and physics. 25 figures. 57pp. 5⅜ × 8½.
60747-X Pa. $2.95

ADVANCED STRENGTH OF MATERIALS, J.P. Den Hartog. Superbly written advanced text covers torsion, rotating disks, membrane stresses in shells, much more. Many problems and answers. 388pp. 5⅜ × 8½. 65407-9 Pa. $9.95

COMPUTABILITY AND UNSOLVABILITY, Martin Davis. Classic graduate-level introduction to theory of computability, usually referred to as theory of recurrent functions. New preface and appendix. 288pp. 5⅜ × 8½. 61471-9 Pa. $6.95

GENERAL CHEMISTRY, Linus Pauling. Revised 3rd edition of classic first-year text by Nobel laureate. Atomic and molecular structure, quantum mechanics, statistical mechanics, thermodynamics correlated with descriptive chemistry. Problems. 992pp. 5⅜ × 8½. 65622-5 Pa. $19.95

AN INTRODUCTION TO MATRICES, SETS AND GROUPS FOR SCIENCE STUDENTS, G. Stephenson. Concise, readable text introduces sets, groups, and most importantly, matrices to undergraduate students of physics, chemistry, and engineering. Problems. 164pp. 5⅜ × 8½. 65077-4 Pa. $6.95

THE HISTORICAL BACKGROUND OF CHEMISTRY, Henry M. Leicester. Evolution of ideas, not individual biography. Concentrates on formulation of a coherent set of chemical laws. 260pp. 5⅜ × 8½. 61053-5 Pa. $6.95

THE PHILOSOPHY OF MATHEMATICS: An Introductory Essay, Stephan Körner. Surveys the views of Plato, Aristotle, Leibniz & Kant concerning propositions and theories of applied and pure mathematics. Introduction. Two appendices. Index. 198pp. 5⅜ × 8½. 25048-2 Pa. $6.95

THE DEVELOPMENT OF MODERN CHEMISTRY, Aaron J. Ihde. Authoritative history of chemistry from ancient Greek theory to 20th-century innovation. Covers major chemists and their discoveries. 209 illustrations. 14 tables. Bibliographies. Indices. Appendices. 851pp. 5⅜ × 8½. 64235-6 Pa. $17.95

DE RE METALLICA, Georgius Agricola. The famous Hoover translation of greatest treatise on technological chemistry, engineering, geology, mining of early modern times (1556). All 289 original woodcuts. 638pp. 6¾ × 11.
60006-8 Pa. $17.95

SOME THEORY OF SAMPLING, William Edwards Deming. Analysis of the problems, theory and design of sampling techniques for social scientists, industrial managers and others who find statistics increasingly important in their work. 61 tables. 90 figures. xvii + 602pp. 5⅜ × 8½. 64684-X Pa. $15.95

THE VARIOUS AND INGENIOUS MACHINES OF AGOSTINO RAMELLI: A Classic Sixteenth-Century Illustrated Treatise on Technology, Agostino Ramelli. One of the most widely known and copied works on machinery in the 16th century. 194 detailed plates of water pumps, grain mills, cranes, more. 608pp. 9 × 12. (EBF)
25497-6 Clothbd. $34.95

LINEAR PROGRAMMING AND ECONOMIC ANALYSIS, Robert Dorfman, Paul A. Samuelson and Robert M. Solow. First comprehensive treatment of linear programming in standard economic analysis. Game theory, modern welfare economics, Leontief input-output, more. 525pp. 5⅜ × 8½. 65491-5 Pa. $13.95

ELEMENTARY DECISION THEORY, Herman Chernoff and Lincoln E. Moses. Clear introduction to statistics and statistical theory covers data processing, probability and random variables, testing hypotheses, much more. Exercises. 364pp. 5⅜ × 8½. 65218-1 Pa. $9.95

THE COMPLEAT STRATEGYST: Being a Primer on the Theory of Games of Strategy, J.D. Williams. Highly entertaining classic describes, with many illustrated examples, how to select best strategies in conflict situations. Prefaces. Appendices. 268pp. 5⅜ × 8½. 25101-2 Pa. $6.95

MATHEMATICAL METHODS OF OPERATIONS RESEARCH, Thomas L. Saaty. Classic graduate-level text covers historical background, classical methods of forming models, optimization, game theory, probability, queueing theory, much more. Exercises. Bibliography. 448pp. 5⅜ × 8¼. 65703-5 Pa. $12.95

CONSTRUCTIONS AND COMBINATORIAL PROBLEMS IN DESIGN OF EXPERIMENTS, Damaraju Raghavarao. In-depth reference work examines orthogonal Latin squares, incomplete block designs, tactical configuration, partial geometry, much more. Abundant explanations, examples. 416pp. 5⅜ × 8¼.
65685-3 Pa. $10.95

THE ABSOLUTE DIFFERENTIAL CALCULUS (CALCULUS OF TENSORS), Tullio Levi-Civita. Great 20th-century mathematician's classic work on material necessary for mathematical grasp of theory of relativity. 452pp. 5⅜ × 8½.
63401-9 Pa. $9.95

VECTOR AND TENSOR ANALYSIS WITH APPLICATIONS, A.I. Borisenko and I.E. Tarapov. Concise introduction. Worked-out problems, solutions, exercises. 257pp. 5⅜ × 8¼. 63833-2 Pa. $6.95

TENSOR CALCULUS, J.L. Synge and A. Schild. Widely used introductory text covers spaces and tensors, basic operations in Riemannian space, non-Riemannian spaces, etc. 324pp. 5⅜ × 8¼. 63612-7 Pa. $7.95

A CONCISE HISTORY OF MATHEMATICS, Dirk J. Struik. The best brief history of mathematics. Stresses origins and covers every major figure from ancient Near East to 19th century. 41 illustrations. 195pp. 5⅜ × 8½. 60255-9 Pa. $7.95

A SHORT ACCOUNT OF THE HISTORY OF MATHEMATICS, W.W. Rouse Ball. One of clearest, most authoritative surveys from the Egyptians and Phoenicians through 19th-century figures such as Grassman, Galois, Riemann. Fourth edition. 522pp. 5⅜ × 8½. 20630-0 Pa. $10.95

HISTORY OF MATHEMATICS, David E. Smith. Nontechnical survey from ancient Greece and Orient to late 19th century; evolution of arithmetic, geometry, trigonometry, calculating devices, algebra, the calculus. 362 illustrations. 1,355pp. 5⅜ × 8½. 20429-4, 20430-8 Pa., Two-vol. set $23.90

THE GEOMETRY OF RENÉ DESCARTES, René Descartes. The great work founded analytical geometry. Original French text, Descartes' own diagrams, together with definitive Smith-Latham translation. 244pp. 5⅜ × 8½. 60068-8 Pa. $6.95

THE ORIGINS OF THE INFINITESIMAL CALCULUS, Margaret E. Baron. Only fully detailed and documented account of crucial discipline: origins; development by Galileo, Kepler, Cavalieri; contributions of Newton, Leibniz, more. 304pp. 5⅜ × 8½. (Available in U.S. and Canada only) 65371-4 Pa. $9.95

THE HISTORY OF THE CALCULUS AND ITS CONCEPTUAL DEVELOPMENT, Carl B. Boyer. Origins in antiquity, medieval contributions, work of Newton, Leibniz, rigorous formulation. Treatment is verbal. 346pp. 5⅜ × 8½. 60509-4 Pa. $7.95

THE THIRTEEN BOOKS OF EUCLID'S ELEMENTS, translated with introduction and commentary by Sir Thomas L. Heath. Definitive edition. Textual and linguistic notes, mathematical analysis. 2,500 years of critical commentary. Not abridged. 1,414pp. 5⅜ × 8½. 60088-2, 60089-0, 60090-4 Pa., Three-vol. set $29.85

GAMES AND DECISIONS: Introduction and Critical Survey, R. Duncan Luce and Howard Raiffa. Superb nontechnical introduction to game theory, primarily applied to social sciences. Utility theory, zero-sum games, n-person games, decision-making, much more. Bibliography. 509pp. 5⅜ × 8½. 65943-7 Pa. $11.95

THE HISTORICAL ROOTS OF ELEMENTARY MATHEMATICS, Lucas N.H. Bunt, Phillip S. Jones, and Jack D. Bedient. Fundamental underpinnings of modern arithmetic, algebra, geometry and number systems derived from ancient civilizations. 320pp. 5⅜ × 8½. 25563-8 Pa. $8.95

CALCULUS REFRESHER FOR TECHNICAL PEOPLE, A. Albert Klaf. Covers important aspects of integral and differential calculus via 756 questions. 566 problems, most answered. 431pp. 5⅜ × 8½. 20370-0 Pa. $8.95

CATALOG OF DOVER BOOKS

CHALLENGING MATHEMATICAL PROBLEMS WITH ELEMENTARY SOLUTIONS, A.M. Yaglom and I.M. Yaglom. Over 170 challenging problems on probability theory, combinatorial analysis, points and lines, topology, convex polygons, many other topics. Solutions. Total of 445pp. 5⅜ × 8½. Two-vol. set.
Vol. I 65536-9 Pa. $6.95
Vol. II 65537-7 Pa. $6.95

FIFTY CHALLENGING PROBLEMS IN PROBABILITY WITH SOLUTIONS, Frederick Mosteller. Remarkable puzzlers, graded in difficulty, illustrate elementary and advanced aspects of probability. Detailed solutions. 88pp. 5⅜ × 8½.
65355-2 Pa. $3.95

EXPERIMENTS IN TOPOLOGY, Stephen Barr. Classic, lively explanation of one of the byways of mathematics. Klein bottles, Moebius strips, projective planes, map coloring, problem of the Koenigsberg bridges, much more, described with clarity and wit. 43 figures. 210pp. 5⅜ × 8½. 25933-1 Pa. $5.95

RELATIVITY IN ILLUSTRATIONS, Jacob T. Schwartz. Clear nontechnical treatment makes relativity more accessible than ever before. Over 60 drawings illustrate concepts more clearly than text alone. Only high school geometry needed. Bibliography. 128pp. 6⅛ × 9¼. 25965-X Pa. $5.95

AN INTRODUCTION TO ORDINARY DIFFERENTIAL EQUATIONS, Earl A. Coddington. A thorough and systematic first course in elementary differential equations for undergraduates in mathematics and science, with many exercises and problems (with answers). Index. 304pp. 5⅜ × 8½. 65942-9 Pa. $7.95

FOURIER SERIES AND ORTHOGONAL FUNCTIONS, Harry F. Davis. An incisive text combining theory and practical example to introduce Fourier series, orthogonal functions and applications of the Fourier method to boundary-value problems. 570 exercises. Answers and notes. 416pp. 5⅜ × 8½. 65973-9 Pa. $9.95

THE THEORY OF BRANCHING PROCESSES, Theodore E. Harris. First systematic, comprehensive treatment of branching (i.e. multiplicative) processes and their applications. Galton-Watson model, Markov branching processes, electron-photon cascade, many other topics. Rigorous proofs. Bibliography. 240pp. 5⅜ × 8½. 65952-6 Pa. $6.95

AN INTRODUCTION TO ALGEBRAIC STRUCTURES, Joseph Landin. Superb self-contained text covers "abstract algebra": sets and numbers, theory of groups, theory of rings, much more. Numerous well-chosen examples, exercises. 247pp. 5⅜ × 8½. 65940-2 Pa. $6.95

Prices subject to change without notice.
Available at your book dealer or write for free Mathematics and Science Catalog to Dept. GI, Dover Publications, Inc., 31 East 2nd St., Mineola, N.Y. 11501. Dover publishes more than 175 books each year on science, elementary and advanced mathematics, biology, music, art, literature, history, social sciences and other areas.